QUIZZES AND TESTS

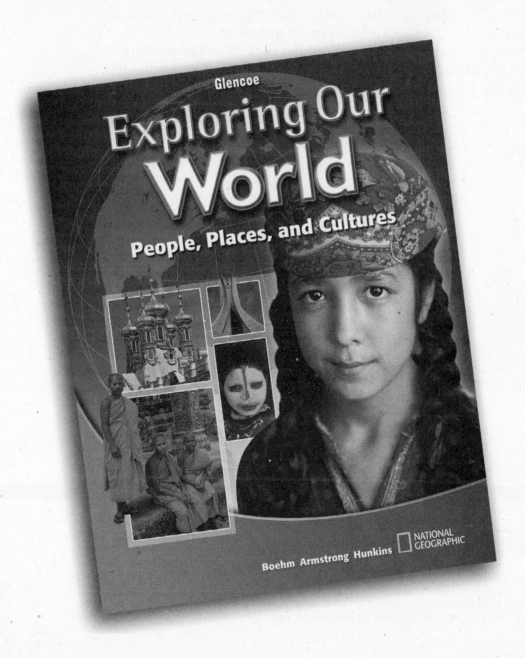

Glencoe

Exploring Our World

People, Places, and Cultures

Boehm Armstrong Hunkins · NATIONAL GEOGRAPHIC

McGraw Hill **Glencoe**

New York, New York   Columbus, Ohio   Chicago, Illinois   Woodland Hills, California

To the Teacher

This *Quizzes and Tests* book offers unit-, section-, and chapter-level assessment for *Exploring Our World*. The book has been organized so that all quizzes and tests appear at the point when you will most likely use them—the Unit Pretest, followed by Section Quizzes, followed by Chapter Tests Forms A and B, followed by the Unit Posttest. Section Quizzes include matching and short-answer questions. The Chapter Tests include matching, multiple-choice, skills application, document-based, and essay questions.

A complete answer key appears at the back of this book. This answer key includes answers for every quiz and test in this book in the order in which they appear in the book.

The McGraw·Hill Companies

 Glencoe

Send all inquiries to:
Glencoe/McGraw-Hill
8787 Orion Place
Columbus, OH 43240-4027

ISBN: 978-0-07-877601-4
MHID: 0-07-877601-5

Printed in the United States of America.

1 2 3 4 5 6 7 8 9 10 045 11 10 09 08 07

Contents

Contents

Contents

Contents

Name_____ Date_____ Class_____

Directions: Matching Match each item in Column A with its description in Column B. Write the correct letters in the blanks. *(5 points each)*

Column A

A. 200 million years ago

B. peninsula

C. lava

D. physical and human features of Earth

E. anthropologist

F. sun

G. 5,500 years ago

H. Rocky Mountains

I. continents

J. migration

Column B

_____ **1.** region known for ranching and mining

_____ **2.** topics studied by geographers

_____ **3.** provides the heat necessary for life on Earth

_____ **4.** magma once it reaches the Earth's surface

_____ **5.** South America and Africa moved apart

_____ **6.** moving from one place to another

_____ **7.** largest landmasses on Earth

_____ **8.** analyzes cultures today to learn how different elements are related

_____ **9.** Florida is an example of this

_____ **10.** approximate number of years ago that people developed writing

Directions: Multiple Choice Write the letter of the choice that best completes the statement or answers the question. *(7 points each)*

_____ **11.** Why might the U.S. government hire geographers?

    A. to decide how land and resources might be used

    B. to interview candidates for diplomatic positions

    C. to build dams and reservoirs in developing countries

    D. to study economic trends abroad

_____ **12.** Why can Earth be compared to a melon?

    A. Both are relatively round.   **C.** Both have several distinct layers.

    B. Both have "rough" outer shells.   **D.** Their innermost portions are rocklike.

_____ **13.** Earth's landforms _____.

    A. are found only on the continents   **C.** are found only on the ocean floors

    B. are found on the continents and on the ocean floors   **D.** have to be a certain height to be labeled "landforms"

_____ **14.** The world's population _____.

    A. is evenly distributed   **C.** has increased rapidly

    B. has decreased slightly   **D.** is relatively stable

_____ **15.** Why are Canada and the United States considered to be one culture region?

    A. They have similar languages and histories.

    B. Canada and the United States share a border.

    C. It is easy to move back and forth between them.

    D. Both use the Great Lakes for shipping goods.

Applying Skills: Reading a Diagram Use the diagram below to answer the questions that follow. *(5 points each)*

World Population, 2005

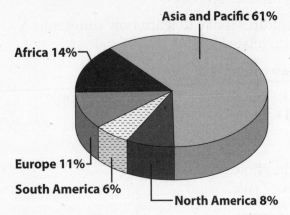

Asia and Pacific 61%

Africa 14%

Europe 11%

South America 6%

North America 8%

Source: *World Population Data Sheet, 2005.*

_____ **16.** Which region has the largest percentage of the world's population?

    A. Africa   **C.** Europe

    B. North America   **D.** Asia and the Pacific

_____ **17.** What percentage of the world's population resides in North and South America?

    A. 8 percent   **C.** 14 percent

    B. 11 percent   **D.** 6 percent

_____ **18.** If the total world population is 6 billion, about how many people live in Asia and the Pacific?

    A. 1.6 billion   **C.** 3.3 billion

    B. 2.5 billion   **D.** 4.5 billion

SCORE

Directions: Matching Match each item in Column A with its description in Column B. Write the correct letters in the blanks. *(10 points each)*

Column A

A. Global Positioning System

B. environment

C. Geographic Information Systems

D. geography

E. absolute location

Column B

_____ **1.** exact spot on Earth where a geographic feature is found

_____ **2.** system that uses radio signals to record the exact location of every place on Earth

_____ **3.** study of Earth and its people

_____ **4.** system of computer hardware and software that gathers, stores, and analyzes geographic information

_____ **5.** natural surroundings

Directions: Short Answer Answer each question or statement below on the line provided. *(10 points each)*

6. What are the five themes of geography?

_____

7. What does a physical geographer study?

_____

8. What are the four long periods of history as defined by Western societies?

_____

9. What types of information do satellites provide for maps?

_____

10. How does the work of geographers in government differ from those in the business world?

_____

SCORE

Directions: Matching Match each item in Column A with its description in Column B. Write the correct letters in the blanks. *(10 points each)*

Column A

A. summer solstice

B. revolution

C. equinoxes

D. axis

E. orbit

Column B

_____ **1.** path of each planet around the sun

_____ **2.** Earth's complete circuit around the sun

_____ **3.** imaginary line passing through the center of Earth from the North Pole to the South Pole

_____ **4.** day with the most hours of sunlight in the Northern Hemisphere

_____ **5.** two days when day and night are of equal length in both hemispheres

Directions: Short Answer Answer each question or statement below on the line provided. *(10 points each)*

6. Describe differences between Jupiter and Mars.

_____

7. What makes up our solar system?

_____

8. How does latitude affect the Earth's temperatures?

_____

9. How many degrees is Earth tilted on its axis?

_____

10. How are the seasons of the midlatitudes affected by air masses from the Tropics and the North and South Poles?

_____

SCORE

Directions: Matching Match each item in Column A with its description in Column B. Write the correct letters in the blanks. *(3 points each)*

Column A

A. Tropics

B. absolute location

C. 24 hours

D. physical features

E. leap year

F. technology

G. Mercury

H. Prehistory

I. axis

J. movement

Column B

_____ **1.** imaginary line that passes through the center of Earth

_____ **2.** a year that contains one extra day

_____ **3.** tools and methods that help people perform tasks

_____ **4.** low-latitude areas near the Equator

_____ **5.** landforms, plants, animals, and weather patterns

_____ **6.** refers to a time before people developed writing

_____ **7.** exact spot on Earth

_____ **8.** explains how and why people, ideas, and goods spread

_____ **9.** amount of time it takes for Earth to make one complete rotation

_____ **10.** relatively small, solid planet

Directions: Multiple Choice In the blank at the left, write the letter of the choice that best completes the statement or answers the question. *(3 points each)*

_____ **11.** Which geography theme describes the characteristics of a location?

    A. location   **C.** regions

    B. movement   **D.** place

_____ **12.** How do people affect their environment?

    A. by changing it to meet their needs

    B. by moving from one place to another

    C. by mapping it

    D. by describing their relative locations

_____ **13.** Approximately how many years ago did Modern History begin?

    A. 500 years ago   **C.** 1,000 years ago

    B. 700 years ago   **D.** 1,500 years ago

_____ **14.** Which of the following might be called upon to help plan a city or aid in international business?

    A. physical geographer   **C.** historical geographer

    B. human geographer   **D.** natural geographer

_____ **15.** The Middle Ages is also known as _____.

    A. the medieval period   **C.** Modern History

    B. Prehistory   **D.** Ancient History

_____ **16.** A millennium is a period of _____.

    A. 1 million years   **C.** 100 years

    B. 1,000 years   **D.** 10 years

_____ **17.** How long does it take for Earth to make one complete circuit around the sun?

    A. 24 hours   **C.** 6 months

    B. 365¼ days   **D.** 30 days

_____ **18.** In which direction does the Earth rotate?

    A. west   **C.** east

    B. southwest   **D.** northeast

_____ **19.** The summer solstice begins on or about _____.

    A. June 21   **C.** March 21

    B. December 22   **D.** September 23

_____ **20.** Where does the noon sun fall during both equinoxes?

    A. directly over the Northern Hemisphere

    B. directly over the Equator

    C. directly over the Tropic of Cancer

    D. directly over the Southern Hemisphere

Applying Skills: Reading a Diagram Use the diagram below to answer the questions that follow. *(5 points each)*

The Solar System

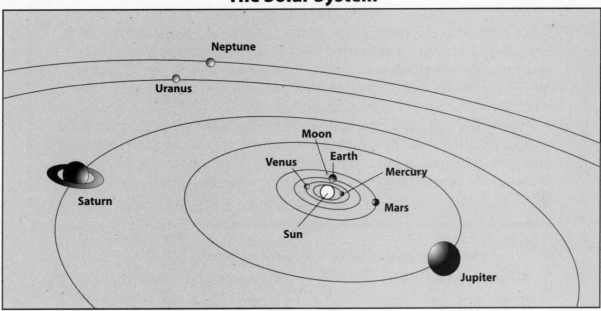

_____ **21.** Which planet is farthest from the sun?

    A. Neptune   **C.** Mercury

    B. Mars   **D.** Saturn

_____ **22.** Which planet is closest to Earth?

    A. Mercury   **C.** Uranus

    B. Jupiter   **D.** Mars

_____ **23.** Which planet is closest to the sun?

    A. Mercury   **C.** Venus

    B. Mars   **D.** Earth

Directions: Document-Based Questions Use the document below to answer the questions that follow. *(5 points each)*

> A radar originally developed for military surveillance and reconnaissance applications is helping a volunteer search-and-rescue group save lives. Rapid Terrain Visualization (RTV) precision-mapping synthetic aperture radar (SAR) data was used for the first time by the Albuquerque Mountain Rescue Council (AMRC) to help find and rescue a hiker stranded in the Sandia Mountains in New Mexico.
>
> The AMRC collected information about the hiker's location and then created detailed maps of the area. The maps were color-coded for height and gave estimates of ground roughness. By using the maps, rescuers were able to zero in on the lost hiker and rescue him.
>
> **Source:** www.sandia.gov/news-center/news-releases/2004/elect-semi-sensors/rescue.html.

_____ **24.** What was the original use for RTV-SAR radar mapping?

    A. locating lost hikers   **C.** search-and-rescue training

    B. military surveillance   **D.** wilderness education

_____ **25.** Where was the hiker lost?

    A. Albuquerque   **C.** Colorado

    B. Arizona   **D.** Sandia Mountains

_____ **26.** Why were these radar-generated maps so helpful to the search-and-rescue teams?

    A. The black-and-white maps were generated quickly and were easy to read.

    B. The maps gave detailed information about the physical geography of the area.

    C. The maps were able to pinpoint the location of the hiker immediately.

    D. Searchers did not have to supply additional information about the hiker.

Directions: Essay On a separate sheet of paper, answer the question below. *(10 points)*

    27. How does the study of history help geographers?

Name_____ Date_____ Class_____

Directions: Matching Match each item in Column A with its description in Column B. Write the correct letters in the blanks. *(3 points each)*

Column A

A. Ancient History

B. March 21

C. regions

D. Pluto

E. 100 years

F. September 23

G. 10 years

H. 88 days

I. geographers

J. 165 years

Column B

_____ **1.** once considered a major planet but now considered a minor one

_____ **2.** people who study Earth and its people

_____ **3.** areas of Earth's surface that have several common characteristics

_____ **4.** amount of time it takes Mercury to orbit the sun

_____ **5.** a decade

_____ **6.** fall equinox

_____ **7.** spring equinox

_____ **8.** time that lasted until about 1,500 years ago

_____ **9.** a century

_____ **10.** amount of time it takes Neptune to orbit the sun

Directions: Multiple Choice In the blank at the left, write the letter of the choice that best completes the statement or answers the question. *(3 points each)*

_____ **11.** The position of a place on the Earth's surface is known as _____.

    A. place

    B. location

    C. environment

    D. movement

_____ **12.** Which is the earliest historical period?

    A. Middle Ages

    B. Ancient History

    C. Prehistory

    D. Modern History

_____ **13.** Religions and languages are part of _____.

    A. human geography

    B. historical geography

    C. physical geography

    D. natural geography

_____ **14.** Why are Geographic Information Systems (GIS) important to geographers?

    A. They are cost-effective and can be purchased easily by geographers.

    B. They make it easier for geographers to communicate from the field.

    C. They are small and easy to carry.

    D. They can gather, store, and analyze geographic information.

_____ **15.** Which geographic theme can be defined by physical features?

    A. movement   **C.** place

    B. absolute location   **D.** culture

_____ **16.** What shape are most planets' orbits around the sun?

    A. nonlinear   **C.** linear

    B. elliptical   **D.** circular

_____ **17.** Every four years, which extra day is added to the calendar?

    A. September 29   **C.** June 31

    B. April 31   **D.** February 29

_____ **18.** Why do the seasons change as Earth makes its circuit around the sun?

    A. Earth is tilted on its axis.

    B. As Earth moves farther from the sun, the weather gets colder.

    C. As Earth moves closer to the sun, the weather gets warmer.

    D. The Earth rotates on its axis.

_____ **19.** During the summer solstice, the North Pole _____.

    A. is tilted away from the sun

    B. does not tilt

    C. experiences some melting of the polar ice cap

    D. is tilted toward the sun

_____ **20.** At noon on or about December 22, the sun's direct rays strike the _____.

    A. Equator   **C.** Prime Meridian

    B. Tropic of Capricorn   **D.** Tropic of Cancer

Applying Skills: Reading a Map Use the map below to answer the questions that follow. *(5 points each)*

Longitude and Latitude

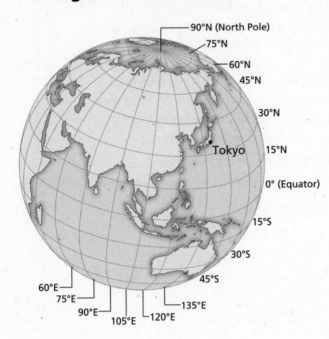

_____ **21.** What is the location of the Equator?

    A. 0° longitude   **C.** 90°N latitude

    B. 0° latitude   **D.** 30°S longitude

_____ **22.** What is located at 90°N latitude?

    A. Tokyo   **C.** Equator

    B. North Pole   **D.** Arctic Circle

_____ **23.** Lines of longitude run _____.

    A. north and south of the Equator

    B. north of the Equator

    C. south of the Equator

    D. from the North Pole to the South Pole

Directions: Document-Based Questions Use the document below to answer the questions that follow. *(5 points each)*

> Summer is the season of greatest plant growth in regions with sufficient summer rainfall. Festivals and rites have been used in many cultures to celebrate summer in recognition of its importance in food production.
>
> A period of exceptionally hot weather, often with high humidity, during the summer is called a heat wave. Such an occurrence in the temperate regions of the Northern Hemisphere in the latter part of summer is sometimes referred to as the dog days.
>
> **Source:** Encyclopaedia Britannica Online. www.britannica.com/eb/article9070305.

_____ **24.** Summer festivals are often held to celebrate _____.
   A. food production   **C.** a heat wave
   B. dog days   **D.** special events

_____ **25.** When do dog days occur?
   A. in the early part of summer
   B. during the equinoxes
   C. during the solstices
   D. in the latter part of summer

_____ **26.** Which of the following is characteristic of a heat wave?
   A. hot weather and low humidity
   B. hot weather and high humidity
   C. milder weather and high humidity
   D. milder weather and low humidity

Directions: Essay On a separate sheet of paper, answer the question below. *(10 points)*

   27. Why do we not feel the Earth moving as it rotates?

Name_____ Date_____ Class_____

Directions: Matching Match each item in Column A with its description in Column B. Write the correct letters in the blanks. *(10 points each)*

Column A

A. erosion

B. crust

C. mantle

D. magma

E. plate tectonics

Column B

_____ **1.** layer of hot, dense rock surrounding the Earth's core

_____ **2.** melted rock that is called lava when it comes from a volcano

_____ **3.** movement of rock by water, wind, and ice

_____ **4.** part of the Earth that includes the continents

_____ **5.** explains how the continents move

Directions: Short Answer Answer each question or statement below on the line provided. *(10 points each)*

6. What are Earth's layers?

_____

7. What is the theory of plate tectonics?

_____

8. What are the seven continents?

_____

9. What causes earthquakes?

_____

10. How do chemicals cause weathering of the Earth's surface?

_____

Name_____ Date_____ Class_____

Directions: Matching Match each item in Column A with its description in Column B. Write the correct letters in the blanks. *(10 points each)*

Column A

A. trench

B. precipitation

C. continental shelf

D. evaporation

E. condensation

Column B

_____ **1.** an underwater plateau off the coast of a continent

_____ **2.** when water changes from gas to liquid

_____ **3.** a deep cut in the ocean floor

_____ **4.** water that falls to the ground from the sky

_____ **5.** when water changes from liquid to gas

Directions: Short Answer Answer each question or statement below on the line provided. *(10 points each)*

6. What is the difference between a plain and a plateau?

_____

7. What is the deepest trench in the ocean, and where is it located?

_____

8. What kind of water is found in oceans, seas, bays, and gulfs?

_____

9. What are aquifers, and how do people utilize them?

_____

10. What is the water cycle?

_____

Directions: Matching Match each item in Column A with its description in Column B. Write the correct letters in the blanks. *(10 points each)*

Column A

A. prevailing winds

B. weather

C. biome

D. climate

E. currents

Column B

_____ **1.** changes in temperature, wind direction and speed, and air moisture over a short period of time

_____ **2.** streams of warm and cold water in the ocean

_____ **3.** area with certain types of plants and animals

_____ **4.** major patterns of movements of air

_____ **5.** predictable patterns of weather

Directions: Short Answer Answer each question or statement below on the line provided. *(10 points each)*

6. What is the difference between trade winds and westerlies?

_____

7. In years of El Niño ocean currents, how does rainfall in the eastern Pacific compare to rainfall in the western Pacific?

_____

8. Name at least three things that affect climate.

_____

9. What is a rain shadow, and how does it affect interior regions?

_____

10. How do urban climates differ from rural climates?

_____

SCORE

Directions: Matching Match each item in Column A with its description in Column B. Write the correct letters in the blanks. *(10 points each)*

Column A

A. conservation

B. biodiversity

C. crop rotation

D. irrigation

E. deforestation

Column B

_____ **1.** cutting down trees without planting new ones

_____ **2.** farmers changing what they plant in their fields from year to year

_____ **3.** using a resource carefully to avoid waste

_____ **4.** the many different kinds of life on Earth

_____ **5.** collecting water and distributing it to crops

Directions: Short Answer Answer each question or statement below on the line provided. *(10 points each)*

6. What is included in the lithosphere?

_____

7. What is global warming?

_____

8. Name three things that threaten the water supply.

_____

9. Why is the destruction of rain forests a concern?

_____

10. What is contour plowing?

_____

Directions: Matching Match each item in Column A with its description in Column B. Write the correct letters in the blanks. *(3 points each)*

Column A

A. westerlies

B. tributary

C. contour plowing

D. continental shelf

E. lithosphere

F. Pangaea

G. steppe

H. aquifer

I. climate

J. Mariana Trench

Column B

_____ **1.** stream that feeds into a larger river

_____ **2.** has a dry climate with grasses and shrubs

_____ **3.** large landmass that at one time was made up of South America and Africa

_____ **4.** deepest place on Earth

_____ **5.** technique used to limit the loss of topsoil

_____ **6.** predictable pattern of weather

_____ **7.** winds that blow over North America

_____ **8.** Earth's crust

_____ **9.** underground layer of rock through which water flows

_____ **10.** underwater plateau

Directions: Multiple Choice In the blank at the left, write the letter of the choice that best completes the statement or answers the question. *(3 points each)*

_____ **11.** Scientists believe Earth's inner core is made up of ____.

    A. steel and iron   **C.** iron and other minerals

    B. iron and nickel   **D.** magma

_____ **12.** What does an isthmus connect?

    A. two larger landmasses   **C.** a peninsula to the mainland

    B. two larger bodies of water   **D.** two continents

_____ **13.** What causes volcanoes and earthquakes?

    A. weathering   **C.** tectonic movement

    B. Earth's tilt   **D.** ocean currents

_____ 14. Condensation occurs when water ____.
   A. changes from a liquid to a gas
   B. collects in rivers, lakes, and oceans
   C. evaporates
   D. changes from gas to a liquid

_____ 15. Where does magma originate?
   A. the inner core   C. the outer core
   B. the crust   D. the outer mantle

_____ 16. Which of the following is directly linked to Earth's climate?
   A. the moon   C. the sun
   B. the tides   D. prevailing winds

_____ 17. Which human-made chemical in particular destroys the ozone layer?
   A. hydrogen   C. chlorofluorocarbon
   B. smog   D. sulfite

_____ 18. Why are scientists concerned that rain forests are being cut down at high rates?
   A. There is no market for the lumber taken from the forests.
   B. The forests help replace oxygen in the atmosphere.
   C. People who live in rain forests are being displaced.
   D. Rain forest habitats are being moved.

_____ 19. Where do most hurricanes occur?
   A. in the western Pacific Ocean
   B. in the western Atlantic and eastern Pacific Oceans
   C. in the eastern Atlantic Ocean
   D. in the Atlantic and Indian Oceans

_____ 20. The process by which water is collected and distributed to crops is known as ____.
   A. conservation   C. hydrospheric action
   B. irrigation   D. condensation

Applying Skills: Reading a Diagram Use the diagram below to answer the questions that follow. *(5 points each)*

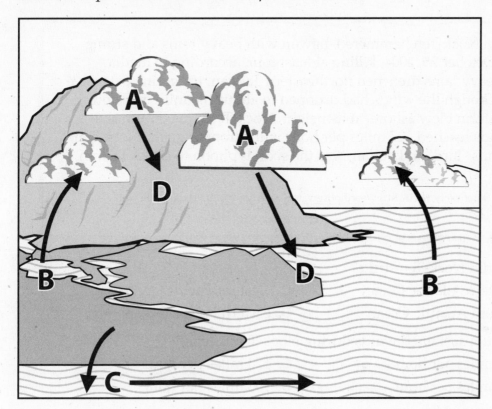

_____ **21.** What is the subject of this diagram?

    A. types of precipitation

    B. the water cycle

    C. how rivers are formed

    D. how erosion occurs

_____ **22.** What does the letter *D* signify?

    A. transpiration   **C.** surface runoff

    B. groundwater   **D.** precipitation

_____ **23.** Which letter signifies evaporation?

    A. A   **C.** C

    B. B   **D.** D

Directions: Document-Based Questions Use the document below to answer the questions that follow. *(5 points each)*

> Typhoon Nock-Ten hammered Taiwan with heavy rains and strong winds on October 25, 2004, killing at least four, according to media reports. Heavy rains drenched northeastern Taiwan, triggering extensive flooding. Though the winds had dropped to about 100 miles per hour when the storm blew ashore, at its height, Nock-Ten's maximum sustained winds reached 127 miles per hour with stronger gusts. Nock-Ten, which means "bird" in Laotian, was the sixth typhoon to strike Taiwan in 2004.
>
> **Source:** *Earth Observatory*, NASA. http://earthobservatory.nasa.gov/NaturalHazards/shownh.php3?img_id=12554.

_____ **24.** Where did Nock-Ten strike?

    A. western Atlantic Ocean   **C.** western Pacific Ocean

    B. eastern Atlantic Ocean   **D.** eastern Pacific Ocean

_____ **25.** Maximum sustained winds during Nock-Ten reached ____.

    A. 127 miles per hour   **C.** 170 miles per hour

    B. 204 miles per hour   **D.** 100 miles per hour

_____ **26.** Which of the following statements is supported by the excerpt?

    A. Typhoons are unusual in Southeast Asia.

    B. Typhoons are unpredictable in South Asia.

    C. Typhoons strike East Asia fairly often.

    D. Typhoons are violent windstorms that form over land.

Directions: Essay On a separate sheet of paper, answer the question below. *(10 points)*

    27. What is the meaning of *El Niño*? What happens during an El Niño event?

Earth's Physical Geography

Chapter 2 Test Form B

Directions: Matching Match each item in Column A with its description in Column B. Write the correct letters in the blanks. *(3 points each)*

Column A

A. El Niño

B. North Atlantic Current

C. inner core

D. tornadoes

E. continental drift

F. leeward

G. weathering

H. hydrosphere

I. plateaus

J. highland climate

Column B

_____ **1.** flatlands at high elevations

_____ **2.** violent, funnel-shaped windstorms

_____ **3.** caused by tectonic plate movement

_____ **4.** side of a mountain that receives little rainfall

_____ **5.** warm waters reach South America's Pacific coast

_____ **6.** made up of nickel and iron

_____ **7.** vegetation changes with altitude

_____ **8.** water, ice, chemicals, and plants break apart rocks

_____ **9.** Earth's surface water and groundwater

_____ **10.** carries warm water to western Europe

Directions: Multiple Choice In the blank at the left, write the letter of the choice that best completes the statement or answers the question. *(3 points each)*

_____ **11.** The Ring of Fire surrounds the ____.
   A. inner core
   B. San Andreas Fault
   C. Pacific Ocean
   D. Tropics

_____ **12.** The Andes of South America were created by the collision of ____.
   A. two continental plates
   B. two continental shelves
   C. two oceanic plates
   D. continental and oceanic plates

_____ **13.** What percentage of Earth's water is salt water?
   A. 97 percent
   B. 96 percent
   C. 3 percent
   D. 70 percent

_____ **14.** The place where a river empties into another body of water
is called its ____.

A. mouth   **C.** source

B. delta   **D.** estuary

_____ **15.** What is evaporation?

A. Water turns from a gas into a liquid.

B. Water falls as rain, snow, or hail.

C. Surface water runs into lakes and seas.

D. Water turns from a liquid into a gas.

_____ **16.** All of the following are biomes EXCEPT ____.

A. rain forest   **C.** rain shadow

B. desert   **D.** tundra

_____ **17.** Winds that blow from east to west between the Tropics and
the Equator are called ____.

A. westerlies   **C.** La Niña

B. prevailing winds   **D.** trade winds

_____ **18.** What is the name for the collection of plants and animals of
all types that live on Earth?

A. biodiversity   **C.** the biosphere

B. the hydrosphere   **D.** an ecosystem

_____ **19.** Why is the presence of ozone in the atmosphere important?

A. It forms a shield against the damaging rays of the sun.

B. It affects the amount of rainfall in any given region.

C. Vitamins are absorbed into the body as a result of the ozone layer.

D. The ozone layer holds down the level of air pollution.

_____ **20.** Why do urban areas have higher temperatures?

A. More people emit body heat in urban areas than in rural areas.

B. Larger buildings cause wind shifts that affect the temperature.

C. Buildings and pavement absorb and reflect the sun's heat.

D. Plants and animals in rural areas absorb more heat.

Applying Skills: Reading a Chart Use the chart below to answer the questions that follow. *(5 points each)*

World Climate Zones				
Category	**Subcategory**	**Characteristics**	**Vegetation**	**Example**
High Latitude	A	Short, mild summers; cold winters	Coniferous forests	Most of Alaska and Canada; western Russia
Midlatitude	Marine west coast	Cool summers, mild winters; ample rainfall	Deciduous or evergreen forests	B
Dry	Steppe	Temperatures can be warm or mild; rainfall low and unreliable	Grasses, shrubs	Western Great Plains; Sahel region south of the Sahara (Africa)
Tropical	Tropical savanna	Warm temperatures throughout year; dry winter	C	Southern half of Brazil; eastern Africa

_____ **21.** Which of the following should be in the chart cell marked *A?*

    A. subarctic   **C.** tundra

    B. ice cap   **D.** highlands

_____ **22.** Which of the following should be in the chart cell marked *B?*

    A. Amazon Basin   **C.** Southeastern United States

    B. Sonoran Desert   **D.** Northwestern Europe

_____ **23.** Which of the following should be in the chart cell marked *C?*

    A. dense rain forests

    B. grasslands dotted by scattered trees

    C. mixed forests

    D. low-lying grasses and mosses

Directions: Document-Based Questions Use the document below to answer the questions that follow. *(5 points each)*

> With no moving air to lift the sails, ships were stranded for weeks in the hot, still weather. Meanwhile, food supplies dwindled and spoiled as the ships sat. To lighten the load so the ships could take advantage of the slightest breeze, sailors would toss supplies overboard, including livestock. This practice gave rise to the name by which the calm areas at the edge of the Tropics are known—the horse latitudes.

_____ **24.** According to this quote, why were the ships stranded?
  A. There were no sea breezes.   **C.** They carried too many horses.
  B. Their engines failed.   **D.** They had no sails.

_____ **25.** How can you tell that this quote is describing an earlier historical period?
  A. Ships are crossing the ocean.
  B. Ships are carrying cargo.
  C. The ships rely on wind currents and sails.
  D. The temperature is hot in the Tropics.

_____ **26.** Where are the horse latitudes located?
  A. near 60°N latitude
  B. near the westerlies
  C. near the Tropic of Cancer and the Tropic of Capricorn
  D. along the Equator

Directions: Essay On a separate sheet of paper, answer the question below. *(10 points)*

  27. How were the Himalaya formed?

SCORE

World Population

Quiz 3-1

Directions: Matching Match each item in Column A with its description in Column B. Write the correct letters in the blanks. *(10 points each)*

Column A

A. urbanization

B. internal migration

C. declining death rates

D. population density

E. pull factor

Column B

_____ **1.** the average number of people living in a square kilometer

_____ **2.** one reason for rapid population growth

_____ **3.** moving from place to place in the same country

_____ **4.** something that attracts immigrants to another place

_____ **5.** the rapid growth of cities

Directions: Short Answer Answer each question or statement below on the line provided. *(10 points each)*

6. Name the five regions that have two-thirds of the world's population. What attracts people to these regions?

_____

_____

_____

7. How do birthrates and death rates work together to contribute to population growth?

_____

8. What is a refugee, and what events create refugee populations?

_____

9. What is international migration?

_____

10. What effects do mass migrations have on the country that people are leaving?

_____

SCORE

Directions: Matching Match each item in Column A with its description in Column B. Write the correct letters in the blanks. *(10 points each)*

Column A

A. ethnic group

B. globalization

C. cultural diffusion

D. civilizations

E. dialect

Column B

_____ **1.** a local variation of a language

_____ **2.** spreading ideas, customs, and language from one culture to another

_____ **3.** highly developed cultures

_____ **4.** the development of a worldwide culture with an interdependent economy

_____ **5.** people who share the same language, history, religion, and physical traits

Directions: Short Answer Answer each question or statement below on the line provided. *(10 points each)*

6. How do anthropologists and archaeologists differ?

_____

7. What is the difference between a dictatorship and a democracy?

_____

8. How do geographers measure the success of an economy?

_____

9. Where were the first four highly developed cultures located?

_____

10. Name three ways that culture spread in the past, and one way that culture spreads today.

_____

SCORE

Directions: Matching Match each item in Column A with its description in Column B. Write the correct letters in the blanks. *(10 points each)*

Column A

A. renewable

B. economic system

C. newly industrialized

D. nonrenewable

E. quota

Column B

_____ **1.** moving toward developed economies

_____ **2.** limit on how much of a particular product can be imported from a certain nation

_____ **3.** resources like iron ore and coal that are limited in supply

_____ **4.** determines what goods and services to produce, how to produce them, and who will receive them

_____ **5.** resources like wind, water, and forests

Directions: Short Answer Answer each question or statement below on the line provided. *(10 points each)*

6. What are the four types of economic systems?

_____

7. What defines a developed economy?

_____

8. Why is trade important?

_____

9. What is a tariff? Why might a country use it?

_____

10. If a country stops producing oil, what are the effects in interdependent countries?

_____

Directions: Matching Match each item in Column A with its description in Column B. Write the correct letters in the blanks. *(3 points each)*

Column A

A. internal migration

B. developed

C. emigration

D. tariff

E. archaeologist

F. Agricultural Revolution

G. geographer

H. Buddhism

I. ethnocentrism

J. Hinduism

Column B

_____ **1.** to leave one's home country to move to another

_____ **2.** uses historical objects of a culture to understand the past

_____ **3.** Siddhartha Gautama founded this religion

_____ **4.** movement of people from farms and villages to cities

_____ **5.** belief that one's culture is superior to other cultures

_____ **6.** country with a mix of agriculture, manufacturing, and service industries

_____ **7.** led people to create civilizations

_____ **8.** tax on imported goods

_____ **9.** looks at physical objects, such as food and housing, to study a culture

_____ **10.** religion whose followers believe in reincarnation

Directions: Multiple Choice In the blank at the left, write the letter of the choice that best completes the statement or answers the question. *(3 points each)*

_____ **11.** In the late 1990s, 2 million refugees fled mass killings in ____.

    A. Nigeria   **C.** Rwanda

    B. Namibia   **D.** Botswana

_____ **12.** Which of the following is expected to experience the largest population growth by the year 2050?

    A. Latin America   **C.** Africa

    B. China   **D.** United States and Canada

_____ **13.** How is population density measured?

    A. total population divided by total land area

    B. average population plus total land area

    C. total land area divided by total population

    D. average land area plus total population

_____ **14.** Which of the following statements about population density is true?

    A. The population density of Buenos Aires is lower than that of Argentina.

    B. Norway's population density is higher than that of Malaysia.

    C. Mongolia has a high population density.

    D. Population density represents an average.

_____ **15.** Trade, migration, and conquest led to _____.

    A. river valley civilizations   **C.** cultural diffusion

    B. representative democracies   **D.** developing countries

_____ **16.** Which of the following is a pull factor for migration?

    A. shortage of farmland   **C.** shortage of jobs

    B. lure of jobs   **D.** natural disaster

_____ **17.** Which of the following is a renewable resource?

    A. timber   **C.** natural gas

    B. coal   **D.** iron ore

_____ **18.** In which economic system do supply and demand guide choices?

    A. market economy   **C.** traditional economy

    B. command economy   **D.** communist economy

_____ **19.** South Korea, Thailand, and Singapore are examples of _____.

    A. developed countries   **C.** newly industrialized countries

    B. developing countries   **D.** industrialized countries

_____ **20.** A barrier to trade that limits the number of imported items from a certain country is a _____.

    A. tariff   **C.** subsidy

    B. pact   **D.** quota

Applying Skills: Reading a Chart Use the chart below to answer the questions that follow. *(5 points each)*

Type of Government	Who Holds Power?	Examples
Direct Democracy	All citizens vote directly on issues.	• Parts of Switzerland • Some New England towns
Representative Democracy	People vote for representatives who lead the country and make laws.	• United States • Russia • France
Constitutional Monarchy	A monarch inherits the right to rule but is limited by laws and a law-making body elected by the people.	• United Kingdom • Japan • Sweden • Jordan
Absolute Monarchy	A monarch inherits the right to rule and has unlimited power.	• Saudi Arabia
Dictatorship	A dictator makes all laws and suppresses any opposition.	• Cuba • Iraq under Saddam Hussein • Germany under Adolf Hitler

_____ **21.** Which type of government does Japan have?

    A. direct democracy   **C.** constitutional monarchy

    B. representative democracy   **D.** dictatorship

_____ **22.** Citizens hold power in all of the following types of governments EXCEPT _____.

    A. constitutional monarchy   **C.** direct democracy

    B. absolute monarchy   **D.** representative democracy

_____ **23.** In which of the following do citizens elect representatives who make laws?

    A. direct democracy   **C.** dictatorship

    B. absolute monarchy   **D.** constitutional monarchy

Directions: Document-Based Questions Use the document below to answer the questions that follow. *(5 points each)*

> Gasoline prices jumped in 2006. U.S. drivers saw prices at the pump reach $3 per gallon. At some point, however, even this price may seem inexpensive. Several reasons account for the high cost of oil. The first is that the demand for oil has risen sharply. Industrialized countries like the United States are demanding it, but now emerging countries—China and India, for example—are competing to buy it. Oil is needed to power many more vehicles in the world than ever before. A huge number of oil-based products are also being manufactured, including CDs, cars, house paint, bicycle helmets, telephones, golf balls, and contact lenses. Another reason for the high cost of oil is that oil supplies are not growing larger.

_____ **24.** What is one reason for the high price of oil?
    A. increased supply   **C.** increased demand
    B. competition among suppliers   **D.** increase in oil substitutes

_____ **25.** What does this statement in the excerpt mean: "oil supplies are not growing larger"?
    A. Oil is a nonrenewable resource.   **C.** There is a shortage of oil.
    B. Oil is a fossil fuel.   **D.** Oil is a natural resource.

_____ **26.** What is a significant result of China and India "emerging"?
    A. More golf balls are being produced.
    B. Oil has been discovered in the two countries.
    C. More automobiles need oil.
    D. More people can afford contact lenses.

Directions: Essay On a separate sheet of paper, answer the question below. *(10 points)*

    27. What are the effects of migration on the home country and the new country?

Directions: Matching Match each item in Column A with its description in Column B. Write the correct letters in the blanks. *(3 points each)*

Column A

A. family

B. Muslim traders

C. trade

D. socialization

E. fossil fuels

F. Muhammad

G. democracy

H. refugees

I. Abraham

J. dialect

Column B

_____ **1.** people who flee to another country to escape war or persecution

_____ **2.** most important social group in all cultures

_____ **3.** process by which people adjust their behavior to meet the rules of the culture

_____ **4.** oil, coal, and natural gas

_____ **5.** power is held by the people

_____ **6.** founder of Islam

_____ **7.** allows nations to import and export goods

_____ **8.** early leader of Judaism

_____ **9.** local form of a language

_____ **10.** example of cultural diffusion

Directions: Multiple Choice In the blank at the left, write the letter of the choice that best completes the statement or answers the question. *(3 points each)*

_____ **11.** Approximately how many people inhabit the Earth today?
   A. more than 6 billion   **C.** less than 4 billion
   B. less than 5 billion   **D.** more than 20 billion

_____ **12.** The type of migration that results in urbanization is known as ____.
   A. immigration   **C.** international migration
   B. internal migration   **D.** emigration

_____ **13.** Approximately what percentage of the Earth's surface is covered by land?
   A. 30 percent   **C.** 55 percent
   B. 10 percent   **D.** 45 percent

_____ **14.** What form of government exists when a leader uses the military to rule by force?

    A. dictatorship   **C.** democracy

    B. monarchy   **D.** limited government

_____ **15.** What can be used to measure the success of an economy?

    A. population density   **C.** the death rate

    B. people's quality of life   **D.** the form of government

_____ **16.** Which of the following countries is a world leader in the use of solar energy?

    A. United States   **C.** France

    B. Germany   **D.** China

_____ **17.** The world remained largely agricultural until the _____.

    A. Agricultural Revolution   **C.** 1700s

    B. river valley civilizations arose   **D.** Internet was invented

_____ **18.** Native Americans' use of the horse is an example of _____.

    A. socialization   **C.** ethnocentrism

    B. internal migration   **D.** cultural diffusion

_____ **19.** Which of the following is a developing country?

    A. Guatemala   **C.** Thailand

    B. Singapore   **D.** South Korea

_____ **20.** Why are tariffs barriers to trade?

    A. All items are affected by tariffs.

    B. Tariffs make imported items more expensive.

    C. Tariffs cause people to purchase more expensive items.

    D. Tariffs limit the amount of items imported from a certain country.

Applying Skills: Reading a Chart Use the chart below to answer the questions that follow. *(5 points each)*

Economic System	WHAT, HOW, and FOR WHOM to produce	Examples (in theory)
Traditional	Customs and traditions determine what and how to produce. Resources are usually shared. Many traditional systems use bartering to exchange goods and services.	• Inuit • Some parts of Africa and South America
Command	Government owns resources and controls production, prices, and wages. Shortages of consumer goods occur because government sets prices low and resources are often used for military goods.	• China • North Korea • Former USSR
Market	Individuals own resources and determine what and how to produce. Prices and wages are determined by producer supply and consumer demand.	• United States
Mixed	Individuals own most resources and determine what and how to produce. Government regulates certain industries.	• Most nations

_____ 21. Who makes key decisions in a command economy?

    A. the government   **C.** individuals

    B. no one; resources are shared   **D.** private businesses

_____ 22. How are goods and services exchanged in a traditional economy?

    A. through prices and wages

    B. through government regulation

    C. through barter

    D. through shortages and surpluses

_____ 23. How are prices and wages determined in a market economy?

    A. by government control   **C** by customs and traditions

    B. by supply and demand   **D.** through federal agencies

Directions: Document-Based Questions Use the document below to answer the questions that follow. *(5 points each)*

> In Native American cultures, birds of prey, especially eagles, are represented in numerous artifacts and legends. The Thunderbird is present throughout North American Indian legends. The form of the Thunderbird is typically a huge eagle or vulture-type bird that exists in the heavens. The bird was believed to cause thunder as it flew, and some Native American nations considered it to be the Great Spirit itself. It was said that if you saw an eagle while you were praying or participating in a ceremony, your prayers would be answered. Some nations believed that the eagle carried prayers directly to the Great Creator.
>
> **Source:** Native Americans and Eagles. www.indiana.edu/~bradwood/eagles/native.htm.

_____ **24.** What aspect of culture does this excerpt represent?

    A. socialization   **C.** history

    B. language   **D.** arts

_____ **25.** What did Native Americans believe would happen if you saw an eagle while praying?

    A. Ancestors would honor your request.

    B. Other birds of prey would intercede on your behalf.

    C. Your prayer would be answered.

    D. The Great Spirit would come to you.

_____ **26.** In Native American legend, the Thunderbird _____.

    A. exists only when one prays

    B. carries prayers to the Great Creator

    C. is a songbird

    D. is rarely seen on artifacts

Directions: Essay On a separate sheet of paper, answer the question below. *(10 points)*

    27. Why has globalization not worked for everyone?

Name_____ Date_____ Class_____

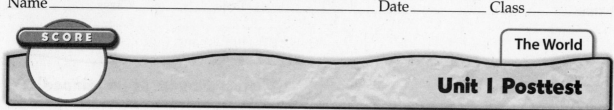
Directions: Matching Match each item in Column A with its description in Column B. Write the correct letters in the blanks. *(5 points each)*

Column A

A. inner planets

B. North Atlantic Current

C. 1,770 miles

D. ozone

E. outer planets

F. arts

G. status

H. human-environment interaction

I. 31 to 62 miles

J. ethnocentrism

Column B

_____ **1.** approximate thickness of Earth's crust

_____ **2.** describes how people affect and are affected by their natural surroundings

_____ **3.** Mercury, Venus, Earth, and Mars

_____ **4.** approximate thickness of Earth's mantle

_____ **5.** carries warm water from the Tropics to western Europe

_____ **6.** refers to a person's importance or rank

_____ **7.** believing that one's own culture is superior to other cultures

_____ **8.** Jupiter, Saturn, Uranus, and Neptune

_____ **9.** dance and literature

_____ **10.** form of oxygen

Directions: Multiple Choice Write the letter of the choice that best completes the statement or answers the question. *(5 points each)*

_____ **11.** Which planet takes the longest time to complete one orbit of the sun?
   A. Mercury   **C.** Venus
   B. Mars   **D.** Neptune

_____ **12.** Which is the location of the Tropic of Cancer?
   A. 23½°E longitude   **C.** 23½°N latitude
   B. 23½°W longitude   **D.** 23½°S latitude

_____ **13.** The temperature of Earth's outer core can reach _____.
   A. 4,700°F   **C.** 2,500°F
   B. 8,500°F   **D.** 10,500°F

_____ **14.** What determines how much water vapor the air holds?
   A. the air's temperature   **C.** the velocity of the wind
   B. the water's temperature **D.** the air pressure

_____ **15.** How many major world religions exist?

    A. 2,000   **C.** 25

    B. 5   **D.** 15

Applying Skills: Reading a Diagram Use the diagram below to answer the questions that follow. *(5 points each)*

Geographic Features

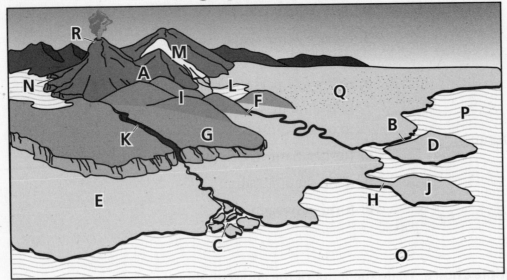

_____ **16.** According to the diagram, what type of landform is letter *H*?

    A. strait   **C.** isthmus

    B. channel   **D.** peninsula

_____ **17.** According to the diagram, what does the letter *M* show?

    A. volcano   **C.** plateau

    B. glacier   **D.** escarpment

_____ **18.** What does the letter *F* signify?

    A. canyon   **C.** mouth

    B. source   **D.** channel

Directions: Essay On a separate sheet of paper, answer the question below. *(10 points)*

    19. Why are mountain peaks cold?

SCORE

Directions: Matching Match each item in Column A with its description in Column B. Write the correct letters in the blanks. *(5 points each)*

Column A

A. humid subtropical

B. Pacific coast

C. separation of powers

D. Midwest

E. Parliament

F. United Nations

G. Asia

H. tariffs

I. Great Plains

J. desert

Column B

_____ **1.** area that stretches west of the Mississippi River

_____ **2.** lawmaking body in Canada

_____ **3.** Cleveland and Detroit are located in this region

_____ **4.** supports the idea of checks and balances

_____ **5.** area where most earthquakes take place

_____ **6.** climate in the inland West

_____ **7.** area that Christopher Columbus was hoping to reach

_____ **8.** taxes on imports

_____ **9.** world organization that promotes cooperation

_____ **10.** climate in the southeastern United States

Directions: Multiple Choice Write the letter of the choice that best completes the statement or answers the question. *(7 points each)*

_____ **11.** The culture of the United States has been shaped mostly by ____.

A. farming

B. Native Americans

C. immigrants

D. wealth

_____ **12.** The Great Lakes were formed thousands of years ago by ____.

A. the St. Lawrence Seaway

B. glaciers

C. Niagara Falls

D. earthquakes

_____ **13.** The descendants of the people who settled the Americas about 15,000 years ago are ____.

A. Native Americans

B. Latinos

C. Asians

D. African Americans

_____ **14.** How do the United States and Canadian free market
economies differ?

    A. The U.S. government provides more services to the public.

    B. The U.S. economy is based on free trade.

    C. Canadian provinces have more power than U.S. states.

    D. The Canadian government provides more services to the public.

_____ **15.** Why is it undesirable for a country to have a long-term
trade deficit?

    A. The country will amass too much purchasing power.

    B. The country is spending more than it earns.

    C. The country is earning more than it spends.

    D. Other countries will find it difficult to export to that country.

Applying Skills: Reading a Graph Use the graph below to answer the
questions that follow. *(5 points each)*

_____ **16.** What percentage of Canadians follow
no established religion?

    A. 16 percent

    B. 11.8 percent

    C. 1.9 percent

    D. 4.4 percent

_____ **17.** Which two religious groups combined
make up more than 60 percent of all
Canadians?

    A. Protestant and Other Christian

    B. Muslim and Roman Catholic

    C. Roman Catholic and Protestant

    D. Roman Catholic and "None"

_____ **18.** What percentage of Canadians are
practicing Muslims?

    A. 11.8 percent

    B. 4.4 percent

    C. 23.3 percent

    D. 1.9 percent

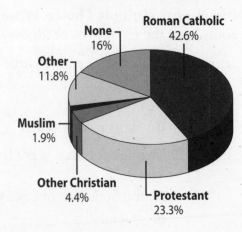

Canada: Religions

None 16%
Roman Catholic 42.6%
Other 11.8%
Muslim 1.9%
Other Christian 4.4%
Protestant 23.3%

Source: *CIA World Factbook*, 2006.

Physical Features

Quiz 4-1

Directions: Matching Match each item in Column A with its description in Column B. Write the correct letters in the blanks. *(10 points each)*

Column A

A. Continental Divide

B. Canadian Shield

C. Grand Banks

D. Niagara River

E. Great Lakes

Column B

_____ **1.** flows north from Lake Erie to Lake Ontario

_____ **2.** formed by glaciers thousands of years ago

_____ **3.** fishing grounds that now suffer from overfishing

_____ **4.** determines which way the rivers flow from the Rocky Mountains

_____ **5.** horseshoe-shaped area with poor soil, a cold climate, but many minerals

Directions: Short Answer Answer each question or statement below on the line provided. *(10 points each)*

6. How do the soils of the Atlantic coast differ from the soils of the Gulf of Mexico coastal plain?

_____

7. Which are older, the Appalachian Mountains or the Rocky Mountains? Compare their features.

_____

8. What area of North America once provided food for millions of buffalo? What is grown and raised on the land today?

_____

9. Why are the St. Lawrence River and the Mississippi River so important to trade?

_____

10. Why are Alberta's oil reserves costly to obtain?

_____

SCORE

Directions: Matching Match each item in Column A with its description in Column B. Write the correct letters in the blanks. *(10 points each)*

Column A

A. humid continental

B. humid subtropical

C. tropical savanna

D. Mediterranean

E. tundra and subarctic

Column B

_____ **1.** climate of the northern parts of Alaska and Canada

_____ **2.** climate of southern California

_____ **3.** climate found in the southeastern United States

_____ **4.** climate of eastern Canada and the northeastern United States

_____ **5.** climate of southern Florida

Directions: Short Answer Answer each question or statement below on the line provided. *(10 points each)*

6. What is the main difference between tornadoes and hurricanes? How are they similar?

_____

7. How are evergreens able to survive the cold winters of the subarctic?

_____

8. What types of vegetation are common in a marine west coast climate?

_____

9. Which receives more rain, the inland West region or the Great Plains? Why?

_____

10. Why do areas of northeastern and southeastern North America have similar climates in the summer?

_____

SCORE

Directions: Matching Match each item in Column A with its description in Column B. Write the correct letters in the blanks. *(3 points each)*

Column A

A. Dust Bowl

B. 1906

C. dormant

D. contiguous

E. Appalachians

F. Continental Divide

G. white-out conditions

H. 2005

I. canyon

J. Houston

Column B

_____ **1.** year of the San Francisco earthquake

_____ **2.** large city on the Gulf coastal plain

_____ **3.** unlikely to erupt

_____ **4.** heavy snowfall problem

_____ **5.** joined together inside a common boundary

_____ **6.** the high ridge of the Rockies

_____ **7.** year of Hurricane Katrina

_____ **8.** experienced drought in the 1930s

_____ **9.** deep valley with steep sides

_____ **10.** oldest mountains in North America

Directions: Multiple Choice In the blank at the left, write the letter of the choice that best completes the statement or answers the question. *(3 points each)*

_____ **11.** Which region covers most of North America?

A. United States and Mexico

B. Canada and Mexico

C. United States and Central America

D. United States and Canada

_____ **12.** Which of the following regions is an important U.S. economic, cultural, and political center?

A. Atlantic megalopolis

B. New England states

C. Piedmont

D. Central Lowlands

_____ **13.** Which is the highest point in North America?

A. Mount St. Helens

B. Mount McKinley

C. Mount Mitchell

D. Mount Hood

_____ **14.** Where does the Mississippi River begin?

    A. Wisconsin   **C.** Gulf of Mexico

    B. Mississippi   **D.** Minnesota

_____ **15.** Which state ranks first in oil and natural gas reserves in the United States?

    A. Texas   **C.** Louisiana

    B. Alaska   **D.** Oklahoma

_____ **16.** Where do most Americans and Canadians live?

    A. near the Great Lakes   **C.** in the middle latitudes

    B. near the Tropic of Cancer   **D.** along the coasts

_____ **17.** Why does the inland West receive little rainfall?

    A. Hot, dry air gets trapped between the Rockies and the Appalachian Mountains.

    B. Cooler air is kept away from the area by the Pacific ranges.

    C. Cooler air flows away from the area toward the Gulf of Mexico.

    D. Hot, dry air gets trapped between the Pacific ranges and the Rockies.

_____ **18.** What is the average January temperature in Atlanta, Georgia?

    A. 41°F   **C.** 20°F

    B. 72°F   **D.** 58°F

_____ **19.** Approximately how many people died during Hurricane Katrina?

    A. 100 people   **C.** 1,000 people

    B. 500 people   **D.** 1,800 people

_____ **20.** How do evergreen trees survive bitterly cold winters?

    A. Sharp needles insulate against the cold.

    B. Waxy needles keep out moisture.

    C. Waxy needles keep in moisture.

    D. Blunt needles help the trees stay warm.

Applying Skills: Reading a Map Use the map below to answer the questions that follow. *(5 points each)*

Great Lakes

_____ **21.** How many states border the Great Lakes?

A. 10　　　　　　　　　　　**C.** 9

B. 8　　　　　　　　　　　　**D.** 6

_____ **22.** Which lake is the largest?

A. Huron　　　　　　　　　**C.** Michigan

B. Ontario　　　　　　　　 **D.** Superior

_____ **23.** The St. Lawrence River connects _____.

A. Lake Ontario and the Atlantic Ocean

B. Lake Superior and Lake Ontario

C. the Great Lakes with each other

D. Lake Michigan with Lake Erie

Directions: Document-Based Questions Use the document below to answer the questions that follow. *(5 points each)*

> The cold Labrador Current and the warmer Gulf Stream meet near the Grand Banks. Air masses passing over this water often produce heavy fogs. Occasional icebergs and severe storms also add to the hazards of this area. However, the mixture of cold and warmer waters favors the growth of plankton, upon which fish rely for their food supply.
>
> Among the most plentiful species of fish are cod, haddock, rosefish, various flatfish, herring, and mackerel. In the mid-twentieth century, overfishing harmed the area and led to Canada's placing some restrictions on the size of fishing nets that could be used. Canada also banned fishing of some species altogether.
>
> **Source:** *Encyclopaedia Britannica.* www.britannica.com/eb/article9037658.

_____ **24.** What caused the Canadian government to place restrictions on the fishing industry?

    A. overfishing   **C.** fog

    B. icebergs   **D.** storms

_____ **25.** Air masses flowing over the cold and warm currents of the Grand Banks produce ____.

    A. ice   **C.** fog

    B. severe storms   **D.** high seas

_____ **26.** The species of fish that inhabit the Grand Banks rely upon what for their food supply?

    A. herring   **C.** flatfish

    B. cod   **D.** plankton

Directions: Essay On a separate sheet of paper, answer the questions below. *(10 points)*

    27. Which two U.S. states lie apart from the contiguous 48 states? Where are these states located?

SCORE

Directions: Matching Match each item in Column A with its description in Column B. Write the correct letters in the blanks. *(3 points each)*

Column A

A. Toronto

B. Piedmont

C. St. Lawrence

D. hurricane

E. storm surge

F. St. Louis

G. Rockies

H. Mississippi

I. Canadian Shield

J. Tornado Alley

Column B

_____ **1.** high levels of seawater

_____ **2.** North America's longest river

_____ **3.** mountain range on the eastern edge of a cordillera

_____ **4.** horseshoe-shaped area of rocky hills, lakes, and evergreens

_____ **5.** central United States

_____ **6.** inland port city

_____ **7.** important Canadian river

_____ **8.** wind system that forms in a tropical area

_____ **9.** fertile, hilly area inland from the Atlantic Ocean

_____ **10.** large city in the Central Lowlands

Directions: Multiple Choice In the blank at the left, write the letter of the choice that best completes the statement or answers the question. *(3 points each)*

_____ **11.** Which country is the second-largest in the world?
  A. Canada   **C.** Mexico
  B. the United States   **D.** Russia

_____ **12.** Which part of the country once provided food for millions of buffalo and for the Native Americans who lived there?
  A. Cordillera   **C.** Canadian Shield
  B. Great Plains   **D.** Eastern Lowlands

_____ **13.** Which of the following empties into the Atlantic Ocean?
  A. St. Lawrence River   **C.** Colorado River
  B. Mississippi River   **D.** Rio Grande

_____ 14. West of the Continental Divide, rivers flow toward the ____.

   A. Arctic Ocean   **C.** Pacific Ocean

   B. Atlantic Ocean   **D.** Mississippi River system

_____ 15. Coal from the Appalachian Mountains, Wyoming, and British Columbia could supply energy for approximately ____.

   A. 250 years   **C.** 300 years

   B. 400 years   **D.** 450 years

_____ 16. In subarctic climates, winters are ____.

   A. brief and cool, while summers are long and warm

   B. long and cold, while summers are long and warm

   C. brief and cool, just like summers

   D. long and cold, while summers are brief and cool

_____ 17. Why did many farmers leave the Great Plains during the 1930s?

   A. Floods ruined crops and destroyed livestock.

   B. Drought caused economic hardships.

   C. Many farms were destroyed by tornadoes.

   D. Blizzards caused devastation to many farms.

_____ 18. During which months of the year do hurricanes normally develop?

   A. November to January   **C.** June to September

   B. March to May   **D.** October to December

_____ 19. What caused many of the fires during the San Francisco earthquake?

   A. underground volcanoes   **C.** tectonic magma that surfaced

   B. broken natural gas lines   **D.** downed power lines

_____ 20. Which of the following is true about the climate of California?

   A. Northern California has a marine climate, and southern California has a Mediterranean climate.

   B. California has a marine west coast climate.

   C. Northern California has a Mediterranean climate, and southern California has a marine climate.

   D. California has a Mediterranean climate.

Applying Skills: Reading a Map Use the map below to answer the questions that follow. *(5 points each)*

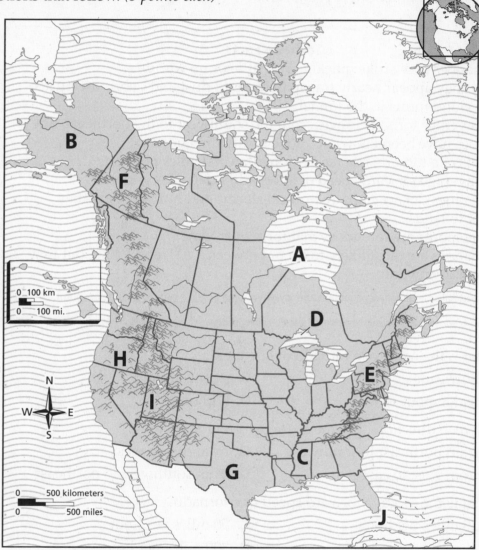

_____ **21.** Which physical feature is labeled *D* on the map?

  A. Lake Erie   **C.** Lake Superior

  B. Lake Huron   **D.** Lake Ontario

_____ **22.** Which physical feature is labeled *E* on the map?

  A. Mount Mitchell   **C.** Ohio River

  B. Appalachians   **D.** Piedmont

_____ **23.** Which letter signifies Hudson Bay?

  A. G   **C.** C

  B. A   **D.** D

Directions: Document-Based Questions Use the document below to answer the questions that follow. *(5 points each)*

Tornado Facts

Tornadoes may strike quickly, with little or no warning.

They may appear nearly transparent, until dust and debris are picked up or a cloud forms in the funnel.

The average tornado moves from the southwest to the northeast, but tornadoes have been known to move in any direction.

Winds of a tornado can reach more than 300 miles per hour.

The average forward speed of a tornado is 30 miles per hour.

Tornadoes can accompany tropical storms and hurricanes as they move onto land.

Waterspouts are tornadoes that form over water.

Tornadoes are most likely to occur between 3 P.M. and 9 P.M., but they can occur at any time.

Source: Federal Emergency Management Agency. www.fema.gov/areyouready/tornadoes.shtm.

_____ **24.** What is the name of a tornado over water?

A. hurricane   **C.** storm surge

B. waterspout   **D.** typhoon

_____ **25.** In which direction does the average tornado move?

A. from northeast to southwest   **C.** from east to west

B. from west to east   **D.** from southwest to northeast

_____ **26.** What is the average forward speed of a tornado?

A. 30 miles per hour   **C.** 50 miles per hour

B. 40 miles per hour   **D.** 300 miles per hour

Directions: Essay On a separate sheet of paper, answer the questions below. *(10 points)*

27. In what two areas of the United States are tropical climates found? What temperatures and amounts of rainfall occur in these areas?

SCORE

Directions: Matching Match each item in Column A with its description in Column B. Write the correct letters in the blanks. *(10 points each)*

Column A

A. France

B. Scandinavia

C. Newfoundland

D. Spain

E. Siberia

Column B

_____ **1.** first Europeans to arrive in Canada came from this area

_____ **2.** first people to arrive in the Americas came from this region

_____ **3.** gained great wealth from gold and silver mines in the Americas

_____ **4.** Vikings lived briefly in this area around A.D. 1000

_____ **5.** ruled the area around the St. Lawrence River and the Great Lakes for 230 years

Directions: Short Answer Answer each question or statement below on the line provided. *(10 points each)*

6. How did the American economy change during the 1800s?

_____

7. What three European countries once had colonies in what is now the United States? What countries had colonies in what is now Canada?

_____

8. How do the United States and Canada differ in the way they gained independence?

_____

9. What are the three branches of the United States government?

_____

10. How did leaders like Martin Luther King, Jr., Rosa Parks, and César Chávez work for civil rights during the 1900s?

_____

SCORE

Directions: Matching Match each item in Column A with its description in Column B. Write the correct letters in the blanks. *(10 points each)*

Column A

A. Mark Twain

B. Winslow Homer

C. Latinos

D. Georgia O'Keeffe

E. Inuit

Column B

_____ **1.** an indigenous people who want self-rule in Canada

_____ **2.** artist who painted the colorful deserts of the Southwest

_____ **3.** wrote about life along the Mississippi River

_____ **4.** the fastest-growing ethnic group in America

_____ **5.** artist who painted the stormy waters of the North Atlantic

Directions: Short Answer Answer each question or statement below on the line provided. *(10 points each)*

6. How has immigration shaped the culture of the United States and Canada?

_____

7. How do Canadians refer to the indigenous people who live there?

_____

8. What are two common themes in American literature?

_____

9. Who are Amy Tan and Oscar Hijuelos? Describe their specialties.

_____

10. How is the film industry important to the economies and cultures of Canada and the United States?

_____

SCORE

History and Cultures of the United States and Canada

Chapter 5 Test Form A

Directions: Matching Match each item in Column A with its description in Column B. Write the correct letters in the blanks. *(3 points each)*

Column A

A. Langston Hughes

B. César Chávez

C. 1783

D. 1950

E. 2.5 million

F. 1867

G. Stratford Festival

H. 1920

I. 5 million

J. Georgia O'Keeffe

Column B

_____ **1.** year that television became a part of American culture

_____ **2.** leader who used peaceful methods for social change

_____ **3.** artist who painted the Southwest

_____ **4.** approximate number of Hindu followers in the U.S.

_____ **5.** year that the Dominion of Canada was formed

_____ **6.** approximate number of Muslim followers in the U.S.

_____ **7.** year that the United States was established

_____ **8.** famous for producing Shakespeare's plays

_____ **9.** poet who wrote about African Americans

_____ **10.** year that American women were given the right to vote

Directions: Multiple Choice In the blank at the left, write the letter of the choice that best completes the statement or answers the question. *(3 points each)*

_____ **11.** How did the first people arrive in the Americas?

    A. Hunters canoed from eastern Siberia to Alaska.

    B. Hunters crossed a land bridge between Siberia and Alaska.

    C. Fishers sailed from Mexico to Florida.

    D. Pilgrims arrived in Massachusetts in a ship.

_____ **12.** The British established colonies ____.

    A. in eastern Canada   **C.** in the Great Lakes area

    B. in the southern United States   **D.** along the Atlantic coast

_____ **13.** Which countries became major world powers after World War II?

    A. United States and Iraq   **C.** United States and Soviet Union

    B. United States and China   **D.** United States and Canada

_____ **14.** How many provinces and territories make up Canada today?

    A. 10 provinces and 3 territories   **C.** 3 provinces and 10 territories

    B. 10 provinces and 5 territories   **D.** 5 provinces and 10 territories

_____ **15.** Which plan explains how the U.S. government is set up and works?

    A. U.S. Constitution   **C.** Fourteenth Amendment

    B. Bill of Rights   **D.** Charter of Rights

_____ **16.** Approximately how many people live in the United States?

    A. 200 million   **C.** 400 million

    B. 300 million   **D.** 500 million

_____ **17.** By the year 2000, less than 15 percent of all U.S. immigrants came from _____.

    A. Latin America   **C.** Canada

    B. Asia   **D.** Europe

_____ **18.** Which religion is most widely practiced in the United States?

    A. Judaism   **C.** Islam

    B. Christianity   **D.** Buddhism

_____ **19.** Which of the following authors wrote about the people of New England?

    A. Amy Tan   **C.** Nathaniel Hawthorne

    B. Willa Cather   **D.** William Faulkner

_____ **20.** What are the two official languages of Canada?

    A. English and Spanish   **C.** French and English

    B. French and Spanish   **D.** English and Inuit

Applying Skills: Reading a Map Use the map below to answer the questions that follow. *(5 points each)*

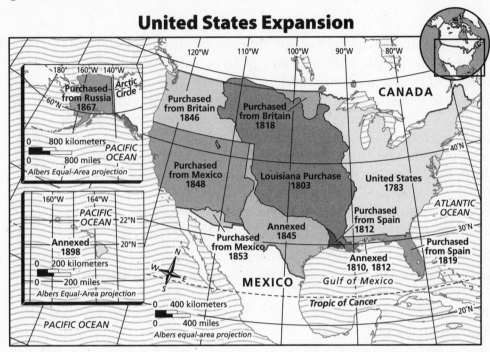

United States Expansion

_____ **21.** The area that is now the state of Florida was purchased from which country?

A. Mexico

B. Canada

C. Britain

D. Spain

_____ **22.** The first U.S. expansion was land purchased from ____.

A. Russia

B. Britain

C. Spain

D. France

_____ **23.** The United States obtained the present-day states of Oregon and Washington by ____.

A. annexing them from Mexico

B. purchasing them from Britain

C. purchasing them from Mexico

D. annexing them from Canada

Directions: Document-Based Questions Use the document below to answer the questions that follow. *(5 points each)*

> Artifacts and archaeological excavation that show human habitation of what is today Ontario date back at least 7,000 years. Many distinct native cultures and languages flourished. In the north, Algonquin, Cree, and Ojibwa people fished and hunted. The first farmers in the south were the Huron, Tobacco (Petun), Neutrals (Attiwandaron), and Iroquois. The Iroquois Five Nations included the Seneca, Cayuga, Onondaga, Oneida, and Mohawk. The Tuscarora joined the Five Nations in 1722, and henceforth they were known as the Six Nations. The Iroquois lived mostly in northern New York State until after the American Revolution when many of them moved to Ontario as Loyalists. Distinct native cultures and languages have continued and evolve to this day.
>
> **Source:** www.gov.on.ca/ont/.

_____ **24.** Which native peoples lived in the north?
   A. Seneca, Cayuga, and Oneida
   B. Algonquin, Cree, and Ojibwa
   C. Huron, Tobacco, and Neutrals
   D. Iroquois, Algonquin, and Tuscarora

_____ **25.** What did many of the Iroquois do after the American Revolution?
   A. moved to New York State
   B. formed the Five Nations
   C. moved to Ontario as Loyalists
   D. moved to the north to hunt and fish

_____ **26.** The Six Nations were formed when the _____ joined the Five Nations.
   A. Tuscarora   **C.** Onondaga
   B. Seneca   **D.** Cayuga

Directions: Essay On a separate sheet of paper, answer the question below. *(10 points)*

   27. In 1882 the U.S. Congress passed a law banning some immigration. What country was most affected by that ban, and why was the ban put into place?

Directions: Matching Match each item in Column A with its description in Column B. Write the correct letters in the blanks. *(3 points each)*

Column A

A. annex

B. Nunavut

C. United States and Soviet Union

D. civil war

E. colony

F. England and France

G. Quebec

H. federalism

I. terrorism

J. Plymouth Rock

Column B

_____ **1.** major world powers after World War II

_____ **2.** occurred after several U.S. states set up a new country in the South

_____ **3.** violence against citizens to obtain political goals

_____ **4.** to declare ownership of a particular area

_____ **5.** countries that claimed areas of Canada in the 1500s

_____ **6.** when power is divided between the national and state governments

_____ **7.** overseas settlement tied to a parent country

_____ **8.** word meaning "Our Land"

_____ **9.** where the Pilgrims first landed

_____ **10.** Canadian province that might separate from the others

Directions: Multiple Choice In the blank at the left, write the letter of the choice that best completes the statement or answers the question. *(3 points each)*

_____ **11.** During the colonial era, Spain gained great wealth from gold and silver mines in _____.

    A. Colorado and Mexico   **C.** Mexico and South America

    B. Mexico and Florida   **D.** South America and Nevada

_____ **12.** By the mid-1800s, what practice was criticized by people in the northern states?

    A. the factory system   **C.** taxes

    B. tariffs   **D.** slavery

_____ **13.** Who were the first Europeans to arrive in Canada?

    A. Spanish explorers   **C.** Portuguese explorers

    B. French explorers   **D.** Viking explorers

_____ **14.** In 1982 Canadians won the right to _____.

    A. govern Saskatchewan and Newfoundland

    B. separate Quebec from the rest of Canada

    C. change their constitution without British approval

    D. elect their own prime minister

_____ **15.** Which amendment requires states to provide their citizens with equal protection?

    A. First   **C.** Tenth

    B. Second   **D.** Fourteenth

_____ **16.** In 1965 an immigration law based entry into the United States on a person's work skills and _____.

    A. race   **C.** links to relatives

    B. country of origin   **D.** age

_____ **17.** What is the most widely spoken language after English in the United States?

    A. Spanish   **C.** Italian

    B. German   **D.** French

_____ **18.** Which of the following artists was known for painting the gritty side of city life?

    A. Georgia O'Keeffe   **C.** John Sloan

    B. Winslow Homer   **D.** Oscar Hijuelos

_____ **19.** About one-fourth of Canadians are of _____.

    A. British ancestry   **C.** Ukrainian ancestry

    B. French ancestry   **D.** Scandinavian ancestry

_____ **20.** Canadians celebrate the founding of their country on _____.

    A. July 4   **C.** July 1

    B. November 11   **D.** November 1

Applying Skills: Reading a Graph Use the graph below to answer the questions that follow. *(5 points each)*

Top Countries for Internet Use

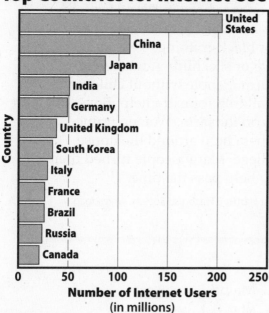

Source: *CIA World Factbook,* 2006.

_____ **21.** Which country shown has the smallest number of Internet users?

    A. France   **C.** Russia

    B. Brazil   **D.** Canada

_____ **22.** The United States has approximately _____ more Internet users than Canada.

    A. four times   **C.** two times

    B. eight times   **D.** ten times

_____ **23.** Approximately how many Indians are Internet users?

    A. 30 million   **C.** 50 million

    B. 30,000   **D.** 50,000

Directions: Document-Based Questions Use the document below to answer the questions that follow. *(5 points each)*

> Noah Webster, political writer and editor, was born in West Hartford, Connecticut, in 1758. Most of the people who lived there were farmers or practiced a trade like cabinet-making or blacksmithing.
>
> Many families in West Hartford had five or six children who were needed to work in the house and on the farm. People without children sometimes "borrowed" their neighbors' children for extra help. Boys learned skills by helping men with chores on the farm. Women trained girls to be wives and mothers by having them help around the house. Unlike boys, girls were unable to go to college. Many people turned their work into games or told stories in order to help pass the time.
>
> **Source:** "Colonial Life in 1770," Noah Webster House & West Hartford Historical Society. www.noah websterhouse.org/lifein1770.html.

_____ **24.** In which state was Noah Webster born?

  A. Connecticut **C.** Maine

  B. Vermont **D.** Massachusetts

_____ **25.** What career options were available for girls in the 1770s?

  A. working as a cabinet maker **C.** working as a blacksmith

  B. teaching at the college level **D.** being wives and mothers

_____ **26.** In the 1700s, it was common for families to have _____.

  A. three children **C.** five or six children

  B. one or two children **D.** ten children

Directions: Essay On a separate sheet of paper, answer the questions below. *(10 points)*

  27. What caused the American colonists to become discontented with Great Britain? What was the outcome?

SCORE

Directions: Matching Match each item in Column A with its description in Column B. Write the correct letters in the blanks. *(10 points each)*

Column A

A. Boston

B. Los Angeles, California

C. Hawaii

D. Halifax

E. Vancouver

Column B

_____ **1.** a major shipping center in the Atlantic Provinces

_____ **2.** an important center of biotechnology research

_____ **3.** sugarcane, pineapples, and coffee grow in its volcanic soil

_____ **4.** Canada's main port on the Pacific Ocean

_____ **5.** center of the world's movie industry

Directions: Short Answer Answer each question or statement below on the line provided. *(10 points each)*

6. Compare and contrast the economies of the United States and Canada.

_____

7. What are the roles of business and consumers in a free market economy?

_____

8. Why has farming been an economic focus of the Midwest and not the Northeast?

_____

9. What do the economic regions of Texas, Louisiana, and Alabama have in common with the economic regions of Manitoba, Saskatchewan, and Alberta?

_____

10. Why are outside businesses reluctant to invest in Quebec's economy?

_____

SCORE

Directions: Matching Match each item in Column A with its description in Column B. Write the correct letters in the blanks. *(10 points each)*

Column A

A. brownfields

B. acid rain

C. tariffs

D. trade deficit

E. peacekeepers

Column B

_____ **1.** results from pollution mixing with water vapor

_____ **2.** United Nations forces sent to troubled areas of the world

_____ **3.** occurs when a country spends more on imports than it earns from exports

_____ **4.** abandoned gas stations and factories containing dangerous chemicals

_____ **5.** taxes on imports

Directions: Short Answer Answer each question or statement below on the line provided. *(10 points each)*

6. In terms of trade deficits and trade surpluses, how do the United States and Canada compare?

_____

7. How are fish and shipping affected by lower water levels on the Great Lakes?

_____

8. How has the North American Free Trade Agreement affected trade between Canada and the United States?

_____

9. How did Canada respond to the U.S. decision to invade Iraq in 2003?

_____

10. What have the United States and Canada done to address the issue of global warming?

_____

SCORE

The United States and Canada Today

Chapter 6 Test Form A

Directions: Matching Match each item in Column A with its description in Column B. Write the correct letters in the blanks. *(3 points each)*

Column A

A. 1800s

B. brownfields

C. British Columbia

D. 60 percent

E. 1994

F. free market

G. Ontario

H. 80 percent

I. trade surplus

J. South

Column B

_____ **1.** percentage of exports that Canada sends to the United States

_____ **2.** time when manufacturing developed in the Midwest

_____ **3.** Canadian province known for extensive forests

_____ **4.** area with rich soils that relied on agriculture

_____ **5.** percentage of imports that Canada buys from the United States

_____ **6.** Canadian province with the largest population

_____ **7.** old, abandoned sites that contain dangerous chemicals

_____ **8.** NAFTA is signed

_____ **9.** limited government involvement in the economy

_____ **10.** earning more from exports than what is spent on imports

Directions: Multiple Choice In the blank at the left, write the letter of the choice that best completes the statement or answers the question. *(3 points each)*

_____ **11.** The northern region of Canada is known for which economic resource?

    A. agriculture   **C.** manufacturing

    B. minerals   **D.** forestry

_____ **12.** Which two key groups make up a free market economy?

    A. business owners and consumers

    B. business owners and employees

    C. employees and government

    D. business owners and government

_____ **13.** How did the United States and Canada work together after the attacks of September 11?

   A. They attacked Iraq.

   B. They increased security along their long border.

   C. They attacked Iraq and Afghanistan.

   D. They sought a peaceful solution through the United Nations.

_____ **14.** What are Florida's major economic activities?

   A. tourism and manufacturing   **C.** trade and communications

   B. manufacturing and ranching   **D.** tourism and trade

_____ **15.** The United States uses _____.

   A. nearly three times the amount of oil it produces

   B. less than the amount of oil it produces

   C. only the amount of oil it produces

   D. nearly six times the amount of oil it produces

_____ **16.** How does the North American Free Trade Agreement assist its member countries?

   A. selectively applies barriers to trade

   B. removes most barriers to trade

   C. forces member nations to trade only with each other

   D. allows any nation in the world to join

_____ **17.** Which city on the St. Lawrence River is a leading financial and industrial center?

   A. Toronto   **C.** Montreal

   B. Ottawa   **D.** Vancouver

_____ **18.** Which U.S. state is the most populous?

   A. California   **C.** Texas

   B. New York   **D.** Florida

_____ **19.** Which country has the world's largest economy?

   A. Canada   **C.** India

   B. China   **D.** United States

_____ **20.** What is the economic focus in the Northeastern region of the United States?

   A. farming and industry   **C.** tourism and mining

   B. business and trade   **D.** manufacturing and tourism

Applying Skills: Reading a Map Use the map below to answer the questions that follow. *(5 points each)*

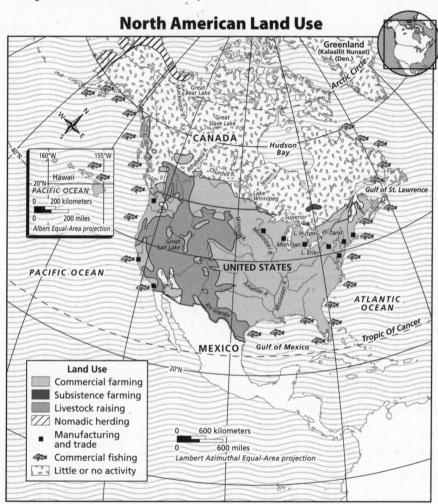

North American Land Use

_____ **21.** In which area of the United States is the land used for raising livestock?

A. Interior West

C. South

B. Midwest

D. Pacific

_____ **22.** The land in Canada's northern region is used primarily for _____.

A. fishing

C. no particular activity

B. farming

D. herding

_____ **23.** Most U.S. manufacturing centers are located in the _____.

A. Midwest and Northeast

C. Pacific and Interior West

B. Pacific and Northwest

D. South and Northeast

Directions: Document-Based Questions Use the document below to answer the questions that follow. *(5 points each)*

"Canada will stand shoulder to shoulder with the United States in defense of freedom and against terrorism," Prime Minister Paul Martin said on Sunday in a ceremony marking the fourth anniversary of the September 11 attacks. Martin stressed the existing friendship between Canadians and Americans.

U.S. ambassador David Wilkins welcomed Martin's remarks and offered thanks for the troops Canada has sent to Afghanistan. However, neither of them mentioned the fact that Canada chose not to join the invasion of Iraq, a decision that chilled relations between the two countries.

Source: "Canada to Stand With US Against Terrorism," *People's Daily Online.* english.peopledaily.com. cn/200509/12/eng20050912_208035.html.

_____ **24.** In what year did this ceremony take place?
    A. 2002   **C.** 2004
    B. 2003   **D.** 2005

_____ **25.** What hindered U.S.–Canadian relations?
    A. David Wilkins insulted the Canadian prime minister.
    B. Canada chose not to fight against terrorism.
    C. Canada chose not to invade Iran.
    D. Canada chose not to invade Iraq.

_____ **26.** After the terrorist attacks on New York City and Washington, D.C., Canada sent troops to _____.
    A. Iran   **C.** Afghanistan
    B. Iraq   **D.** Syria

Directions: Essay On a separate sheet of paper, answer the question below. *(10 points)*

    27. Why do some consumers save by putting their money in a bank instead of buying stock?

SCORE

Directions: Matching Match each item in Column A with its description in Column B. Write the correct letters in the blanks. *(3 points each)*

Column A

A. global warming

B. Nova Scotia

C. Pacific

D. biotechnology

E. urban sprawl

F. Manitoba

G. Los Angeles

H. Nunavut

I. Toronto

J. profit

Column B

_____ **1.** money remaining after business expenses are paid

_____ **2.** the spread of human settlement into natural areas

_____ **3.** one of Canada's western provinces

_____ **4.** Ontario's capital

_____ **5.** study of cells to find ways of improving health

_____ **6.** worldwide center of the movie industry

_____ **7.** phenomenon that many believe will lead to changing weather patterns

_____ **8.** region that has fish, timber, and mineral resources

_____ **9.** one of Canada's northern areas

_____ **10.** one of the Atlantic provinces

Directions: Multiple Choice In the blank at the left, write the letter of the choice that best completes the statement or answers the question. *(3 points each)*

_____ **11.** A free market economy allows people to _____.

  A. trade goods between countries without any restrictions

  B. buy goods from any country without paying taxes

  C. buy, sell, and produce what they want with limited government involvement

  D. buy, sell, and produce what they want with strict government involvement

_____ **12.** Mining, ranching, and lumbering used to be the main economic activities of what U.S. region?

  A. South   **C.** Northeast

  B. Interior West   **D.** Midwest

_____ 13. Why would the melting of the polar ice caps cause a problem for Florida's economy?

   A. Colder water would keep people from the beaches.

   B. Rising sea levels would cause major flooding.

   C. Rising salt water would destroy the citrus groves.

   D. Colder water would destroy the sea life.

_____ 14. The United States _____.

   A. spends very little on imports

   B. earns most of its money from exports

   C. spends more on exports than it earns from imports

   D. spends more on imports than it earns from exports

_____ 15. Because Canada's exports have been growing, Canada has _____.

   A. a trade deficit   **C.** serious economic problems

   B. a trade surplus   **D.** been able to lower taxes

_____ 16. Which country is the second-largest trading partner of the United States?

   A. Mexico   **C.** Saudi Arabia

   B. Canada   **D.** China

_____ 17. Unlike the United States, Canada's national and provincial governments provide _____.

   A. financial help for needy families   **C.** health care for citizens

   B. food stamps   **D.** education reforms

_____ 18. Iron ore, coal, lead, and zinc are mined in which U.S. region?

   A. Midwest   **C.** South

   B. Northeast   **D.** Eastern

_____ 19. Industries found in the Pacific area include _____.

   A. steel manufacturing

   B. textile manufacturing

   C. paper manufacturing

   D. airplane construction and computer software development

_____ 20. How has the United States addressed the problem of global warming?

   A. enacted strict antipollution laws

   B. created programs in grade schools to educate people about global warming

   C. funded research to find less harmful energy sources

   D. mandated the size and efficiency of all motor vehicles

Applying Skills: Reading a Map Use the map below to answer the questions that follow. *(5 points each)*

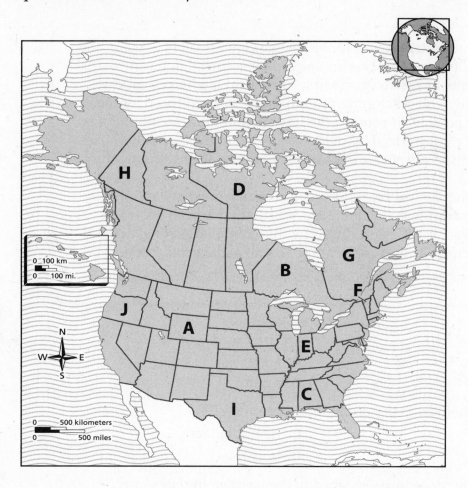

_____ **21.** Which of the following is signified by the letter *C?*

    A. Louisiana   **C.** Mississippi

    B. Alabama   **D.** Georgia

_____ **22.** The letter *D* is located on _____.

    A. Yukon Territory   **C.** Nunavut

    B. Northwest Territories   **D.** Saskatchewan

_____ **23.** Which state is signified by the letter *J?*

    A. Oregon   **C.** Idaho

    B. Washington   **D.** Wyoming

Directions: Document-Based Questions Use the document below to answer the questions that follow. *(5 points each)*

Boston is an important center for biotechnology research. Some of the most dramatic advances in biotechnology have occurred in recent years. One advance came in 1986 with the first significant laboratory production of factor VIII, a blood-clotting protein that is not produced, or has greatly reduced activity, in people who have hemophilia. Hemophilia is a disease that is characterized by delayed clotting of the blood. Because of this, hemophiliacs are at risk of bleeding to death after suffering minor cuts or bruises.

In this biotechnological procedure, the human gene that controls blood-clotting is transferred to hamster cells that have been grown in the laboratory. Factor VIII is produced by this combination of genes and cells. In 1992 factor VIII was approved for commercial production.

Source: "Biotechnology," *Encarta.* encarta.msn.com/encyclopedia_76157885/Biotechnology.html.

_____ **24.** What is factor VIII?
  A. a fat   **C.** a gene
  B. a protein   **D.** a clot

_____ **25.** Who will benefit from the production of factor VIII?
  A. scientists   **C.** hemophiliacs
  B. hamsters   **D.** doctors

_____ **26.** How does the procedure described in the passage fit the definition of *biotechnology*?
  A. It uses computers to manage the data from the procedure.
  B. It involves the study of cells.
  C. It uses high-tech equipment to conduct the procedure.
  D. It combines technology with biology.

Directions: Essay On a separate sheet of paper, answer the question below. *(10 points)*

  27. What problems occur when climate conditions cause the water level in the Great Lakes to drop?

SCORE

Directions: Matching Match each item in Column A with its description in Column B. Write the correct letters in the blanks. *(5 points each)*

Column A

A. Newfoundland

B. Niagara Falls

C. Canadian Shield

D. Bill of Rights

E. newsprint

F. central United States

G. 1763

H. Vancouver

I. 1991

J. southeastern Atlantic coast

Column B

_____ 1. horseshoe-shaped area around Hudson Bay

_____ 2. area where the Vikings lived briefly

_____ 3. major port in Canada

_____ 4. area that sees more tornadoes each year than any other place on Earth

_____ 5. major source of hydroelectric power

_____ 6. when Great Britain won France's North American colonies

_____ 7. when the Cold War ended

_____ 8. area that sees many hurricanes

_____ 9. what Canada is the world's largest producer of

_____ 10. first 10 amendments to the U.S. Constitution

Directions: Multiple Choice Write the letter of the choice that best completes the statement or answers the question. *(5 points each)*

_____ 11. The Central Lowlands are located _____.

   A. north of the Canadian Shield
   B. west of the Great Plains
   C. south of the Canadian Shield
   D. in the coastal plain

_____ 12. The province of Ontario is located in the _____.

   A. North
   B. Central and Eastern region
   C. West
   D. Atlantic Provinces

_____ 13. Which would most likely be found only in the Pacific region?

   A. pineapples and coffee
   B. coal mines
   C. auto manufacturing plants
   D. corn, wheat, and soybeans

_____ 14. When the United States expanded west in the 1800s, the _____ suffered.

   A. French
   B. British
   C. enslaved Africans
   D. Native Americans

_____ 15. Who were the first Canadian artists?

   A. indigenous peoples
   B. traders from Asia
   C. the Vikings
   D. French explorers

Applying Skills: Reading a Map Use the map below to answer the questions that follow. *(5 points each)*

Path of Hurricane Katrina

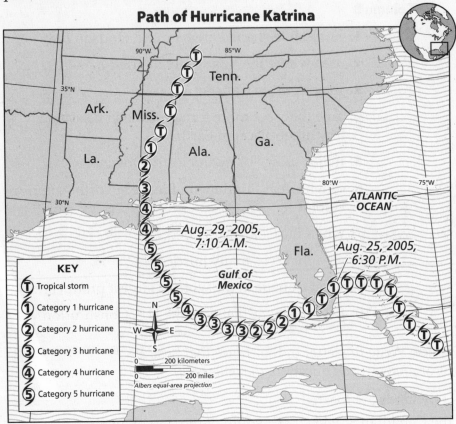

_____ **16.** At 6:30 P.M. on August 25, 2005, which area was receiving the force of the storm?

A. the Florida Keys

C. Florida's southern coast

B. the Bahamas

D. the Gulf of Mexico

_____ **17.** Which of the following carries the most force?

A. Category 2 hurricane

C. tropical storm

B. Category 4 hurricane

D. Category 1 hurricane

_____ **18.** After touching land in Louisiana, Hurricane Katrina _____.

A. gained in strength

C. lost strength

B. stayed the same

D. lost and then gained strength

Directions: Essay On a separate sheet of paper, answer the question below. *(10 points)*

19. Sequence the events that happened after Abraham Lincoln was elected president.

SCORE

Unit 3 Pretest

Directions: Matching Match each item in Column A with its description in Column B. Write the correct letters in the blanks. *(5 points each)*

Column A

A. 2.7 million square miles

B. Pampas

C. A.D. 1200

D. Colombia

E. Miguel Hidalgo

F. José de San Martín

G. 600 miles

H. terracing

I. A.D. 900

J. Chile

Column B

_____ **1.** Aztec civilization arose

_____ **2.** world's largest exporter of copper

_____ **3.** vast, treeless plains

_____ **4.** priest who urged poor Mexicans to fight for freedom from Spanish rule

_____ **5.** farming method that involves cutting "steps" into mountainsides

_____ **6.** country with Caribbean Sea and Pacific coasts

_____ **7.** how far inland the city of Brasília was located

_____ **8.** approximate size of the Amazon Basin

_____ **9.** Mayan civilization collapsed

_____ **10.** soldier who led his army from Argentina across the Andes into Chile

Directions: Multiple Choice Write the letter of the choice that best completes the statement or answers the question. *(7 points each)*

_____ **11.** Most of Latin America gained independence in the ____.

    A. 1600s   **C.** 1800s

    B. 1700s   **D.** 1900s

_____ **12.** Most people in Central America depend on ____.

    A. farming   **C.** fishing

    B. mining   **D.** manufacturing

_____ **13.** What has kept some countries in Latin America from fully using their vast natural resources?

    A. disagreements over trade   **C.** lack of ports

    B. political and economic troubles   **D.** low literacy rates

_____ **14.** What are some Caribbean countries turning to in order to help their economies grow?

    A. farming   **C.** mining

    B. Native American crafts   **D.** tourism

_____ **15.** Where is much of Latin America located?

A. between the Tropic of Cancer and the Tropic of Capricorn

B. south of the Tropic of Capricorn

C. north of the Tropic of Cancer

D. in the area surrounding the Caribbean Sea

Applying Skills: Reading a Chart Use the chart below to answer the questions that follow. *(5 points each)*

Statistics for Selected Latin American Countries					
Country	**Literacy Rate**	**Population and Density**	**Land Area**	**Life Expectancy**	**GDP Per Capita (U.S. dollars)**
Bahamas	95.6%	300,000 60 per sq. mi.	5,359 sq. mi.	70	$17,700
Brazil	86.4%	184,200,000 56 per sq. mi.	3,300,154 sq. mi.	71	$8,100
Mexico	92.2%	107,000,000 142 per sq. mi.	756,082 sq. mi.	75	$9,600
Nicaragua	67.5%	5,800,000 116 per sq. mi.	50,193 sq. mi.	69	$2,300

Source: *CIA World Factbook*, 2005. *World Population Data Sheet*, 2005.

_____ **16.** In which country do people have the longest life expectancy?

A. Bahamas

B. Mexico

C. Brazil

D. Nicaragua

_____ **17.** Which country has the greatest population density?

A. Bahamas

B. Brazil

C. Mexico

D. Nicaragua

_____ **18.** What is the land area of the Bahamas?

A. 50,193 square miles

B. 756,082 square miles

C. 3,300,154 square miles

D. 5,359 square miles

SCORE

Directions: Matching Match each item in Column A with its description in Column B. Write the correct letters in the blanks. *(10 points each)*

Column A

A. Andes

B. Orinoco

C. Greater Antilles

D. Central America

E. Brazilian Highlands

Column B

_____ **1.** Cuba, Hispaniola, Puerto Rico, and Jamaica

_____ **2.** ends in a series of steep cliffs

_____ **3.** cordillera along the Pacific coast of South America

_____ **4.** isthmus that links North America and South America

_____ **5.** carries fertile soil into the Llanos of western Venezuela

Directions: Short Answer Answer each question or statement below on the line provided. *(10 points each)*

6. Why are Jamaica's large deposits of bauxite unique to the Caribbean islands?

_____

7. What is unique about Lake Titicaca?

_____

8. Why is transporting goods difficult in Central America?

_____

9. What products do Brazil's rain forests provide?

_____

10. Where are the Pampas, and what do they provide?

_____

SCORE

Directions: Matching Match each item in Column A with its description in Column B. Write the correct letters in the blanks. *(10 points each)*

Column A

A. desert

B. Amazon Basin

C. Caribbean islands

D. humid subtropical climate

E. Mediterranean climate

Column B

_____ **1.** the short winters and long, humid summers of Argentina's Pampas

_____ **2.** climate of northern Mexico

_____ **3.** holds the world's largest rain forest

_____ **4.** enables central Chile to grow large amounts of fruit

_____ **5.** developed a tourism industry despite hurricanes

Directions: Short Answer Answer each question or statement below on the line provided. *(10 points each)*

6. How does El Niño affect Peru's coast and northeastern Brazil differently?

_____

7. Where is the Atacama Desert? How do the Andes and the cold Peru Current make this one of the driest places on Earth?

_____

8. What are the four altitude zones of the Andes, from lowest to highest elevation?

_____

9. What is a rain forest canopy, and how is it formed?

_____

10. Why are the climates south of the Tropic of Capricorn temperate rather than tropical?

_____

SCORE

Directions: Matching Match each item in Column A with its description in Column B. Write the correct letters in the blanks. *(3 points each)*

Column A

A. canopy

B. bauxite

C. *tierra caliente*

D. Argentina

E. Brazil

F. Atacama

G. *tierra helada*

H. El Niño

I. West Indies

J. silver

Column B

_____ **1.** another name for the Caribbean islands

_____ **2.** largest country in Latin America

_____ **3.** mineral mined in Mexico

_____ **4.** one of the driest places on Earth

_____ **5.** mineral mined in Jamaica

_____ **6.** changes in air pressure, temperature, and rainfall in the Pacific Ocean

_____ **7.** country that is mostly covered by the Pampas

_____ **8.** zone of highest elevation in the Andes

_____ **9.** "hot land"

_____ **10.** umbrella-like covering of leaves

Directions: Multiple Choice In the blank at the left, write the letter of the choice that best completes the statement or answers the question. *(3 points each)*

_____ **11.** How many tectonic plates meet in Middle America?

    A. two   **C.** four

    B. three   **D.** five

_____ **12.** The Andes have four altitude zones of climate. Which zone begins at 6,000 feet?

    A. *tierra helada*   **C.** *tierra caliente*

    B. *tierra fría*   **D.** *tierra templada*

_____ **13.** To produce gasohol, Brazil uses gasoline mixed with alcohol produced from _____.

    A. sugar beets   **C.** Brazil nuts

    B. palm oil   **D.** sugarcane

_____ **14.** El Niño takes place when the temperature of the Pacific waters off Peru's coast are ____.
   A. unusually warm   **C.** very cold
   B. unusually cold   **D.** very warm

_____ **15.** Where is the Amazon Basin located?
   A. west of the Andes   **C.** north of the Andes
   B. east of the Andes   **D.** south of the Andes

_____ **16.** What are the tropical grasslands that stretch through eastern Colombia and Venezuela?
   A. Pampas   **C.** Patagonia
   B. Llanos   **D.** Maracaibo

_____ **17.** Which country is the world's largest exporter of copper?
   A. Mexico   **C.** Colombia
   B. Jamaica   **D.** Chile

_____ **18.** Ships use the Panama Canal to shorten travel time between the ____.
   A. Atlantic and Pacific Oceans
   B. Atlantic Ocean and Gulf of Mexico
   C. Caribbean Sea and Pacific Ocean
   D. Pacific Ocean and Gulf of Mexico

_____ **19.** Vast rain forests are found in which climate zone?
   A. humid subtropical   **C.** tropical wet
   B. tropical dry   **D.** marine west coast

_____ **20.** What is the Paraná?
   A. a canal in Middle America
   B. the highest peak in the Andes
   C. a lake in Venezuela
   D. a river that flows into an estuary

Applying Skills: Reading a Chart Use the chart below to answer the questions that follow. *(5 points each)*

Average Monthly Rainfall in Latin America (inches)		
Month	**Manaus, Brazil**	**Lima, Peru**
January	9.8	0.1
February	9.0	0.0
March	10.3	0.0
April	8.7	0.0
May	6.7	0.2
June	3.3	0.2
July	2.3	0.3
August	1.5	0.3
September	1.8	0.3
October	4.2	0.1
November	5.6	0.1
December	8.0	0.0

Source: BBC Weather Center, 2006.

_____ **21.** In March, approximately how much rain falls in Manaus, Brazil?

    A. 0.0 inches   **C.** 10.3 inches

    B. 2.3 inches   **D.** 0.1 inch

_____ **22.** When is the rainy season in Lima, Peru?

    A. July–September   **C.** April–June

    B. October–December   **D.** January–March

_____ **23.** In which month does Manaus, Brazil, record the least amount of rainfall?

    A. September   **C.** December

    B. October   **D.** August

Directions: Document-Based Questions Use the document below to answer the questions that follow. *(5 points each)*

> The ruins of an ancient temple have been found by international archaeologists under Lake Titicaca, the world's highest lake. A terrace for crops, a long road, and a 2,600-foot-long wall were also found under the lake, located in the Andes between Bolivia and Peru. The explorers found the temple after following the submerged road. The ruins, which date back 1,000 to 1,500 years, are pre-Incan.
>
> More than 200 dives were made into the lake, to depths of as much as 100 feet, to record the ruins on film. The Bolivian government has said it will provide financial and technical support to preserve the ruins.
>
> **Source:** "Ancient Temple Found Under Lake Titicaca," news.bbc.co.uk/2/hi/americas/892616.stm.

_____ 24. Where is Lake Titicaca located?
   A. in the Andes   **C.** Peru
   B. Bolivia   **D.** Chile

_____ 25. How many dives were made into the lake in order to record the ruins on film?
   A. approximately 150 dives   **C.** 190 dives
   B. 170 dives   **D.** more than 200 dives

_____ 26. The terrace found under Lake Titicaca had been used at one time ____.
   A. for entering the temple
   B. for farming
   C. to hold decorative hedges and flowers
   D. as a means of defense for the temple

Directions: Essay On a separate sheet of paper, answer the question below. *(10 points)*

27. Into what three groups are the islands of the Caribbean Sea divided? Describe each group.

SCORE

Directions: Matching Match each item in Column A with its description in Column B. Write the correct letters in the blanks. *(3 points each)*

Column A

A. emeralds

B. Pampas

C. archipelago

D. northern Mexico

E. Venezuela

F. coffee

G. central Chile

H. nickel

I. estuary

J. Andes

Column B

_____ **1.** world's longest mountain system

_____ **2.** a dry climate is found here

_____ **3.** area where river currents and ocean tides meet

_____ **4.** similar to the Great Plains of North America

_____ **5.** group of islands

_____ **6.** a Mediterranean climate is found here

_____ **7.** mined in Colombia

_____ **8.** has largest reserves of oil in Latin America

_____ **9.** important export crop in Latin America

_____ **10.** mined in Cuba

Directions: Multiple Choice In the blank at the left, write the letter of the choice that best completes the statement or answers the question. *(3 points each)*

_____ **11.** The Amazon River is approximately how long?

    A. 4,000 miles   **C.** 6,000 miles

    B. 5,000 miles   **D.** 7,000 miles

_____ **12.** Powerful hurricanes often strike the Caribbean islands during which months?

    A. April and May

    B. October to December

    C. June to November

    D. January through March

_____ **13.** Which of the following is grown in the *tierra caliente?*

    A. bananas   **C.** barley

    B. potatoes   **D.** wheat

_____ **14.** Which of the following make up Middle America?

    A. Mexico and the Caribbean islands

    B. the Caribbean islands and Brazil

    C. Mexico and Central America

    D. Colombia and Brazil

_____ **15.** In which of the following altitude zones can the temperature be as low as 20°F?

    A. *tierra caliente*   **C.** *tierra helada*

    B. *tierra fría*   **D.** *tierra templada*

_____ **16.** The Andes form _____.

    A. an archipelago   **C.** an escarpment

    B. a cordillera   **D.** El Niño

_____ **17.** The rain forests of South America provide _____.

    A. barley   **C.** corn

    B. rubber   **D.** silver

_____ **18.** Which of the following is an isthmus?

    A. Mexico   **C.** Central America

    B. Cuba   **D.** Lesser Antilles

_____ **19.** Which of the following is Latin America's largest lake?

    A. Lake Titicaca   **C.** Lake Nicaragua

    B. Laguna Palcacocha   **D.** Lake Maracaibo

_____ **20.** What makes the soil fertile in Middle America?

    A. fertilizer

    B. grazing livestock

    C. coastal marshes

    D. ash and lava

Applying Skills: Reading a Map Use the map below to answer the questions that follow. *(5 points each)*

_____ **21.** On the map, which feature is labeled *G?*

   A. Pampas

   B. Llanos

   C. Brazilian Highlands

   D. Amazon Basin

_____ **22.** What feature is represented by the letter *C?*

   A. Amazon River

   B. Río de la Plata

   C. Uruguary River

   D. Orinoco River

_____ **23.** Which letter on the map is pointing to the Gulf of California?

   A. B

   B. D

   C. E

   D. F

Directions: Document-Based Questions Use the document below to answer the questions that follow. (*5 points each*)

> The Amazon rain forest, also known as Amazonia, is one of the world's greatest natural resources. Because its vegetation continuously recycles carbon dioxide into oxygen, it has been described as the "Lungs of Our Planet." About 20 percent of Earth's oxygen is produced by the Amazon rain forest.
>
> Some of the animals found in the canopy are harpy eagles, which prey on monkeys; the sloth; reptiles; and other birds. Sloths spend most of their lives in the treetops. Their diet of leaves forces them to conserve energy, causing the sloth to spend 80 percent of its time resting. A large portion of a howler monkey's diet consists of leaves, which are hard to digest. Leaf-cutter ants are responsible for harvesting a sixth of the area's leaves. They play a critical role in the rain forest's ecosystem by pruning the vegetation, which stimulates new growth, and breaking down the leaves to renew the soil.
>
> **Source:** "Amazon Rain Forest," www.blueplanetbiomes.org/amazon.htm.

_____ **24.** Why has the Amazon rain forest been called the "Lungs of Our Planet"?
  A. The rain forest recycles carbon dioxide into oxygen.
  B. All of the animals and insects in the rain forest have lungs.
  C. The rain forest actually breathes.
  D. Viewed from above, observers can see oxygen rising into the air.

_____ **25.** Which of the following spend most of their lives in the treetops?
  A. howler monkeys   **C.** sloths
  B. harpy eagles   **D.** leaf-cutter ants

_____ **26.** Approximately how much of Earth's oxygen is produced by the Amazon rain forest?
  A. 20 percent   **C.** 50 percent
  B. 80 percent   **D.** 75 percent

Directions: Essay On a separate sheet of paper, answer the question below. (*10 points*)

  27. What is the *tierra templada*? Where is it located, and why do many people choose to live there?

SCORE

Directions: Matching Match each item in Column A with its description in Column B. Write the correct letters in the blanks. *(10 points each)*

Column A

A. Aztec

B. Toltec

C. Olmec

D. Inca

E. caudillos

Column B

_____ **1.** held a monopoly on the obsidian trade

_____ **2.** Latin America's first civilization in southern Mexico

_____ **3.** ruled as dictators and did little to help the poor

_____ **4.** built a huge empire in central Mexico

_____ **5.** empire that stretched more than 2,500 miles along the Andes

Directions: Short Answer Answer each question or statement below on the line provided. *(10 points each)*

6. What people did Hernán Cortés and Francisco Pizarro conquer?

_____

7. What were three achievements of the Maya?

_____

8. What countries colonized Brazil and Bolivia, and how did the colonies differ in the way they gained their independence?

_____

9. Who led Latin America's first successful revolt against European rule, and where did it take place?

_____

10. How is Cuba's government different from other governments in Latin America?

_____

SCORE

Directions: Matching Match each item in Column A with its description in Column B. Write the correct letters in the blanks. *(10 points each)*

Column A

A. Quechua

B. São Paulo

C. Central America

D. Cuba

E. Rio de Janeiro

Column B

_____ **1.** country whose music shaped American jazz

_____ **2.** region of high birthrates in Latin America

_____ **3.** ancient and current language of Peru and Bolivia

_____ **4.** has a large Japanese community

_____ **5.** this city's Carnival is famous for its color and excitement

Directions: Short Answer Answer each question or statement below on the line provided. *(10 points each)*

6. Why do African Latin Americans form a high percentage of the populations in the Caribbean islands?

_____

7. What effect has Asian immigration had on religion in Latin America?

_____

8. What do rural Latin Americans expect to find when they move to cities, and what do they actually find?

_____

9. How does family leadership in some parts of the Caribbean differ from most of Latin America?

_____

10. What is magic realism? How has it affected culture around the world?

_____

SCORE

Directions: Matching Match each item in Column A with its description in Column B. Write the correct letters in the blanks. *(3 points each)*

Column A

A. caudillos

B. Brazil

C. Quechua

D. Roman Catholic

E. 65 percent

F. Cuba

G. Tenochtitlán

H. Cuzco

I. 80 percent

J. Spanish

Column B

_____ **1.** percentage of people in Central America and the Caribbean who live in cities

_____ **2.** major religion in Latin America

_____ **3.** percentage of people in South America who live in cities

_____ **4.** focus of war between the United States and Spain in 1898

_____ **5.** language spoken centuries ago by the Inca

_____ **6.** capital of the Aztec Empire

_____ **7.** high-ranking military officers who often ruled as dictators

_____ **8.** home to the largest number of Japanese in one place outside of Japan

_____ **9.** most widely spoken language in Latin America

_____ **10.** capital of the Inca Empire

Directions: Multiple Choice In the blank at the left, write the letter of the choice that best completes the statement or answers the question. *(3 points each)*

_____ **11.** Latin America's first civilization was the ____.

    A. Olmec   **C.** Inca

    B. Aztec   **D.** Maya

_____ **12.** How did a monopoly in obsidian help the Toltec maintain their rule?

    A. The Toltec were able to trade obsidian for gunpowder.

    B. Other peoples believed that obsidian held magical powers.

    C. Obsidian was used to pay soldiers for their service to the Toltec.

    D. The most powerful weapons of the time were made from obsidian.

_____ **13.** François-Dominique Toussaint-Louverture was ____.

    A. a leader who helped Brazil break away from Portugal

    B. an enslaved African who led a revolt in Haiti

    C. a priest who urged Mexicans to fight for freedom from Spain

    D. a soldier who led his army from Argentina into Chile

_____ **14.** During colonial times, tobacco, gold, and silver were shipped from Latin America to Europe. What did the ships often carry on the return trip?

    A. seeds to plant for crops   **C.** enslaved people from Africa

    B. luxuries such as spices and silk   **D.** tea and coffee

_____ **15.** Who led the fight for freedom for Venezuela, Colombia, Ecuador, and Bolivia?

    A. Miguel Hidalgo   **C.** Simón Bolívar

    B. José de San Martín   **D.** José María Morelos

_____ **16.** Which Latin American style of writing combines fantastic events with the ordinary?

    A. fantasy   **C.** magic realism

    B. fiction   **D.** mystery

_____ **17.** What is an official language of Peru and Bolivia?

    A. Portuguese   **C.** Japanese

    B. Quechua   **D.** Creole

_____ **18.** During the 1400s, the Inca had a powerful civilization in what is now _____.

    A. Peru   **C.** Bolivia

    B. Mexico   **D.** Argentina

_____ **19.** Why did Panama give the United States permission to build the Panama Canal?

    A. The United States helped Panama win its freedom from Spain.

    B. The United States helped Panama win its freedom from Colombia.

    C. The United States threatened to take over Panama's government.

    D. The United States supported Panama's dictator and paid $250 million.

_____ **20.** Who led a revolution in Cuba in 1959?

    A. Simón Bolívar   **C.** Fidel Castro

    B. Toussaint-Louverture   **D.** José de San Martín

Applying Skills: Reading a Chart Use the chart below to answer the questions that follow. *(5 points each)*

Internet and Cell Phone Users in Central America			
Country	Population	Internet Users	Cell Phone Users
Belize	287,730	35,000	93,100
Honduras	7,326,496	223,000	1,282,000
Guatemala	12,293,545	756,000	3,168,300
Costa Rica	4,075,261	1,000,000	1,101,000

Source: *CIA World Factbook.*

_____ **21.** Which country has the highest percentage of Internet users?

    A. Belize   **C.** Guatemala

    B. Costa Rica   **D.** Honduras

_____ **22.** What is the approximate proportion of cell phone users to population in Guatemala?

    A. 1 of every 4 people   **C.** 3 of every 10 people

    B. 2 of every 4 people   **D.** 8 of every 10 people

_____ **23.** Which country has the highest percentage of cell phone users?

    A. Costa Rica   **C.** Honduras

    B. Guatemala   **D.** Belize

Directions: Document-Based Questions Use the document below to answer the questions that follow. *(5 points each)*

> Like most agricultural people, the Aztec worshiped gods whom they believed controlled the forces of nature. In addition to the sun god, they worshiped the god of rain and the serpent Quetzalcoatl, who was the god of wind and resurrection [rebirth].
>
> Archaeologists have learned about the Aztec gods and religious ceremonies from the artwork found in the ruins of their cities. The images of the gods are seen in stone sculptures and carved wall sculptures on the temples. The inside walls of the buildings have brilliantly colored paintings showing ceremonial events. One especially famous Aztec sculpture—an enormous calendar stone—is a carved stone circle that is 12 feet in diameter. The calendar represents the Aztec universe with the face of the sun god in the center. He is surrounded by symbols that represent the days and the months and the locations of heavenly bodies at different times of the year.
>
> **Source:** "The Aztecs," lsa.colorado.edu/~lsa/texts/Aztecs.html.

_____ **24.** The Aztec god of wind and resurrection has been shown in sculptures as a _____.

    A. serpent   **C.** cross

    B. cloud   **D.** star

_____ **25.** How have archaeologists learned about Aztec gods?

    A. through written accounts that have been discovered

    B. through artwork

    C. through legendary accounts passed down by word of mouth

    D. through historical records kept by conquerors

_____ **26.** What was located in the middle of the large, carved Aztec calendar?

    A. symbols representing heavenly bodies

    B. a carved serpent

    C. the face of the sun god

    D. symbols representing days and months

Directions: Essay On a separate sheet of paper, answer the question below. *(10 points)*

    27. What are some of the challenges facing Latin America today?

Directions: Matching Match each item in Column A with its description in Column B. Write the correct letters in the blanks. *(3 points each)*

Column A

A. Tenochtitlán

B. murals

C. Fidel Castro

D. Portugal

E. Carnival

F. Day of the Dead

G. Argentina

H. Haiti

I. Diego Rivera

J. Creole

Column B

_____ **1.** set up a communist state in Latin America

_____ **2.** pidgin language

_____ **3.** colonial ruler of Brazil

_____ **4.** has a mostly Spanish and Italian population

_____ **5.** had huge temples and "floating gardens"

_____ **6.** Mexican holiday

_____ **7.** only nation created as a result of a successful revolt by enslaved people

_____ **8.** symbolize the artistic traditions of the ancient Maya and Aztec

_____ **9.** famous Latin American painter

_____ **10.** holiday celebrated before Lent

Directions: Multiple Choice In the blank at the left, write the letter of the choice that best completes the statement or answers the question. *(3 points each)*

_____ **11.** What language do most Brazilians speak?

    A. Spanish   **C.** French

    B. Portuguese   **D.** Creole

_____ **12.** Who landed on Mexico's Gulf coast with the goal of conquering the Aztec?

    A. Hernán Cortés   **C.** José de San Martín

    B. Simón Bolívar   **D.** Francisco Pizarro

_____ **13.** Which people of the Yucatán Peninsula developed a calendar, hieroglyphics, and a number system based on 20?

    A. Toltec   **C.** Aztec

    B. Inca   **D.** Maya

_____ **14.** Which of these countries has a large Native American population?

    A. Argentina   **C.** Uruguay

    B. Guyana   **D.** Peru

_____ **15.** Who liberated Argentina and Chile from Spanish rule?

    A. François-Dominique Toussaint-Louverture

    B. Simón Bolívar

    C. José de San Martín

    D. Miguel Hidalgo

_____ **16.** Which of the following is one of the largest urban areas in the world?

    A. Cuzco   **C.** Tula

    B. Tenochtitlán   **D.** São Paulo

_____ **17.** African Latin Americans form a high percentage of the population in ____.

    A. Uruguay   **C.** Mexico

    B. Chile   **D.** the Caribbean islands

_____ **18.** What seriously weakened Latin American economies in the mid-1900s?

    A. cash crops   **C.** increasing debt

    B. mineral exports   **D.** foreign investment

_____ **19.** Which country was the second country in the world to play baseball?

    A. the United States **C.** Cuba

    B. Japan   **D.** Argentina

_____ **20.** Approximately what percentage of the population of Guyana is of Asian ancestry?

    A. 20 percent   **C.** 40 percent

    B. 30 percent   **D.** 50 percent

Applying Skills: Reading a Map Use the map below to answer the questions that follow. *(5 points each)*

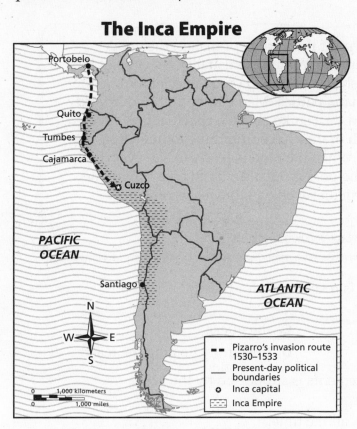

The Inca Empire

_____ **21.** Which present-day country was the starting point for the Spanish invasion of the Inca Empire?

A. Colombia   **C.** Panama

B. Venezuela   **D.** Ecuador

_____ **22.** In how many present-day countries was the Inca Empire located?

A. two   **C.** four

B. three   **D.** five

_____ **23.** About how long did it take the Spanish to conquer the capital city of the Inca?

A. 3 years   **C.** 30 years

B. 10 years   **D.** 33 years

History and Cultures of Latin America

Chapter 8 Test Form B (continued)

Directions: Document-Based Questions Use the document below to answer the questions that follow. *(5 points each)*

> Typical Cuban food is known for the variety of dishes, the good seasoning, and the amounts served. Women are usually in charge of the black beans, yucca (with garnishes of chopped onion and lemon), white rice, corn fritters, and fried banana patties. Men gather in the courtyard to roast the pig, which is placed on a spike above a charcoal fire, covered with leaves, and sprinkled with orange juice from time to time. Roasting the pig can take several hours. When the food is ready to eat, everything is served in dishes except for the pork, which is placed on a tray in the center of the table. Cubans particularly enjoy large feasts on family occasions.
>
> **Source:** "Cuban Cuisine," www.cubanculture.com/english/cocina.asp.

_____ **24.** During a Cuban feast, who is responsible for roasting the pig?

    A. the women   **C.** the guests

    B. the men   **D.** the family hosting the feast

_____ **25.** Which of the following statements is supported by the excerpt?

    A. Cubans have large feasts all the time.

    B. Meat is scarce in Cuba.

    C. Females are the primary chefs in Cuba.

    D. Cuban food is normally seasoned.

_____ **26.** If bananas are served at a Cuban feast, they are usually prepared ____.

    A. in a salad   **C.** in fried patties

    B. in their skins   **D.** peeled, but not cut up

Directions: Essay On a separate sheet of paper, answer the question below. *(10 points)*

    27. What is family life typically like in Latin American cultures?

Directions: Matching Match each item in Column A with its description in Column B. Write the correct letters in the blanks. *(10 points each)*

Column A

A. vaqueros

B. mestizos

C. subsistence farms

D. plantations

E. maquiladoras

Column B

_____ **1.** factories in which workers assemble parts made in other countries

_____ **2.** Mexican cowhands

_____ **3.** large farms that raise a single crop for sale

_____ **4.** small plots where farmers grow enough food to feed their families

_____ **5.** people with a Spanish and Native American heritage

Directions: Short Answer Answer each question or statement below on the line provided. *(10 points each)*

6. How do Mexican cities reflect Spanish culture?

_____

7. What was different about the Mexican presidential election in 2000 than the elections of the previous 70 years? Why?

_____

8. Where is the center of Mexico's energy industry, and why is it located there?

_____

9. What types of economic activities occur in Mexico's North region?

_____

10. Why is the climate of Central Mexico comfortable, even though it is located in the Tropics?

_____

SCORE

Directions: Matching Match each item in Column A with its description in Column B. Write the correct letters in the blanks. *(10 points each)*

Column A

A. remittances

B. Costa Rica

C. Haiti

D. literacy rate

E. commonwealth

Column B

_____ **1.** the percentage of people who can read and write

_____ **2.** a self-governing territory

_____ **3.** money sent back home by Haitians who work in other countries

_____ **4.** located on the western half of Hispaniola

_____ **5.** country with no army

Directions: Short Answer Answer each question or statement below on the line provided. *(10 points each)*

6. How has the political stability of Guatemala and Costa Rica differed?

_____

7. What are recent signs of economic change in Guatemala?

_____

8. How has Cuba's government affected the success of its economy?

_____

9. What is the difference between tourism in Cuba and tourism in Puerto Rico?

_____

10. How does Panama profit from the Panama Canal?

_____

SCORE

Directions: Matching Match each item in Column A with its description in Column B. Write the correct letters in the blanks. *(10 points each)*

Column A

A. gaucho

B. Caracas

C. Bogotá

D. selva

E. favela

Column B

_____ **1.** Amazon rain forest

_____ **2.** overcrowded slum area

_____ **3.** national symbol of Argentina

_____ **4.** capital city of Venezuela

_____ **5.** capital city of Colombia

Directions: Short Answer Answer each question or statement below on the line provided. *(10 points each)*

6. How does the ancestry of Brazil's population compare with the ancestry of Argentina's population?

_____

7. What resulted when Argentina borrowed large amounts from foreign banks in the late 1900s?

_____

8. How did President Hugo Chávez plan to better the lives of Venezuela's poor?

_____

9. How do the governments of Chile and Argentina today differ from their governments in the past?

_____

10. How does agriculture provide energy for Brazil?

_____

SCORE

Directions: Matching Match each item in Column A with its description in Column B. Write the correct letters in the blanks. *(3 points each)*

Column A

A. Cancun

B. vaqueros

C. Buenos Aires

D. Frida Kahlo

E. Fidel Castro

F. Panama

G. Juan Perón

H. Amazon rain forest

I. Ciudad Juárez

J. Hugo Chávez

Column B

_____ **1.** famous Mexican artist

_____ **2.** resort city on the Yucatán Peninsula

_____ **3.** important banking center

_____ **4.** capital of Argentina

_____ **5.** president of Venezuela

_____ **6.** Brazil's greatest natural resource

_____ **7.** manufacturing city on the Mexico–U.S. border

_____ **8.** Mexican cowhands

_____ **9.** became dictator of Argentina in the late 1940s

_____ **10.** Cuba's longtime dictator

Directions: Multiple Choice In the blank at the left, write the letter of the choice that best completes the statement or answers the question. *(3 points each)*

_____ **11.** More than two-thirds of Argentina's people live in ____.

A. Buenos Aires

B. the Pampas

C. Patagonia

D. the Llanos

_____ **12.** About half of Guatemala's people descend from the ____.

A. Portuguese

B. ancient Aztecs

C. ancient Maya

D. Inca

_____ **13.** Why have millions of Brazilians recently moved from rural to coastal areas?

A. to work in the capital city

B. to escape drought

C. to live in favelas

D. to find better jobs

_____ **14.** What is considered to be the backbone of Chile's economy?
    A. mining   **C.** ranching
    B. farming   **D.** tourism

_____ **15.** Mexico's president can serve _____.
    A. two three-year terms   **C.** one six-year term
    B. two four-year terms   **D.** one eight-year term

_____ **16.** How many countries make up Central America?
    A. six   **C.** seven
    B. eight   **D.** nine

_____ **17.** About 85 percent of Argentina's people are Spanish and
    ____.

    A. Native American   **C.** German
    B. Italian   **D.** French

_____ **18.** Which region of Mexico has industrial cities and more than
half of Mexico's people?
    A. Central Mexico   **C.** the West
    B. the North   **D.** the South

_____ **19.** Which country grows more coffee, oranges, and cassava
than any other country in the world?
    A. Peru   **C.** Chile
    B. Colombia   **D.** Brazil

_____ **20.** Why has the United States tightened controls along its
border with Mexico?
    A. to keep U.S. citizens from taking jobs in Mexico
    B. to help the Mexican economy
    C. to reduce illegal immigration
    D. to keep U.S. firms from building factories in Mexico

Name_____ Date_____ Class_____

Applying Skills: Reading a Graph Use the graph below to answer the questions that follow. *(5 points each)*

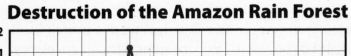

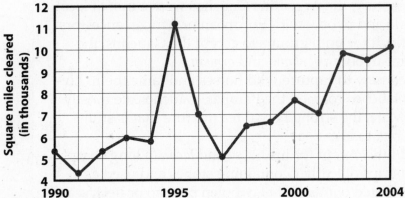

Destruction of the Amazon Rain Forest

Square miles cleared (in thousands)

Source: National Institute of Space Research.

_____ **21.** In what year were approximately 11,500 square miles of the Amazon rain forest cleared?

    A. 1995   **C.** 1996

    B. 1991   **D.** 1993

_____ **22.** During which two years did the least amount of deforestation occur?

    A. 1991 and 1999   **C.** 1991 and 1997

    B. 1994 and 1997   **D.** 1997 and 2001

_____ **23.** Approximately how many square miles were cleared during 2004?

    A. 10,000 square miles   **C.** 9,000 square miles

    B. 8,000 square miles   **D.** 11,000 square miles

Directions: Document-Based Questions Use the document below to answer the questions that follow. *(5 points each)*

> In the seventeenth century, the Argentina Gauchos were a mix of local Native American people and people with European or African ancestors. At the time, it was difficult for both groups to accept the Gauchos; the word *Gaucho* came to mean both *vagabond* and *orphan*.
>
> The Gauchos learned how to capture wild horses and tame them. Living a solitary life, the Gauchos roamed the Pampas. Gauchos ate mostly beef and drank Yerba Mate, the strong herbal tea mixture that is still popular in South America today.
>
> The Gaucho owned little except for his horse and *facon* (a long sharp knife) and a *boleadora* (strips of leather containing stones and used as a lariat). His clothing consisted of a wide hat, woolen poncho or neck scarf, baggy trousers called *bombachas*, and knee-high leather boots. The boots were made from skinned hides that were fastened to the Gaucho's legs. Over time, they would shrink to a custom fit.
>
> Eventually, Spanish landowners in need of good ranch hands took the Gauchos in as herdsmen for their ranches. This brought an end to the Gauchos' nomadic lifestyle.
>
> **Source:** "Argentina Gauchos—The Nomads of the Pampas," www.the-allure-of-argentina.com/argentinagauchos.html.

_____ **24.** What did the Gauchos do for a living?

A. capture and tame wild horses

B. work in the Argentine mines

C. serve as slaves for wealthy landowners

D. act as trail bosses during round-up

_____ **25.** What is a *facon*?

A. a neck scarf

B. a hat

C. a knife

D. a lariat

_____ **26.** The popular drink Yerba Mate is ____.

A. Argentine coffee

B. a tea mixture

C. cassava juice

D. goats' milk

Directions: Essay On a separate sheet of paper, answer the question below. *(10 points)*

27. How does Costa Rica differ from most of its neighbors?

SCORE

Directions: Matching Match each item in Column A with its description in Column B. Write the correct letters in the blanks. *(3 points each)*

Column A

A. Puerto Rico

B. Patagonia

C. Chile

D. Octavio Paz

E. Juan Perón

F. Falklands

G. smog

H. Brasília

I. plaza

J. default

Column B

_____ **1.** author who writes about the values of Mexico's people

_____ **2.** capital of Brazil

_____ **3.** miss a debt payment

_____ **4.** public square

_____ **5.** makes more money from tourism than any other Caribbean island

_____ **6.** plateau in Argentina

_____ **7.** thick haze of fog and chemicals

_____ **8.** country with unusual ribbonlike shape

_____ **9.** also known as the Malvinas

_____ **10.** dictator of Argentina

Directions: Multiple Choice In the blank at the left, write the letter of the choice that best completes the statement or answers the question. *(3 points each)*

_____ **11.** In the early 2000s, Guatemala entered an agreement with the United States to _____.

    A. provide national security   **C.** add tariffs

    B. patrol its borders   **D.** remove trade barriers

_____ **12.** How many state governments does Brazil have?

    A. 16   **C.** 23

    B. 26   **D.** 19

_____ **13.** What are Argentina's chief exports?

    A. bananas and cassava   **C.** beef and beef products

    B. zinc and copper   **D.** oil and coffee

_____ **14.** Which is Mexico's largest city?

    A. Mexico City   **C.** Cancun

    B. Guadalajara   **D.** Monterrey

_____ **15.** What do Brazilians call their country's Amazon rain forest?

    A. favela   **C.** pampa

    B. selva   **D.** maquiladora

_____ **16.** Which of Mexico's economic regions is irrigated and has cattle ranches with vaqueros?

    A. the South   **C.** Central Mexico

    B. the West   **D.** the North

_____ **17.** Which of the following is a self-governing territory of the United States?

    A. Puerto Rico   **C.** Panama

    B. Cuba   **D.** Costa Rica

_____ **18.** What was the first and largest European group to settle Brazil?

    A. Native Americans   **C.** Portuguese

    B. Asians   **D.** Africans

_____ **19.** Why were the 1970s a time of fear in Argentina?

    A. Military officers took control and killed thousands of people.

    B. The country was governed by a dictator.

    C. Argentina was losing a war with Great Britain.

    D. Argentina was in the midst of a civil war.

_____ **20.** What is replacing coffee, meat, and seafood as Nicaragua's primary source of income?

    A. copper   **C.** sugar

    B. oil   **D.** ecotourism

Chapter 9 Test Form B (continued)

Applying Skills: Reading a Map Use the map below to answer the questions that follow. *(5 points each)*

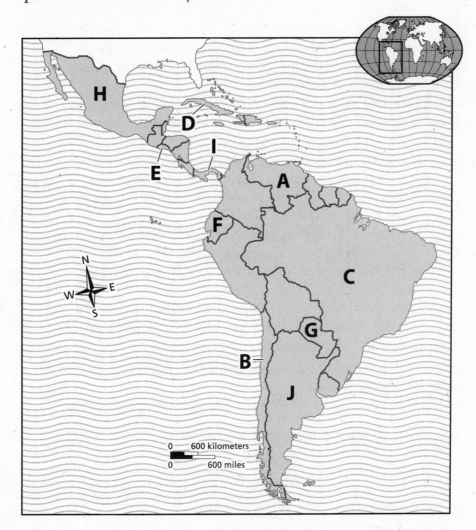

_____ **21.** Which country is signified by the letter *A*?
    A. Colombia   **C.** Costa Rica
    B. Uruguay   **D.** Venezuela

_____ **22.** Which letter is located on Argentina?
    A. J   **C.** G
    B. H   **D.** F

_____ **23.** What is letter *D* pointing to?
    A. Puerto Rico   **C.** Cuba
    B. Haiti   **D.** Jamaica

Directions: Document-Based Questions Use the document below to answer the questions that follow. *(5 points each)*

From 5 A.M. to noon in the harvest season, coffee pickers carrying heavy buckets of fruit walk backward down the steep slopes of the Hacienda Ana plantation. After noon, it's too hot!

This day, a cooling morning rain and stiff breeze keep the air temperature at a comfortable 80 degrees. There's a beautiful double rainbow off to the east.

But if your objective is to strip bushy, 10-foot Arabica coffee trees of as many ripe, red "cherries" as possible, there's not a lot of time to look at rainbows. Even though there are many pickers, there are never enough workers to get the job done on schedule.

Coffee picking is challenging work that involves a great deal of stretching and stooping. Using both hands, a picker will grab a branch, center it over a 5-gallon bucket slung around his neck on a rope, and use his thumbs to release only the ripe fruit.

In days to come, the fruit will be pulped, dried, and milled to remove a parchment covering on the coffee bean. Roasting will follow, another labor-intensive step on the road to a steaming cup of hot coffee.

Source: "It's a Labor-Intensive Trip from the Slope to the Sip," www.washingtonpost.com/wp-dyn/content/article/2007/01/09/AR2007010900589_pf.html.

_____ **24.** When coffee is harvested, what color is the ripe fruit?

A. red   **C.** black

B. brown   **D.** gray

_____ **25.** Why do the coffee pickers work only in the mornings?

A. The coffee pickers have other jobs in the afternoon.

B. A new shift of coffee pickers takes over at noon.

C. The afternoons are too hot for work of that kind.

D. All of the coffee that is ripe has been picked by noon.

_____ **26.** Why is the fruit milled?

A. to crush the beans   **C.** to clean soil from the beans

B. to remove a parchment layer   **D.** to package the beans

Directions: Essay On a separate sheet of paper, answer the question below. *(10 points)*

27. What are Colombia's economic strengths?

SCORE

Unit 3 Posttest

Directions: Matching Match each item in Column A with its description in Column B. Write the correct letters in the blanks. *(5 points each)*

Column A

A. Cuba

B. Hispaniola

C. 55°F

D. cricket

E. Atahuallpa

F. Michelle Bachelet

G. Panama

H. Carlos Fuentes

I. 75°F to 80°F

J. empire

Column B

_____ **1.** the last Inca ruler

_____ **2.** country that lies about 90 miles south of Florida

_____ **3.** average temperature in the *tierra caliente*

_____ **4.** large territory under one ruler

_____ **5.** island that holds two countries

_____ **6.** sport popular in Caribbean countries that were once ruled by the British

_____ **7.** country at the narrowest part of Central America

_____ **8.** author who wrote about the values of Mexicans

_____ **9.** average yearly temperature in the *tierra fría*

_____ **10.** first female president of Chile

Directions: Multiple Choice Write the letter of the choice that best completes the statement or answers the question. *(5 points each)*

_____ **11.** Cuban music is famous for its use of ____.
  A. African rhythms   **C.** Caribbean rhythms
  B. Spanish rhythms   **D.** Mexican rhythms

_____ **12.** What is the "River of Silver"?
  A. Río de la Plata   **C.** Paraguay River
  B. Paraná River   **D.** Amazon River

_____ **13.** When did Mexico become a republic?
  A. 1800   **C.** 1840
  B. 1850   **D.** 1823

_____ **14.** What is the capital of Venezuela?
  A. Bridgetown   **C.** Santiago
  B. Nassau   **D.** Caracas

_____ **15.** Why does sunlight seldom reach the Amazon rain forest floor?
  A. The sun does not shine there.   **C.** Equipment blocks the sun.
  B. The canopy is too dense.   **D.** Clouds block the sun.

Applying Skills: Reading a Graph Use the graph below to answer the
questions that follow. *(5 points each)*

Comparing Population

Source: *World Population Data Sheet, 2005.*

_____ **16.** Mexico has approximately half the population of what
other country shown in the graph?

    A. the United States   **C.** Peru

    B. Argentina   **D.** Brazil

_____ **17.** Approximately how many people live in Honduras?

    A. 500,000,000   **C.** 50,000,000

    B. 10,000,000   **D.** 600,000,000

_____ **18.** Approximately 30,000,000 people live in ____.

    A. Peru   **C.** Honduras

    B. Argentina   **D.** Mexico

Directions: Essay On a separate sheet of paper, answer the question
below. *(10 points)*

    19. During the 1900s, why did so many Latin Americans dis-
trust the United States? What did the United States do to
improve relations?

Name_____ Date_____ Class_____

Directions: Matching Match each item in Column A with its description in Column B. Write the correct letters in the blanks. *(5 points each)*

Column A

A. Enlightenment

B. Scotland

C. Greece

D. European Union

E. Ireland

F. feudalism

G. Rome

H. Switzerland

I. Vikings

J. Renaissance

Column B

_____ **1.** where European civilization began

_____ **2.** Age of Reason

_____ **3.** had senators, consuls, and the Twelve Tables

_____ **4.** northern region of Great Britain

_____ **5.** home of the Celts

_____ **6.** Scandinavian sailors of the Middle Ages

_____ **7.** protected from invasion by the Alps

_____ **8.** rebirth of learning and focus on humanism

_____ **9.** political and social system between lords and knights

_____ **10.** trade association

Directions: Multiple Choice Write the letter of the choice that best completes the statement or answers the question. *(7 points each)*

_____ **11.** Europe is not a separate landmass but is connected to ____.

   A. North America

   B. South America

   C. Asia

   D. Antarctica

_____ **12.** A marine west coast climate has warm temperatures and ____.

   A. abundant rainfall

   B. frequent hailstorms

   C. dry winters

   D. high pressure

_____ **13.** Europe's major religions include Roman Catholic, Protestant, Islam, Judaism, and ____.

   A. Hinduism

   B. Gothic

   C. Daoism

   D. Eastern Orthodox

_____ **14.** About 25 percent of this country lies below sea level.

   A. Iceland

   B. Netherlands

   C. Greece

   D. Poland

_____ **15.** Which nation split into two separate countries in 1993?

   A. United Kingdom

   B. Germany

   C. Finland

   D. Czechoslovakia

Applying Skills: Reading a Chart Use the chart below to answer the questions that follow. (*5 points each*)

GODS AND GODDESSES OF ANCIENT GREECE	
Name	**Power**
Zeus—Ruler of Mount Olympus	• King of the gods and the rain god • Wielded a thunderbolt
Poseidon—Zeus's brother	• God of the sea and earthquakes; carried a trident • Giver of horses to mortals
Hades—Zeus's brother	• God of the underworld (ruled over the dead)
Hera—Zeus's wife	• Protector of marriage and children
Hestia—Zeus's sister	• Goddess of the hearth and home
Ares—Son of Zeus	• God of war
Athena—Daughter of Zeus	• Goddess of wisdom • Protector of cities, especially Athens
Apollo—Son of Zeus	• God of the sun • Patrol of truth, archery, music, medicine
Aphrodite—Daughter of Zeus	• Goddess of love and beauty
Hermes—Son of Zeus	• Messenger to mortals • God of public speakers, writers, and trade • Protector of thieves and mischief-makers
Artemis—Apollo's twin sister	• Goddess of the moon and a mighty huntress • Guardian of cities, young animals, and women
Hephaestus—Aphrodite's husband	• God of fire and the forge

_____ **16.** Where did the ancient Greeks believe their gods and goddesses lived?

    A. Sparta   **C.** Macedonia

    B. Mount Olympus   **D.** Athens

_____ **17.** Who would Greek healers turn to for advice and help?

    A. Hera   **C.** Poseidon

    B. Zeus   **D.** Apollo

_____ **18.** What does this chart tell you about the ancient Greeks?

    A. They did not respect public speakers or tradespeople.

    B. They used science to explain supernatural events.

    C. They did not value music or learning.

    D. They used religious beliefs to explain natural events.

SCORE

Directions: Matching Match each item in Column A with its description in Column B. Write the correct letters in the blanks. *(10 points each)*

Column A

A. Alpine Mountain System

B. Northern European Plain

C. Meseta

D. Northwest Uplands

E. Hungarian Plain

Column B

_____ **1.** extend from Sweden through Northern Great Britain to Iceland

_____ **2.** highland in Spain

_____ **3.** includes the Pyrenees and Carpathians

_____ **4.** stretches from France to Belarus and Ukraine

_____ **5.** large lowland that lies east of the Alps

Directions: Short Answer Answer each question or statement below on the line provided. *(10 points each)*

6. How are Poland's people hurt and helped by coal?

_____

7. How does acid rain form?

_____

8. Why are hydroelectric power and wind power called "clean" energy? What three countries are the world's leaders in building wind farms?

_____

9. How is fertilizer from European farms affecting the fish of the Danube?

_____

10. Why is the Mediterranean Sea important to Europeans?

_____

Directions: Matching Match each item in Column A with its description in Column B. Write the correct letters in the blanks. *(10 points each)*

Column A

A. polar easterlies

B. steppe

C. mistral

D. siroccos

E. Pyrenees

Column B

_____ **1.** cold, dry wind that blows into southern France

_____ **2.** gives eastern Europe cooler summers and colder winters

_____ **3.** a dry, treeless plain with short grasses

_____ **4.** hot, dry winds that blow out of Africa into southern Europe

_____ **5.** block cold winds from reaching Spain and Italy

Directions: Short Answer Answer each question or statement below on the line provided. *(10 points each)*

6. Why are deciduous trees able to grow well in the marine west coast climate zone?

_____

7. What effect does the North Atlantic Current have on northwestern Europe?

_____

8. What are the three main climate zones of most of Europe?

_____

9. How do mountains affect rainfall within a climate zone? Name two countries that experience this effect.

_____

10. Why are the Netherlands and Venice, Italy, especially concerned about global warming?

_____

Directions: Matching Match each item in Column A with its description in Column B. Write the correct letters in the blanks. *(3 points each)*

Column A

A. coniferous

B. Mont Blanc

C. lignite coal

D. mistral

E. Pyrenees

F. Kyoto Treaty

G. tundra

H. Danube

I. Sicily

J. Mediterranean

Column B

_____ **1.** vast treeless plains near the North Pole

_____ **2.** attempt to eliminate greenhouse gases

_____ **3.** cold, dry wind that crosses France

_____ **4.** causes acid rain when burned

_____ **5.** evergreens

_____ **6.** one of Europe's longest rivers

_____ **7.** southern European climate zone

_____ **8.** island in the Mediterranean Sea

_____ **9.** located between France and Spain

_____ **10.** Europe's highest mountain

Directions: Multiple Choice In the blank at the left, write the letter of the choice that best completes the statement or answers the question. *(3 points each)*

_____ **11.** Which of the following are European islands?

    A. Denmark, Ireland, and Italy   **C.** Sicily, Crete, and Cyprus

    B. Elbe, Rhine, and Tiber   **D.** Balkans

_____ **12.** Which of these descriptions fits most European countries?

    A. They have colder winters than the United States.

    B. They are near an ocean or a sea.

    C. They are larger than Texas.

    D. They have dry climates.

_____ **13.** What plentiful resource fueled Europe's industry in the 1800s?

    A. coal   **C.** oil

    B. natural gas   **D.** wood

_____ **14.** Rich soil, abundant resources, and dense population describe which European region?

 A. Northern Uplands   **C.** Alpine Mountain System

 B. Central Uplands   **D.** Northern European Plain

_____ **15.** Where do Europe's most productive oil fields lie?

 A. beneath the Alps   **C.** beneath the North Sea

 B. in the Central Uplands   **D.** near the Mediterranean Sea

_____ **16.** Which of these problems threatens Europe's forests, lakes, and rivers?

 A. severe drought   **C.** acid rain

 B. poor sewage disposal   **D.** frequent flooding

_____ **17.** Which of the following best describes Europe's natural resources?

 A. abundant and varied   **C.** inadequate for the current population

 B. scarce and overused   **D.** limited to minerals and fuel

_____ **18.** The climate in northwestern and central Europe _____.

 A. is hot in summer and cold in winter

 B. has mild temperatures and much rain

 C. is cool and usually dry

 D. is influenced by the Mediterranean

_____ **19.** Where is Europe's most forested area?

 A. Italy and France   **C.** Spain and Portugal

 B. Poland and Austria   **D.** Norway and Sweden

_____ **20.** Why is northwestern Spain cool, wet, and green, but inland Spain is hot, dry, and brown?

 A. because of the rain shadow effect of the Pyrenees Mountains

 B. because of the influence of the Mediterranean Sea

 C. because tropical winds come from the east

 D. because of the difference in the angle of the sun's rays in each area

Applying Skills: Reading a Map Use the map below to answer the questions that follow. *(5 points each)*

Europe: Currents and Wind Patterns

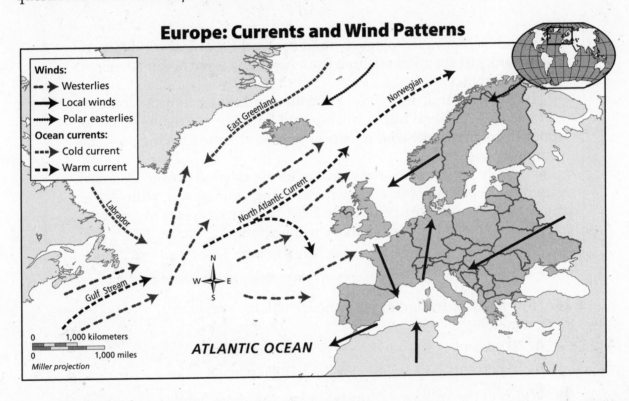

_____ **21.** Westerlies flow in the same general direction as the _____.

    A. cold currents   **C.** polar easterlies

    B. warm currents   **D.** local winds

_____ **22.** Which current flows around the United Kingdom?

    A. Gulf Stream   **C.** North Atlantic Current

    B. Labrador   **D.** Norwegian

_____ **23.** The polar easterlies are a _____.

    A. warm wind   **C.** cold wind

    B. cold current   **D.** warm current

Directions: Document-Based Questions Use the document below to answer the questions that follow. *(5 points each)*

> Ireland has approved plans to build the world's largest wind farm on a sandbank just six miles offshore from Arklow, a town about 40 miles south of Dublin.
>
> The Arklow Sandbank . . . is one of the windiest locations in Ireland and will seat 200 wind turbines. The wind farm is expected to generate about 10 percent of the country's energy needs by the time the project is complete. . . .
>
> Currently Europe leads the world in its use of wind power. Denmark generates 15 percent of its energy needs using wind power, with Germany and Sweden close behind. By 2020, Denmark expects to generate 50 percent of its power demands by using wind.
>
> **Source:** Bijal P. Trivedi, *National Geographic Today*, January 15, 2002.

_____ **24.** How much of Ireland's energy needs will the wind farm generate?

   A. 50 percent   **C.** 40 percent

   B. 10 percent   **D.** 90 percent

_____ **25.** Which of the following countries generates more wind power than the others?

   A. Ireland   **C.** Sweden

   B. Germany   **D.** Denmark

_____ **26.** Why was the Arklow Sandbank chosen as the location for the wind farm?

   A. It is near the large city of Dublin.

   B. It is near the ocean.

   C. It is one of Ireland's windiest locations.

   D. It is a sandy location.

Directions: Essay On a separate sheet of paper, answer the question below. *(10 points)*

   27. How has Europe's nearness to the ocean affected its historical development?

Directions: Matching Match each item in Column A with its description in Column B. Write the correct letters in the blanks. *(3 points each)*

Column A

A. Alpine Mountain System

B. marine west coast

C. iron ore

D. Chernobyl

E. Central Uplands

F. Crete

G. sirocco

H. subarctic

I. Carpathians

J. Ukrainian Steppe

Column B

_____ **1.** island in the Mediterranean

_____ **2.** climate of Ireland and the United Kingdom

_____ **3.** used to make steel

_____ **4.** contains much of Europe's coal

_____ **5.** stretches from Spain to the Balkan Peninsula

_____ **6.** mountains in East Central Europe

_____ **7.** broad grassy plain north of the Black Sea

_____ **8.** hot, dry wind

_____ **9.** covers parts of Norway, Sweden, and Finland

_____ **10.** a nuclear disaster occurred here

Directions: Multiple Choice In the blank at the left, write the letter of the choice that best completes the statement or answers the question. *(3 points each)*

_____ **11.** Only a few European countries _____.

    A. are warmed by ocean winds   **C.** are landlocked

    B. are capable of growing trees   **D.** are rich in natural resources

_____ **12.** Which of the following is true about the continent of Europe?

    A. Europe includes more than 40 countries.

    B. Few areas of Europe are suitable for farming.

    C. Europe has only three language groups.

    D. Europe has unlimited oil and gas reserves.

_____ **13.** Most of Europe's rivers are navigable, which means that _____.

    A. they provide good sources of irrigation

    B. they provide excellent drinking water

    C. ships can travel inland

    D. fishing is a productive industry

_____ 14. Which of these are Europe's major clean energy sources?
   A. hydroelectric and wind power   **C.** solar and nuclear power
   B. natural gas and oil   **D.** coal and oil

_____ 15. Europe's farmland can best be described as ____.
   A. scarce but productive
   B. depleted in minerals after centuries of farming
   C. not important to its economy
   D. some of the richest in the world

_____ 16. Why is burning lignite coal a problem in eastern Europe?
   A. It is an abundant energy source.   **C.** It cannot compete with oil.
   B. It is cheap.   **D.** It causes acid rain.

_____ 17. Sewage, garbage, and farm runoff in Europe are sources of
   ____.
   A. air pollution   **C.** acid rain
   B. water pollution   **D.** recycling

_____ 18. Where do coniferous trees dominate the landscape of
   Europe?
   A. southern Sweden and Norway
   B. Spain and parts of southern France
   C. the eastern slopes of the highlands
   D. the Mediterranean climate zone

_____ 19. Southern France experiences a wind called the ____.
   A. timberline   **C.** sirocco
   B. mistral   **D.** rain shadow

_____ 20. How are Norway and Sweden tackling the effects of acid
   rain?
   A. adding lime to their lakes
   B. prohibiting factories from producing
   C. limiting agriculture
   D. reducing the number of tourists

Applying Skills: Reading a Map Use the map below to answer the questions that follow. *(5 points each)*

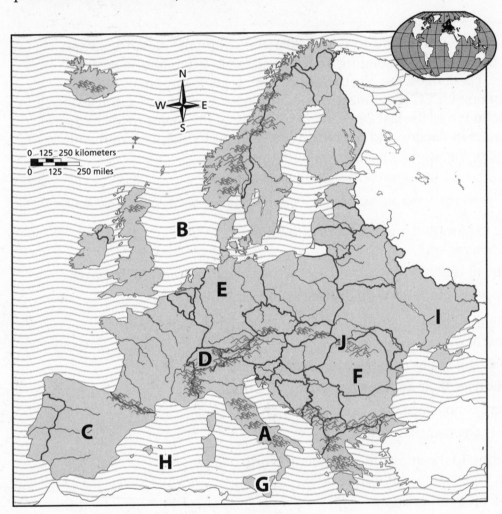

_____ **21.** Which of the following is signified by the letter *C*?

    A. Northern European Plain   **C.** Hungarian Plain

    B. Meseta   **D.** Pyrenees

_____ **22.** Where is the letter *D* located?

    A. Carpathian Mountains   **C.** Alps

    B. Apennine Mountains   **D.** Po River Valley

_____ **23.** The letter *B* is located in the ____.

    A. North Sea   **C.** Baltic Sea

    B. English Channel   **D.** Arctic Ocean

Directions: Document-Based Questions Use the document below to answer the questions that follow. *(5 points each)*

> With severe wind gusts and waves 30 meters high, the North Sea has been one of the most challenging areas for oil exploration and recovery. Despite the challenges, the North Sea has been a key component of the increase in non-OPEC [Organization of Petroleum Exporting Countries] oil production over the last 20 years. Now many of the major fields in the North Sea are in decline and the North Sea is about to lose its prominent role as one of the world's leading oil domains.
>
> **Source:** Energy Security, Institute for the Analysis of Global Security, 2004.

_____ **24.** Why is exploration and recovery of oil difficult in the North Sea region?

    A. little oil is left   **C.** strong winds and high waves

    B. shipping interferes with drilling   **D.** too many oil spills

_____ **25.** Despite the difficulties, why did Great Britain and Norway explore for oil in the North Sea?

    A. Oil is still easier to extract than coal.

    B. It reduces their dependence on OPEC oil.

    C. There is no alternative fuel.

    D. Oil is cheaper than coal.

_____ **26.** According to the quote, the decline in North Sea oil production means that Europe will ____.

    A. seek oil in other areas

    B. purchase oil from other regions

    C. join OPEC

    D. lose its role as a leading oil producer

Directions: Essay On a separate sheet of paper, answer the question below. *(10 points)*

    27. How does climate make life in Norway different from life in Italy?

SCORE

Directions: Matching Match each item in Column A with its description in Column B. Write the correct letters in the blanks. *(10 points each)*

Column A

A. Christianity

B. Alexander the Great

C. *Pax Romana*

D. Renaissance

E. Enlightenment

Column B

_____ **1.** the peaceful first 200 years of the Roman Empire

_____ **2.** strongly influenced society during the Middle Ages

_____ **3.** a time of revolutions in scientific and political thought

_____ **4.** spread Greek culture to Egypt and Persia

_____ **5.** a time of "rebirth" in art and learning

Directions: Short Answer Answer each question or statement below on the line provided. *(10 points each)*

6. How is a republic a limited form of democracy?

_____

7. What did Charlemagne's empire do in A.D. 800 that the European Union is doing today?

_____

8. How did the Black Death lead to the decline of the feudal system?

_____

9. How did the Reformation affect the authority of the Catholic Church and of monarchs?

_____

10. How did thinkers of the Renaissance and the Enlightenment differ in their beliefs about faith and reason?

_____

SCORE

Directions: Matching Match each item in Column A with its description in Column B. Write the correct letters in the blanks. *(10 points each)*

Column A

A. Gothic architecture

B. Romanticism

C. the government

D. Eastern Orthodox

E. service industries

Column B

_____ **1.** strong in the southern part of eastern Europe

_____ **2.** provides Europe with most of its jobs

_____ **3.** supports the needy, sick, and elderly in a welfare state

_____ **4.** a new style developed by musicians, writers, and artists in the 1800s

_____ **5.** arose during the Middle Ages

Directions: Short Answer Answer each question or statement below on the line provided. *(10 points each)*

6. What is the general trend of Europe's population rate?

_____

7. What was the result of the ethnic conflict that took place in Yugoslavia in the 1990s?

_____

8. What are four recreational activities that many Europeans enjoy?

_____

9. What is the Chunnel, and why is it unique?

_____

10. How is abstract painting different from the Romantic and Impressionist styles?

_____

SCORE

Directions: Matching Match each item in Column A with its description in Column B. Write the correct letters in the blanks. *(3 points each)*

Column A

A. Chunnel

B. Byzantine Empire

C. Rome

D. Miguel de Cervantes

E. London

F. Athens

G. *Pax Romana*

H. Venice

I. Palestine

J. Aristotle

Column B

_____ **1.** home of the first democracy

_____ **2.** time of peace in the Roman Empire

_____ **3.** a leading Renaissance city

_____ **4.** called the Holy Land by Crusaders

_____ **5.** became a republic in 509 B.C.

_____ **6.** eastern part of the Roman Empire

_____ **7.** links England and France

_____ **8.** Renaissance writer

_____ **9.** one of the world's largest cities

_____ **10.** ancient Greek philosopher

Directions: Multiple Choice In the blank at the left, write the letter of the choice that best completes the statement or answers the question. *(3 points each)*

_____ **11.** Ancient Greece was made up of ____.

    A. nation states

    B. city-states

    C. democracies

    D. counties

_____ **12.** Before Christianity became the official religion of Rome, leaders of the Roman Empire ____.

    A. ignored Christians

    B. persecuted Christians

    C. made most Christians citizens

    D. enslaved Christians

_____ **13.** What was one early effect of the Crusades?

    A. The Roman Catholic Church declined.

    B. Trade increased.

    C. Nobles gained more land.

    D. Peasants revolted.

_____ 14. The Black Death helped end feudalism by creating _____.

A. a shortage of labor

C. more advanced medicine

B. a revolution

D. stronger families

_____ 15. As a result of the Scientific Revolution, the 1700s became known as the Age of what?

A. Learning

C. Empire

B. Discovery

D. Enlightenment

_____ 16. Starting in the 1700s, Europe changed to _____.

A. a rural, farming society

C. a rural, industrial society

B. an urban, industrial society

D. an urban, agricultural society

_____ 17. How is Europe's overall population changing?

A. It is increasing slowly.

C. It is staying the same.

B. It is decreasing.

D. It is doubling in size.

_____ 18. What kind of art did Renaissance artists create?

A. realistic

C. impressions

B. iconic

D. abstract

_____ 19. Protestants dominate which region of Europe?

A. eastern Europe

C. western Europe

B. southern Europe

D. northern Europe

_____ 20. The Holocaust occurred in Europe during _____.

A. the Franco-Prussian War

B. World War I

C. World War II

D. the Cold War

Applying Skills: Reading a Map Use the map below to answer the questions that follow. *(5 points each)*

Spread of the Black Death

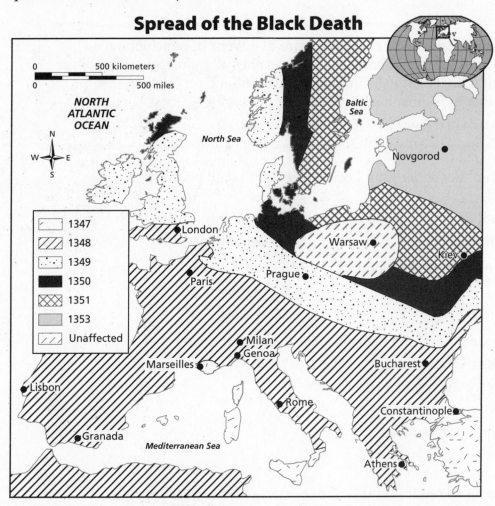

_____ **21.** In which general direction did the Black Death spread through Europe?

    A. from south to north   **C.** from west to east

    B. from north to south   **D.** from east to west

_____ **22.** Which city on the map was the first to be struck by the bubonic plague?

    A. Rome   **C.** Prague

    B. Athens   **D.** Constantinople

_____ **23.** By what year were most of Europe's major cities affected?

    A. 1347   **C.** 1351

    B. 1348   **D.** 1353

Directions: Document-Based Questions Use the document below to answer the questions that follow. *(5 points each)*

> The state of nature has a law of nature to govern it, which obliges every one, and reason which is that law, teaches all mankind who will but consult it, that being all equal and independent, no one ought to harm another in his life, health, liberty, or possessions.
>
> **Source:** John Locke, *The Second Treatise of Civil Government*, 1690.

_____ **24.** English philosopher John Locke believed that all people are created _____.

    A. equal   **C.** by nature

    B. natural   **D.** dependent

_____ **25.** Locke equates the law of nature with what?

    A. life   **C.** mankind

    B. liberty   **D.** reason

_____ **26.** Americans used John Locke's ideas to support their _____.

    A. Industrial Revolution

    B. war for independence

    C. westward movement

    D. colonial settlements

Directions: Essay On a separate sheet of paper, answer the question below. *(10 points)*

    27. How did the Enlightenment and the Industrial Revolution lead to conflict in Europe?

SCORE

Directions: Matching Match each item in Column A with its description in Column B. Write the correct letters in the blanks. *(3 points each)*

Column A

A. Copernicus

B. Alexander

C. Charlemagne

D. Spain

E. Leonardo da Vinci

F. Martin Luther

G. Socrates

H. John Locke

I. Florence

J. Romanticism

Column B

_____ **1.** artistic movement in the 1800s

_____ **2.** a Renaissance city

_____ **3.** built the first colonial empire in America

_____ **4.** Renaissance artist

_____ **5.** early Germanic king

_____ **6.** his empire stretched into Greece, Egypt, Persia, and India

_____ **7.** Polish mathematician who said the sun is the center of the universe

_____ **8.** believed people had natural rights

_____ **9.** started the Reformation

_____ **10.** ancient Greek thinker

Directions: Multiple Choice In the blank at the left, write the letter of the choice that best completes the statement or answers the question. *(3 points each)*

_____ **11.** The classical world refers to which of the following?

    A. Reformation   **C.** Middle Ages

    B. Renaissance   **D.** ancient Greece and Rome

_____ **12.** The Twelve Tables led to ____.

    A. units of measurement

    B. standards of justice

    C. the banking system

    D. the American Revolution

_____ **13.** Where did Christianity originate?

    A. Palestine   **C.** Athens

    B. Rome   **D.** Macedonia

_____ **14.** Which cultural elements are important Roman influences in the Western world today?

    A. science, art, philosophy   **C.** feudalism, drama, sports

    B. language, architecture, law   **D.** medicine, business, farming

_____ **15.** Which of the following best describes Europe's major transportation system today?

    A. government-owned, high-speed rail

    B. poorly developed rural roads

    C. interconnected river systems

    D. private toll roads and highways

_____ **16.** In the 1300s, people all over Europe were battling _____.

    A. an Ice Age   **C.** the Catholic Church

    B. Germanic invaders   **D.** the Black Death

_____ **17.** One result of the Enlightenment was the beginning of the _____.

    A. Protestant Revolution   **C.** Scientific Revolution

    B. French Revolution   **D.** Renaissance

_____ **18.** As Europeans became more secular, fewer people did which of the following?

    A. joined a political party

    B. lived in a single country

    C. belonged to a religious group

    D. donated to the arts

_____ **19.** Which of these is a result of the Industrial Revolution?

    A. People moved to the countryside.

    B. People could afford fewer things.

    C. The population of Europe decreased.

    D. Farms required less labor.

_____ **20.** Which of the following is the best description of Europeans today?

    A. They are well-educated city dwellers with comfortable incomes.

    B. They have large families and live on farms.

    C. Most are poorly educated city dwellers who would like to migrate.

    D. Most are wealthy landowners who value their religious heritage.

Applying Skills: Reading a Map Use the map below to answer the questions that follow. *(5 points each)*

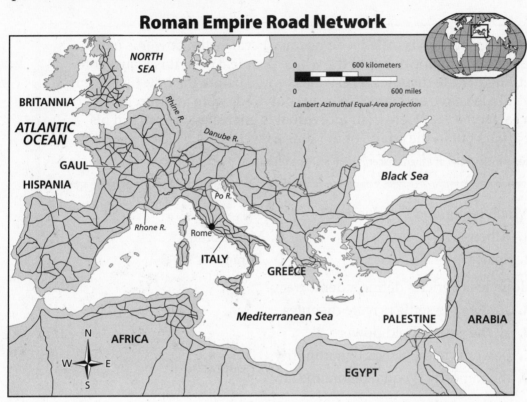

Roman Empire Road Network

_____ **21.** Which two rivers did the northern extent of the Roman Empire follow?

    A. Rhone and Po   **C.** Po and Danube

    B. Rhine and Rhone   **D.** Rhine and Danube

_____ **22.** What was the farthest north that the Roman Empire built roads?

    A. Africa   **C.** Gaul

    B. Britannia   **D.** Hispania

_____ **23.** Why did Rome build so many roads?

    A. so tax collectors could move quickly among the towns

    B. to enable grain shipments to get to the cities quickly

    C. to allow foreigners quick access to the capital

    D. so armies could quickly protect its borders

Directions: Document-Based Questions Use the document below to answer the questions that follow. *(5 points each)*

> Our Constitution is called a democracy because the power is in the hands not of a minority but of the whole people. When it is a question of settling private disputes, everyone is equal before the law. Just as our political life is free and open, so is our day-to-day life in our relations with each other. . . . Here each individual is interested not only in his own affairs but in the affairs of the state as well.
>
> **Source:** Pericles, ruler of Athens, excerpt from his *Funeral Oration.*

_____ **24.** Which region did Pericles rule?

    A. Athens   **C.** Macedonia

    B. Sparta   **D.** Thrace

_____ **25.** How does Pericles define a democracy?

    A. as a way to settle private disputes

    B. all the people hold power

    C. power is in the hands of a minority

    D. the minority is equal before the law

_____ **26.** According to Pericles, what is the relationship between the individual and the state in a democracy?

    A. The individual is interested only in his or her own affairs.

    B. State affairs must come first before individual affairs.

    C. The individual is interested in personal and state affairs.

    D. Political life is secondary to living a free and open private life.

Directions: Essay On a separate sheet of paper, answer the question below. *(10 points)*

    27. Where have many immigrants to Europe come from since World War II? Describe the various ways European countries deal with immigration.

Directions: Matching Match each item in Column A with its description in Column B. Write the correct letters in the blanks. *(10 points each)*

Column A

A. fjords

B. constitutional monarchy

C. geysers

D. parliamentary democracy

E. bog

Column B

_____ **1.** contains plants partly decayed in water

_____ **2.** government run by a prime minister who is the leader of the party with most elected officials

_____ **3.** government run by elected officials with a king and queen as head of state

_____ **4.** springs that shoot hot water and steam into the air

_____ **5.** narrow inlets of the sea surrounded by steep cliffs

Directions: Short Answer Answer each question or statement below on the line provided. *(10 points each)*

6. What form of energy is common in Iceland? What is its source?

_____

7. Why do many large ships unload their cargoes at Copenhagen?

_____

8. Name the four countries in Northern Europe that have constitutional monarchies.

_____

9. How do Finland's people differ from other Scandinavians? What is the reason for these differences?

_____

10. Who were the ancestors of the Irish? How is their influence still part of Irish culture?

_____

Name_____ Date_____ Class_____

Directions: Matching Match each item in Column A with its description in Column B. Write the correct letters in the blanks. *(10 points each)*

Column A

A. European Union

B. Germany

C. Austria

D. Liechtenstein

E. Benelux

Column B

_____ **1.** another name for Belgium, Netherlands, and Luxembourg

_____ **2.** headquartered in Brussels

_____ **3.** country smaller than Washington, D.C.

_____ **4.** Mozart lived and performed here

_____ **5.** country with the largest population in Europe

Directions: Short Answer Answer each question or statement below on the line provided. *(10 points each)*

6. What do growing populations of African and Asian immigrants face in France, Belgium, the Netherlands, and Luxembourg?

_____

7. What are the specialized products of France? What does specialization allow France to do?

_____

8. What are polders, and how do the Dutch use them?

_____

9. What has industry done for Germany's economy?

_____

10. What are the three regions of Belgium? How are the people who live in these regions identified?

_____

SCORE

Directions: Matching Match each item in Column A with its description in Column B. Write the correct letters in the blanks. *(10 points each)*

Column A

A. Vatican City

B. Parthenon

C. Balkan

D. Iberian

E. Euskera

Column B

_____ **1.** Basque language unrelated to any other language in the world

_____ **2.** ancient Greek religious site popular with tourists

_____ **3.** Athens is found on this peninsula

_____ **4.** peninsula bordered by the Mediterranean Sea and Atlantic Ocean

_____ **5.** Roman Catholic Church headquarters

Directions: Short Answer Answer each question or statement below on the line provided. *(10 points each)*

6. What do southern Italy and the Meseta in Spain have in common?

_____

7. In what major countries of southern Europe has agriculture declined in importance?

_____

8. Why did Spain's regions have little autonomy before the 1970s?

_____

9. What are the capitals of Spain and Italy?

_____

10. How are cultural traditions important to Spain's economy? Name two popular examples of these traditions.

_____

Directions: Matching Match each item in Column A with its description in Column B. Write the correct letters in the blanks. *(10 points each)*

Column A

A. Bulgaria

B. Dnieper River

C. Carpathian Mountains

D. Poland

E. Albania

Column B

_____ **1.** divides Ukraine into two regions

_____ **2.** tourists come to its scenic Black Sea resorts

_____ **3.** major geographic feature of Slovakia

_____ **4.** only country in Europe with a majority Muslim population

_____ **5.** Pope John Paul II had a strong influence here

Directions: Short Answer Answer each question or statement below on the line provided. *(10 points each)*

6. How did the economies of many eastern European nations change after the fall of communism?

_____

7. Why did Yugoslavia break up into six countries? What are the countries?

_____

8. How has rapid industrialization helped and hurt the Czech Republic?

_____

9. How do Hungarians differ from most other eastern Europeans in ancestry?

_____

10. Name the three countries that are known as the Baltic Republics.

_____

Name_____ Date_____ Class_____

Directions: Matching Match each item in Column A with its description in Column B. Write the correct letters in the blanks. *(3 points each)*

Column A

A. Scandinavia

B. Benelux

C. Serbs

D. Gaelic

E. Albania

F. Alpine countries

G. Solidarity

H. Ukraine

I. United Kingdom

J. Magyars

Column B

_____ **1.** labor group that helped bring down communism

_____ **2.** England, Scotland, Wales, Northern Ireland

_____ **3.** one of Ireland's languages

_____ **4.** ancestors of the Hungarians

_____ **5.** Norway, Sweden, Finland, Denmark

_____ **6.** Belgium, Netherlands, Luxembourg

_____ **7.** farmers outnumber factory workers here

_____ **8.** "breadbasket of Europe"

_____ **9.** carried out ethnic cleansing in Yugoslavia

_____ **10.** Switzerland, Austria, Liechtenstein

Directions: Multiple Choice In the blank at the left, write the letter of the choice that best completes the statement or answers the question. *(3 points each)*

_____ **11.** Most Scandinavians are _____.
   A. Roman Catholic   **C.** Protestant Lutherans
   B. Finnish   **D.** Eastern Orthodox

_____ **12.** About 25 percent of which country lies below sea level?
   A. Spain   **C.** Italy
   B. Iceland   **D.** Netherlands

_____ **13.** What form of government does the United Kingdom have?
   A. federal republic   **C.** direct democracy
   B. parliamentary democracy **D.** confederation

_____ **14.** The Irish trace their ancestry to the ____.
- **A.** Vikings
- **B.** Celts
- **C.** Picts
- **D.** Scots

_____ **15.** Which is the smallest Scandinavian country with a high population density?
- **A.** Norway
- **B.** Sweden
- **C.** Denmark
- **D.** Iceland

_____ **16.** Which country has more than 60 million people and relies on tourism, wines, cheeses, and high-tech industries?
- **A.** Spain
- **B.** France
- **C.** Ireland
- **D.** Belgium

_____ **17.** Which country was separated by communism but reunited in 1990?
- **A.** Germany
- **B.** France
- **C.** Norway
- **D.** Denmark

_____ **18.** Refusing to take sides in wars, which country enjoyed a stable democratic government for 700 years?
- **A.** Austria
- **B.** Italy
- **C.** Luxembourg
- **D.** Switzerland

_____ **19.** In which country can one hear Castilian, Catalonian, and Basque spoken?
- **A.** Italy
- **B.** Spain
- **C.** the Netherlands
- **D.** Germany

_____ **20.** Which country and its 2,000 islands are often shaken by earthquakes?
- **A.** Portugal
- **B.** Austria
- **C.** Greece
- **D.** Finland

Applying Skills: Reading a Map Use the map below to answer the questions that follow. *(5 points each)*

The Danube River

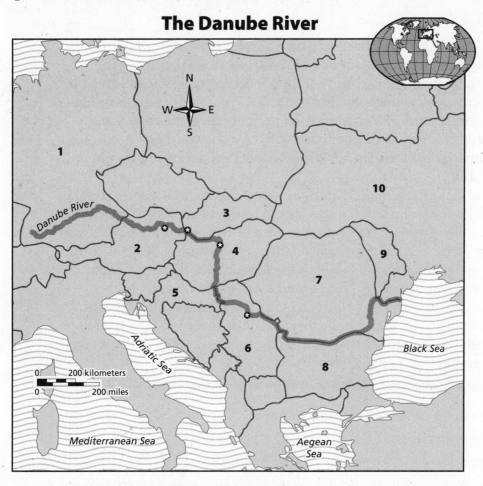

_____ **21.** The source of the Danube River is located in country 1. What is this country?

    A. Germany   **C.** Czech Republic

    B. Austria   **D.** Switzerland

_____ **22.** The Danube River flows through four capital cities. Which capital in country 4 is split in two by the Danube?

    A. Vienna   **C.** Belgrade

    B. Bratislava   **D.** Budapest

_____ **23.** Where is the mouth of the Danube River?

    A. Alps   **C.** Black Sea

    B. Carpathian Mountains   **D.** Aegean Sea

Directions: Document-Based Questions Use the document below to answer the questions that follow. *(5 points each)*

Known as the "Queen of the Adriatic," Venice, Italy, is built on more than 100 islands connected by about 150 canals and 400 bridges. The bridges are for pedestrian use only, and no motor vehicles are allowed on the city's narrow, ancient streets. For centuries, Venetians used gondolas as their primary means of transportation in navigating the canals. Gondolas are long, flat-bottomed boats propelled by one oar. Now gondolas are used primarily for tourists, with motorboats used to carry freight and passenger traffic.

The Grand Canal, the main waterway winding through Venice, is 80 to 175 feet wide and about two miles long. Lining its banks are nearly 200 palaces and other great works of architecture built between the 1100s and 1700s. Today, Venice faces enormous challenges. Although beaches form protective barriers on the outer side of the lagoon, floods are a major threat. A devastating flood in 1966 served as a "wake-up call" to the international community, and efforts to save the Queen of the Adriatic began. Still, Venice's land and buildings continue to sink. The city also struggles with damage to structures from air and water pollution, as well as a loss of population to other areas.

_____ **24.** On which body of water is Venice located?

A. Mediterranean Sea   **C.** Aegean Sea

B. Adriatic Sea   **D.** Tiber River

_____ **25.** Visitors to Venice will see all of the following EXCEPT ____.

A. gondolas   **C.** pedestrian bridges

B. motorboats   **D.** automobiles

_____ **26.** Which of the following is a problem Venice faces?

A. overpopulation   **C.** drought

B. sinking   **D.** loss of tourism

Directions: Essay On a separate sheet of paper, answer the question below. *(10 points)*

27. How do northern and southern Italy differ in terms of physical geography, economy, and standard of living?

Directions: Matching Match each item in Column A with its description in Column B. Write the correct letters in the blanks. *(3 points each)*

Column A

A. United Kingdom

B. Spain

C. Germany

D. France

E. Ireland

F. Switzerland

G. Denmark

H. Ukraine

I. Vatican City

J. Austria

Column B

_____ **1.** revolution here led to the rise of democracy

_____ **2.** its capital is Copenhagen

_____ **3.** Parliamentary democracy with 60 million people

_____ **4.** Catholic descendants of Celts

_____ **5.** reunified as a nation in 1990

_____ **6.** neutral country during wars

_____ **7.** its capital is Madrid

_____ **8.** one of the original republics of the Soviet Union

_____ **9.** home of great composers like Mozart

_____ **10.** smallest independent country in the world

Directions: Multiple Choice In the blank at the left, write the letter of the choice that best completes the statement or answers the question. *(3 points each)*

_____ **11.** What body of water separates Great Britain from the continent of Europe?

    A. North Sea   **C.** Baltic Sea

    B. English Channel   **D.** Bering Strait

_____ **12.** What provision was included in the Petition of Right that Parliament forced King Charles I of England to sign in 1628?

    A. Taxes could be enacted only if Parliament approved.

    B. The king would also pay taxes.

    C. Parliament could meet every year.

    D. Taxes could never be enacted unless England was at war.

_____ **13.** Why did more than one million Irish people die in the 1840s?

    A. War broke out with Scotland.   **C.** Disease destroyed the potato crop.

    B. The plague swept across the country.   **D.** An earthquake struck Dublin.

_____ **14.** Iceland's hot springs and geysers are caused by which of the following?

    A. underground rivers   **C.** the movement of tectonic plates

    B. the strong North Atlantic Current   **D.** drilling for oil

_____ **15.** Which industry gives employment to more than 1 in 12 workers in France?

    A. agriculture   **C.** tourism

    B. banking   **D.** fishing

_____ **16.** Flanders, Wallonia, and Brussels are three regions of which country?

    A. Wales   **C.** Belgium

    B. Norway   **D.** Italy

_____ **17.** Which country has polders reclaimed from the sea?

    A. Netherlands   **C.** Austria

    B. Portugal   **D.** Sweden

_____ **18.** Which phrase describes historic conditions in the Czech Republic, Slovakia, and Hungary?

    A. part of Russia   **C.** descendants of the Magyars

    B. under Communist rule   **D.** parliamentary democracies

_____ **19.** Which European country still has strong ties to Russia?

    A. Poland   **C.** Bulgaria

    B. Belarus   **D.** Romania

_____ **20.** Which Baltic Republic has the highest average incomes and exports telecommunications equipment?

    A. Estonia   **C.** Lithuania

    B. Latvia   **D.** Moldova

Applying Skills: Reading a Map Use the map below to answer the
questions that follow. *(5 points each)*

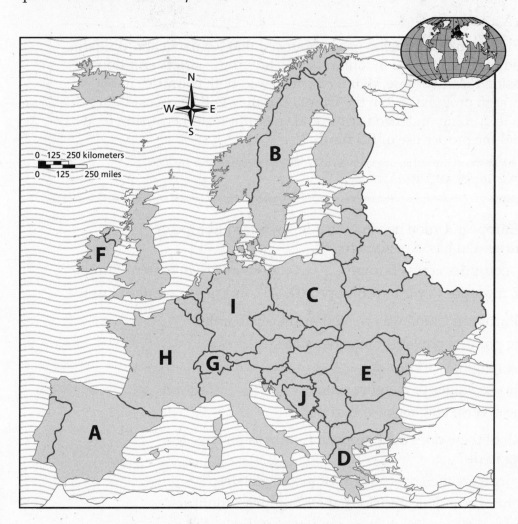

_____ **21.** Which country is signified by the letter *B*?

    A. Finland   **C.** Denmark

    B. Norway   **D.** Sweden

_____ **22.** Letter *E* is located on which country?

    A. Romania   **C.** Moldova

    B. Bulgaria   **D.** Hungary

_____ **23.** Which country is labeled with the letter *C*?

    A. Germany   **C.** Poland

    B. Czech Republic   **D.** Belarus

Directions: Document-Based Questions Use the document below to answer the questions that follow. *(5 points each)*

> The European Commission has announced that Romania and Bulgaria will be admitted to the EU in January 2007, but under strict conditions. Commission President Jose Manuel Barroso said both countries had made enough progress to join the Union. But they will be checked for progress in curbing organized crime and corruption, and ensuring food safety and the proper use of EU funds.
>
> **Source:** "New Members Expand European Union to 27," BBC News, September 26, 2006, news.bbc.co.uk/2/hi/europe/5380024.stm.

_____ **24.** The European Union began with a few western European countries and has expanded to ____.
  A. 27 countries across Europe   **C.** 25 countries in eastern Europe
  B. 27 countries in western Europe   **D.** 25 countries in western Europe

_____ **25.** The European Union was created primarily to unify ____.
  A. the political powers of member states
  B. the religions of Europe
  C. the economies of member states
  D. the diverse languages of Europe

_____ **26.** Which of these does the European Commission have the power to do?
  A. reorganize the governments of member states
  B. control economic decisions of all European countries
  C. redraw the borders between member states
  D. judge the economic, social, and political conditions of member states

Directions: Essay On a separate sheet of paper, answer the question below. *(10 points)*

  27. What is the dispute over Northern Ireland?

Directions: Matching Match each item in Column A with its description in Column B. Write the correct letters in the blanks. *(5 points each)*

Column A

A. Bosnia and Herzegovina

B. Chunnel

C. North Atlantic Current

D. Rhine

E. Romania

F. Mediterranean

G. Pyrenees

H. Scandinavia

I. North Sea

J. Ukraine

Column B

_____ **1.** drove out Communists in a bloody revolt in 1989

_____ **2.** mountains between France and Spain

_____ **3.** scene of ethnic cleansing

_____ **4.** location of oil reserves

_____ **5.** warms Iceland

_____ **6.** largest European country

_____ **7.** important river in Germany

_____ **8.** links France and England

_____ **9.** climate of Italy and Greece

_____ **10.** northernmost part of Europe

Directions: Multiple Choice Write the letter of the choice that best completes the statement or answers the question. *(5 points each)*

_____ **11.** The Tower of London, Germany's Cologne Cathedral, and ancient monuments in Athens all show damage from what?

    A. vandalism   **C.** tornadoes

    B. fires   **D.** acid rain

_____ **12.** All of the following are major port cities today EXCEPT _____.

    A. London   **C.** Hamburg

    B. Copenhagen   **D.** Antwerp

_____ **13.** The Crusades and the bubonic plague weakened _____.

    A. European nation-states   **C.** trade

    B. feudalism   **D.** European monarchs

_____ **14.** Which of these is a constitutional monarchy?

    A. United Kingdom   **C.** Germany

    B. France   **D.** all of these

_____ **15.** The Valley of Roses is located in _____.

    A. Italy   **C.** Spain

    B. Bulgaria   **D.** Greece

Name_____ Date_____ Class_____

Applying Skills: Reading a Time Line Use the time line below to answer the questions that follow. *(5 points each)*

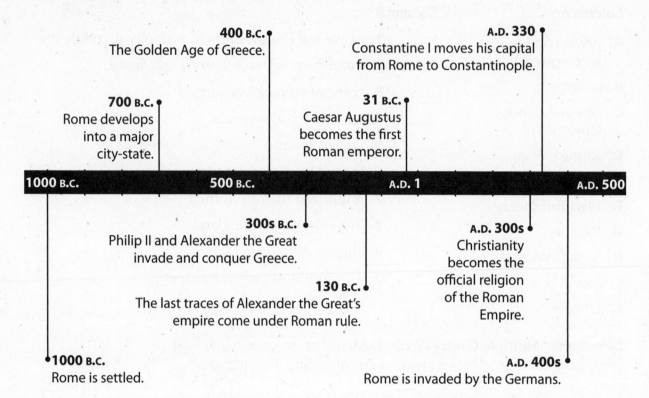

400 B.C.
The Golden Age of Greece.

A.D. 330
Constantine I moves his capital from Rome to Constantinople.

700 B.C.
Rome develops into a major city-state.

31 B.C.
Caesar Augustus becomes the first Roman emperor.

1000 B.C.   500 B.C.   A.D. 1   A.D. 500

300s B.C.
Philip II and Alexander the Great invade and conquer Greece.

A.D. 300s
Christianity becomes the official religion of the Roman Empire.

130 B.C.
The last traces of Alexander the Great's empire come under Roman rule.

1000 B.C.
Rome is settled.

A.D. 400s
Rome is invaded by the Germans.

_____ **16.** Where was the capital of the eastern Roman Empire located?

    A. northern Italy   **C.** Constantinople

    B. Greece   **D.** Germany

_____ **17.** About how long did Alexander the Great's empire exist?

    A. 130 years   **C.** 300 years

    B. 200 years   **D.** 350 years

_____ **18.** Who was the first Roman emperor?

    A. Julius Caesar   **C.** Philip II

    B. Charlemagne   **D.** Caesar Augustus

Directions: Essay On a separate sheet of paper, answer the question below. *(10 points)*

    19. What elements of ancient Rome are found in Western cultures today?

Directions: Matching Match each item in Column A with its description in Column B. Write the correct letters in the blanks. *(5 points each)*

Column A

A. Siberia

B. *War and Peace*

C. Peter the Great

D. Cold War

E. Eastern Orthodox Christianity

F. cell phone

G. Moscow

H. *Swan Lake*

I. Ivan the Great

J. Muscovy

Column B

_____ **1.** ballet written by Tchaikovsky

_____ **2.** Slavic territory that became Russia

_____ **3.** prince who rejected Mongol rule

_____ **4.** capital of Russia

_____ **5.** one of the most popular possessions in Russia today

_____ **6.** struggle between the United States and the Soviet Union

_____ **7.** Russia's major religion

_____ **8.** czar who built a new capital close to Europe

_____ **9.** novel written by Tolstoy

_____ **10.** Asian Russia

Directions: Multiple Choice Write the letter of the choice that best completes the statement or answers the question. *(7 points each)*

_____ **11.** Which of the following is a challenge to Russia as it tries to build a democracy?

  A. People are fearful of their government.

  B. Russia's oil and gas exports are not bringing in much money.

  C. Many citizens understand little about how their government works.

  D. Too many new businesses are being built at too rapid a pace.

_____ **12.** What led to the Russian revolution?

  A. shortages of food

  B. Mongol invasions

  C. civil war between ethnic groups

  D. religious differences

_____ **13.** Nearly half of Russia's waterway traffic is carried on the ____.

  A. Lena

  B. Volga

  C. Baltic Sea

  D. Urals

_____ **14.** Why is so much of Russia's climate cool to cold?

  A. It sits at high elevations.

  B. It is close to the Arctic Ocean.

  C. It is located at high latitudes.

  D. It is located at low latitudes.

_____ **15.** The Soviet policy of perestroika was important because it allowed ____.

    A. Soviet citizens to say what they thought without fear of being punished

    B. newspapers to publish any story without fear of being punished

    C. factory workers more freedom to make economic decisions

    D. Soviet citizens to form new political parties

Applying Skills: Reading a Graph Use the graph below to answer the questions that follow. *(5 points each)*

_____ **16.** Russian citizens living outside of Moscow are most concerned about ____.

    A. deforestation

    B. diseases caused by pollution

    C. high radiation

    D. water pollution

_____ **17.** What percentage of people who live in Moscow are concerned about deforestation?

    A. 3 percent

    B. 7 percent

    C. 4 percent

    D. 1 percent

_____ **18.** What problem do citizens living in Moscow worry about least?

    A. high radiation

    B. diseases caused by pollution

    C. water pollution

    D. air pollution

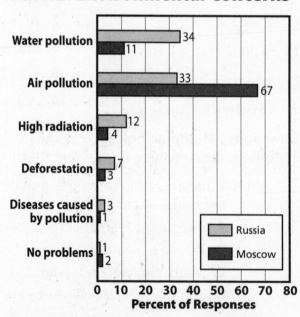

Russia: Environmental Concerns*

*Russians were asked, "What ecological problems trouble the citizens of your place of residence most of all?"

Source: Public Opinion Foundation, 2006 (http://bd. english.fom.ru/).

SCORE

Directions: Matching Match each item in Column A with its description in Column B. Write the correct letters in the blanks. *(10 points each)*

Column A

A. Ob'

B. Black Sea

C. Caspian Sea

D. Volga

E. softwood

Column B

_____ **1.** an inland saltwater lake that is important for fishing

_____ **2.** waterway that flows through European Russia

_____ **3.** natural resource found in the evergreen forests of Siberia

_____ **4.** Russia's warm-water route to the Mediterranean Sea

_____ **5.** waterway that flows through Asian Russia

Directions: Short Answer Answer each question or statement below on the line provided. *(10 points each)*

6. How do European and Asian Russia differ in terms of climate and population?

_____

7. What is unusual about the port of St. Petersburg?

_____

8. What fossil fuels are found in Asian Russia? What inhibits their use?

_____

9. Where is Lake Baikal? Why is it so important to humans?

_____

10. Where is the Kamchatka Peninsula located? What occurs in this region?

_____

SCORE

Climate and the Environment

Quiz 13-2

Directions: Matching Match each item in Column A with its description in Column B. Write the correct letters in the blanks. *(10 points each)*

Column A

A. taiga

B. cold winters

C. subarctic

D. smog

E. humid continental

Column B

_____ **1.** world's largest coniferous forest

_____ **2.** played an important role in Russia's history

_____ **3.** thick haze of fog and chemicals

_____ **4.** Russia's largest climate area

_____ **5.** climate of western Russia

Directions: Short Answer Answer each question or statement below on the line provided. *(10 points each)*

6. How does Russia's geography in the north and south contribute to the country's generally cool to cold climate?

_____

7. What types of vegetation survive in the tundra?

_____

8. Why does Russia have high levels of pollution today?

_____

9. How do the effects of smog on the Russian people compare to those of chemical pollution on Lake Baikal's wildlife?

_____

10. What are other countries doing to help Russia clean up its pollution problems?

_____

Directions: Matching Match each item in Column A with its description in Column B. Write the correct letters in the blanks. *(3 points each)*

Column A	Column B
A. Volga	_____ **1.** world's largest coniferous forest
B. softwood	_____ **2.** plain where only mosses, lichens, or small shrubs can survive
C. Lake Baikal	_____ **3.** haze that blankets many Russian cities
D. tundra	_____ **4.** European Russia's major river
E. Siberia	_____ **5.** river that flows north into the Arctic Ocean
F. Northern European Plain	_____ **6.** world's deepest freshwater lake
G. smog	_____ **7.** area with one of the coldest climates in the world
H. Kamchatka Peninsula	_____ **8.** area of Russia that contains many volcanoes
I. taiga	_____ **9.** Russian resource used in buildings and furniture
J. Lena	_____ **10.** home to about 75 percent of all Russians

Directions: Multiple Choice In the blank at the left, write the letter of the choice that best completes the statement or answers the question. *(3 points each)*

_____ **11.** Russia is _____ as the United States.
    A. nearly twice as large   **C.** three times as large
    B. half as large   **D.** about the same size

_____ **12.** The capital of Russia is _____.
    A. St. Petersburg   **C.** Omsk
    B. Grozny   **D.** Moscow

_____ **13.** Which of the following jobs would most likely be held by a resident of northern Siberia?
    A. steel worker   **C.** farmer
    B. reindeer herder   **D.** ship builder

_____ **14.** The Lena, the Yenisey, and the Ob' are among the _____.
    A. widest rivers in the world   **C.** deepest rivers in the world
    B. longest rivers in Russia   **D.** longest rivers in the world

____ **15.** Why is it difficult to access Siberia's resources?

    A. Siberia lacks fossil fuels and softwood.

    B. Too much volcanic activity occurs in the area.

    C. The climate is too cold, and no infrastructure exists.

    D. There is no direct route to the ocean from Siberia.

____ **16.** Russia has a warm-water route to the Mediterranean Sea through the ____.

    A. Baltic Sea   **C.** Caspian Sea

    B. Black Sea   **D.** North Sea

____ **17.** The warm currents of the Atlantic and Pacific Oceans ____.

    A. are vital to Russia's shipping industries because they keep port waters from freezing

    B. magnify the sun's heat and help keep the Russian climate as moderate as possible

    C. increase summer temperatures and provide relief from the harsh Russian winters

    D. are too far away from much of Russia to help moderate the climate

____ **18.** Which best summarizes Russia's seasons?

    A. Spring and summer are very brief.

    B. Winter and spring are very long.

    C. Summer and autumn are very long.

    D. Spring and autumn are very brief.

____ **19.** What causes permafrost?

    A. warm temperatures followed by sudden freezing

    B. cold temperatures and heavy rainfall

    C. arctic air blasts followed by heavy precipitation

    D. cold temperatures and a lack of precipitation

____ **20.** Which of the following is a major cause of water pollution in Russia?

    A. oil spills from tanker ships

    B. people throwing garbage into lakes and streams

    C. chemicals used in agriculture and industry

    D. gasoline and other pollutants used in the fishing industry

Name_____ Date_____ Class_____

Applying Skills: Reading a Graph Use the graphs below to answer
the questions that follow. *(5 points each)*

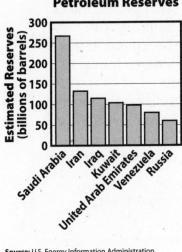

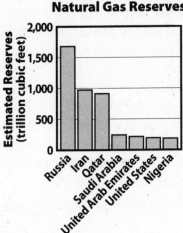

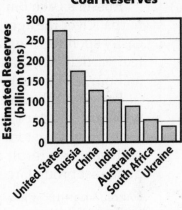

Source: U.S. Energy Information Administration.

____ **21.** Of which natural resource does Russia have the least
amount?

    A. natural gas   **C.** coal

    B. petroleum   **D.** minerals

____ **22.** Of which resource does Russia have the largest reserves?

    A. petroleum   **C.** natural gas

    B. gasoline   **D.** coal

____ **23.** About how much more coal does Russia have than China?

    A. 50 billion tons   **C.** 25 billion tons

    B. 100 billion tons   **D.** 150 billion tons

Directions: Document-Based Questions Use the document below to answer the questions that follow. *(5 points each)*

> Russia's Lake Baikal is the last preserve of a unique seal species, the nerpa. Over the ages, nerpas have developed amazing skills and can easily spend as long as 20 minutes underwater without breathing. If they feel particularly threatened, they can remain below the surface for up to an hour, an astonishing achievement for mammals.
>
> Between February and April, baby seals are born with their distinctive white fur, much prized by Russia's fashion industry. This makes them a tempting target for hunters. Around 10,000 nerpas, mostly young, die each year as a result of hunting or disease, the Russian office of environmentalist group Greenpeace says.
>
> **Source:** Adapted from "Russia's Unique Seals Struggle for Survival." animal.discovery.com/news/afp/20030825/nerpas.html.

____ **24.** How long can nerpas remain underwater without breathing?

    A. from 20 minutes to an hour   **C.** one hour and 20 minutes

    B. less than 20 minutes   **D.** more than an hour

____ **25.** During which months are baby seals born?

    A. between April and May   **C.** between November and February

    B. between February and April   **D.** between December and February

____ **26.** Why are baby seals hunted?

    A. for their meat   **C.** for sport

    B. for their oil   **D.** for their fur

Directions: Essay On a separate sheet of paper, answer the question below. *(10 points)*

    27. What is the Ring of Fire? How does it affect Asian Russia?

SCORE

Physical Geography of Russia

Chapter 13 Test Form B

Directions: Matching Match each item in Column A with its description in Column B. Write the correct letters in the blanks. *(3 points each)*

Column A

A. economic growth

B. Lake Baikal

C. 16°F

D. Mediterranean Sea

E. Caucasus

F. 66°F

G. St. Petersburg

H. pollutants

I. Ural Mountains

J. Caspian Sea

Column B

_____ **1.** large port city near the Baltic Sea

_____ **2.** mountains in southern Russia

_____ **3.** dividing line between the European and Asian parts of Russia

_____ **4.** world's deepest freshwater lake

_____ **5.** Moscow's average July temperature

_____ **6.** focus of Russia's leaders for most of the 1900s

_____ **7.** largest inland body of water

_____ **8.** Black Sea provides access to this

_____ **9.** Moscow's average January temperature

_____ **10.** chemicals and smoke particles

Directions: Multiple Choice In the blank at the left, write the letter of the choice that best completes the statement or answers the question. *(3 points each)*

_____ **11.** Besides fossil fuels, Russia's other great resource is _____.

    A. natural gas   **C.** softwood

    B. fish   **D.** technology

_____ **12.** Which of the following areas lies near a fault line and is prone to destructive earthquakes?

    A. northern Russia   **C.** Siberia

    B. Ural Mountains   **D.** Caucasus

_____ **13.** Russians have long relied on which of the following rivers for transportation?

    A. Volga   **C.** Yenisey

    B. Lena   **D.** Ob'

_____ **14.** Russia's largest climate area is the _____ zone.

    A. subarctic   **C.** humid continental

    B. tundra   **D.** permafrost

____ 15. The Caspian Sea is actually ____.

    A. the beginning point for several of Russia's largest rivers

    B. the world's deepest freshwater lake

    C home to one of Russia's major seaports

    D. a saltwater lake

____ 16. Why does Russia have a cool to cold climate?

    A. Mountain ranges block warm air coming from the Pacific Ocean.

    B. Russia's many bodies of water cause the air to be cooler.

    C Most of Russia is located in the high latitudes.

    D. Permafrost holds the cold climate in the soil.

____ 17. Why can icy Arctic air flow into Russia?

    A. The northern mountains do not present a united front to the Arctic Circle.

    B. Elevations are low in northern Russia.

    C. Russia's forests lie in the rain shadow of the Caucasus.

    D. No large buildings act as windbreaks.

____ 18. During World War II, bitter cold weather halted the advance of ____ into Russia.

    A. German troops   **C.** Communist troops

    B. Napoleon's troops   **D.** British troops

____ 19. How large is the taiga?

    A. about 400 miles across   **C.** about 6,200 miles across

    B. about 4,000 miles across   **D.** about 8,000 miles across

____ 20. Which of the following can be said about Russia's economy and environment?

    A. Both Russia's economy and environment have improved dramatically.

    B. As Russia's economy expanded, the environment became worse.

    C. Both Russia's economy and environment have declined over the past few years.

    D. As Russia's environmental problems improved, the economy declined.

Name_____ Date_____ Class_____

Applying Skills: Reading a Map Use the map below to answer the questions that follow. *(5 points each)*

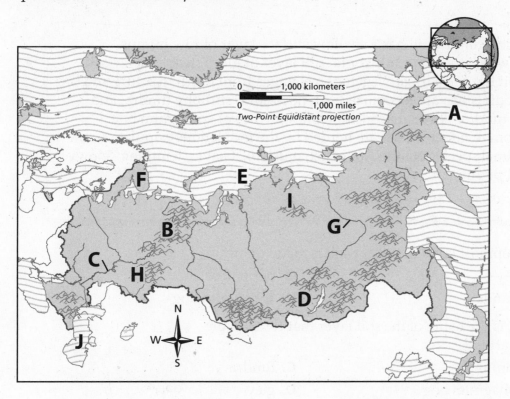

____ **21.** Which feature is represented by the letter *C?*

    A. Caspian Sea   **C.** Caucasus Mountains

    B. Ural Mountains   **D.** Volga

____ **22.** Which feature is represented by the letter *F?*

    A. Kola Peninsula   **C.** Siberia

    B. Kamchatka Peninsula   **D.** Kaliningrad

____ **23.** Which feature is represented by the letter *J?*

    A. Black Sea   **C.** Caspian Sea

    B. Yenisey   **D.** Baltic Sea

Directions: Document-Based Questions Use the document below to answer the questions that follow. *(5 points each)*

> A typical tundra soil has a shallow surface layer of raw humus, beneath which there is a horizontal soil layer of gley (sticky, clayey soil) resting on the permafrost. Vegetation changes from north to south, and three subdivisions are recognized: Arctic tundra, shrubby tundra, and wooded tundra. There are considerable stretches of sphagnum bog. Apart from reindeer, which are herded by the indigenous population, the main animal species are the Arctic fox, musk ox, beaver, lemming, snowy owl, and ptarmigan.
>
> **Source:** *Encyclopaedia Britannica.* www.britannica.com/eb/article38590.

____ **24.** The topmost layer of tundra soil is made up of ____.

  A. gley   **C.** permafrost

  B. humus   **D.** sphagnum bog

____ **25.** What is the name of the soil layer that rests on the permafrost?

  A. humus   **C.** tundra

  B. sphagnum bog   **D.** gley

____ **26.** Which of the following is a species that would likely be found in the Russian wooded tundra?

  A. elk   **C.** snowy owl

  B. horse   **D.** seal

Directions: Essay On a separate sheet of paper, answer the question below. *(10 points)*

  27. Why do so many Russians suffer from lung diseases and cancer?

SCORE

Directions: Matching Match each item in Column A with its description in Column B. Write the correct letters in the blanks. *(10 points each)*

Column A

A. Ivan the Great

B. Kievan Rus

C. St. Petersburg

D. Moscow

E. Ivan the Terrible

Column B

_____ **1.** name of civilization built around the city of Kyiv in the A.D. 800s

_____ **2.** ancient trading post that became the Soviet capital

_____ **3.** prince of Muscovy who rejected Mongol rule and declared independence

_____ **4.** the first czar of Russia

_____ **5.** built to increase contact and trade with Europe

Directions: Short Answer Answer each question or statement below on the line provided. *(10 points each)*

6. Why did serfs have little freedom?

_____

7. Who turned the Russian Empire into the Union of Soviet Socialist Republics? What did he do to try to make everyone in Soviet society more equal?

_____

8. How did the policy of perestroika lead the people of the Soviet Union to doubt communism?

_____

9. What does the word *glasnost* mean in English, and how did it affect Soviet citizens?

_____

10. How has Vladimir Putin dealt with challenges he has faced as president?

_____

SCORE

Cultures and Lifestyles

Quiz 14-2

Directions: Matching Match each item in Column A with its description in Column B. Write the correct letters in the blanks. *(10 points each)*

Column A

A. The Hermitage

B. Bolshoi

C. Yakut

D. Trans-Siberian Railroad

E. Peter Ilich Tchaikovsky

Column B

_____ **1.** ethnic group that herds reindeer in eastern Siberia

_____ **2.** writer of *Swan Lake* and *The Nutcracker*

_____ **3.** famous Moscow ballet school

_____ **4.** famous museum in St. Petersburg

_____ **5.** runs from Moscow to Vladivostok

Directions: Short Answer Answer each question or statement below on the line provided. *(10 points each)*

6. Who wrote *War and Peace*? How did this novel reflect the Russians' sense of nationalism?

_____

7. What does *Maslenitsa* celebrate? Name three ways Russians celebrate it.

_____

8. What has been the primary means of transportation in Russia? How are people and the government changing this?

_____

9. What are three main influences on the Russian lifestyle?

_____

10. In what areas have Russians excelled?

_____

SCORE

Directions: Matching Match each item in Column A with its description in Column B. Write the correct letters in the blanks. *(3 points each)*

Column A

A. Slavs

B. Kirov

C. Tatars

D. 1941

E. Warsaw Pact

F. dachas

G. coup

H. 1985

I. Igor Stravinsky

J. Karl Marx

Column B

_____ **1.** year Mikhail Gorbachev became the Soviet leader

_____ **2.** country homes owned by wealthy Russians

_____ **3.** what hard-line Communists tried to do to Yeltsin

_____ **4.** German political thinker

_____ **5.** famous ballet company in St. Petersburg

_____ **6.** composer of *The Firebird Suite*

_____ **7.** group of Communist countries that included most of Eastern Europe

_____ **8.** ancestors of modern Russians

_____ **9.** year that Germany invaded the Soviet Union

_____ **10.** Muslim descendants of the Mongols

Directions: Multiple Choice In the blank at the left, write the letter of the choice that best completes the statement or answers the question. *(3 points each)*

_____ **11.** Kievan Rus prospered from river trade between Scandinavia and ____.
  A. the Mongol Empire   **C.** France
  B. the Byzantine Empire   **D.** Ukraine

_____ **12.** In A.D. 988, missionaries brought a new religion to Kievan Rus. What else did they bring?
  A. the plantation system   **C.** food and clothing
  B. a new form of government **D.** a written language

_____ **13.** Which Russian czar freed the serfs?
  A. Peter the Great   **C.** Czar Alexander II
  B. Ivan the Terrible   **D.** Catherine the Great

____ **14.** When the Union of Soviet Socialist Republics (U.S.S.R.) was created, how many republics made up this nation?

A. 15   **C.** 25

B. 20   **D.** 30

____ **15.** Which ruler overthrew Mongol rule?

A. Ivan III   **C.** Peter the Great

B. Ivan IV   **D.** Catherine the Great

____ **16.** What is Russia's largest ethnic group?

A. Tatars   **C.** Ukrainians

B. Slavs   **D.** Yakut

____ **17.** What is the major religion in Russia today?

A. Muslim   **C.** Roman Catholic

B. Protestant   **D.** Eastern Orthodox Christianity

____ **18.** Which Russian work of art describes the Russians' defense against the French invasion of 1812?

A. *War and Peace*   **C.** *The Firebird Suite*

B. *Swan Lake*   **D.** *The Nutcracker*

____ **19.** Which policy aimed to rebuild the Soviet economy?

A. glasnost   **C.** krasnoyarsk

B. collectivization   **D.** perestroika

____ **20.** What was the primary means of transportation in Russia during the Soviet era?

A. trucks   **C.** railroads

B. shipping   **D.** private car

Applying Skills: Reading a Map Use the map below to answer the questions that follow. *(5 points each)*

Expansion of Russia

KEY
- Kievan Territory
- 1360–1533
- 1533–1689
- 1689–1917
- Boundary of the Soviet Union in 1945
- Present-day Russian boundary

_____ **21.** St. Petersburg is located in a part of Russia that was ____.

    A. added between 1533 and 1689

    B. added between 1360 and 1533

    C. once known as the Kievan Territory

    D. added between 1689 and 1917

_____ **22.** The size of present-day Russia ____.

    A. is about the same today as it was in 1917

    B. includes all of the Kievan Territory

    C. is about half the size that it was during the Soviet Union

    D. includes almost all of the land acquired by 1689

_____ **23.** Which inland body of water became part of Russia between 1533 and 1689?

    A. Aral Sea   **C.** Kara Sea

    B. Black Sea   **D.** Lake Baikal

Directions: Document-Based Questions Use the document below to answer the questions that follow. *(5 points each)*

> Two spacewalking astronauts successfully rewired half of the international space station on Thursday, a job that when finished will allow the orbiting outpost to double the size of its crew and add two more labs in the coming years. . . .
>
> Before the start of the spacewalk, NASA flight controllers on the ground powered down sections of the station. . . . Half the lights in the station's U.S. laboratory went dark. Cameras at the station stopped working and some ventilation ducts were turned off. Communication between the U.S. and Russian sides of the space station was cut off.
>
> **Source:** "Astronauts Reroute Space Station Power," MSNBC. www.msnbc.msn.com/id/16205412.

_____ **24.** Why were the astronauts spacewalking?

   A. to reroute some wiring on the space station

   B. to check that heat shields were in place

   C. to set up a new means of communication with NASA

   D. to conduct experiments in weightlessness

_____ **25.** What will be added to the space station in the coming years?

   A. communication equipment   **C.** more cameras

   B. two more labs   **D.** ventilation ducts

_____ **26.** Why is it called the "international" space station?

   A. The station orbits the entire Earth.

   B. Cameras broadcast images of the station all over Earth.

   C. The station includes components from many different countries.

   D. The astronauts are from the United States and Russia.

Directions: Essay On a separate sheet of paper, answer the question below. *(10 points)*

   27. How did Russia's cold climate affect the invasion led by Napoleon Bonaparte?

Directions: Matching Match each item in Column A with its description in Column B. Write the correct letters in the blanks. *(3 points each)*

Column A

A. competition

B. Vladimir Lenin

C. Joseph Stalin

D. glasnost

E. Alexander Solzhenitsyn

F. Leo Tolstoy

G. Ukrainians

H. Boris Yeltsin

I. collectivization

J. Yuri Gagarin

Column B

_____ **1.** first president of Russia

_____ **2.** first person to fly in space

_____ **3.** author who wrote about harsh conditions in a Communist society

_____ **4.** created the Union of Soviet Socialist Republics

_____ **5.** resulted in factorylike farms run by the government

_____ **6.** Soviet dictator after 1924

_____ **7.** policy of openness

_____ **8.** author of *War and Peace*

_____ **9.** Soviet government eliminated this in the economy

_____ **10.** descendants of Slavs who settled near Kyiv

Directions: Multiple Choice In the blank at the left, write the letter of the choice that best completes the statement or answers the question. *(3 points each)*

_____ **11.** The civilization called Kievan Rus was settled by _____.

    A. Ivan the Terrible   **C.** early Slavs

    B. Mongol warriors   **D.** Ivan the Great

_____ **12.** How did Ivan IV expand the Russian Empire?

    A. by conquering neighboring territories

    B. by diplomatic agreements with other countries

    C. by forcing his children to marry into the royal households of other countries

    D. by popular election

_____ **13.** What did Vladimir Lenin end?

    A. World War II   **C.** serfdom

    B. private ownership   **D.** collectivization

____ **14.** The German political thinker Karl Marx believed that ____.

    A. the government had too much power and factory owners had too little power

    B. factory owners had too much power and factory workers had too little power

    C. factory owners had little power and factory workers had too much power

    D. factory owners should have power over their workers and the government

____ **15.** Which Soviet leader is most associated with perestroika?

    A. Boris Yeltsin   **C.** Vladimir Putin

    B. Mikhail Gorbachev   **D.** Joseph Stalin

____ **16.** Which of the following ethnic groups herd reindeer and raise horses and cattle in eastern Siberia?

    A. Tatars   **C.** Yakut

    B. Mongols   **D.** Slavs

____ **17.** The Bolshoi of Moscow and the Kirov in St. Petersburg are ____.

    A. museums   **C.** ballet companies

    B. famous sculptures   **D.** famous opera companies

____ **18.** Peter Carl Fabergé is famous for creating which of the following works of art?

    A. famous novels   **C.** jewel-encrusted eggs

    B. ballets   **D.** opera scores

____ **19.** The Trans-Siberian Railroad connects Moscow with ____.

    A. Kyiv   **C.** Vladivostok

    B. St. Petersburg   **D.** Chechnya

____ **20.** Why is it sometimes difficult to use the Internet in Russia?

    A. Russia does not have many people who are trained to install and repair computers.

    B. Many Russian people are too poor to buy computers.

    C. Computer technology has not yet reached Russia.

    D. Phone service is either not available or needs improvement in many areas.

Applying Skills: Reading a Chart Use the chart below to answer the questions that follow. *(5 points each)*

Russian Rituals		
	A	
Maslenitsa (Farewell-to-Winter) Rituals	A bonfire is lit to symbolize an invitation for dead ancestors to come for a hearty meal.	
	Snowball fights are organized.	
B	Young, married couples are made to kiss in public.	
	Women invite their sons-in-law to pancake parties.	
	Young, unmarried men and women are "punished" by having logs hung on their necks to represent their "missing halves."	
Farming Rituals	Sleigh rides are planned to encourage good crops.	
	Rituals center around hemp and flax.	

____ **21.** Which ritual below should be included as a farewell-to-winter ritual in the space marked *A?*

    A. A fir tree is decorated.   **C.** Evergreen branches are burned.

    B. A broom is hung over a door.   **D.** Straw dolls are burned.

____ **22.** Which category does the letter *B* represent?

    A. Wedding and Family Rituals   **C.** Cooking Rituals

    B. Hunting Rituals   **D.** Gift-Giving Rituals

____ **23.** What do the logs worn around the necks of young, unmarried men and women represent?

    A. the end of winter   **C.** the missing partner

    B. the desire for healthy crops   **D.** the souls of dead ancestors

Directions: Document-Based Questions Use the document below to answer the questions that follow. *(5 points each)*

> Ivan IV succeeded his father to the throne at the age of three, although others (called *regents*) ruled for him until he was 16 years old. Ivan suffered under the regents. Although he was treated with respect in public, in private he was often neglected and tortured. He also witnessed others in the royal household fighting for power. These two things are believed to have caused Ivan IV to be cruel. As a child, he was known to torture animals; as an adult, his actions earned him the name *Ivan the Terrible*.
>
> Ivan IV became famous for torturing and executing thousands of people. Even members of the Russian Orthodox Church, of which Ivan was a member, were often included in the executions. Ivan offered prayers for those he had executed.
>
> **Source:** "Ivan the Terrible." www.mnsu.edu/emuseum/history/russia/ivantheterrible.html.

_____ **24.** At what age did Ivan IV succeed to the throne?
   A. 10   **C.** 3
   B. 12   **D.** 16

_____ **25.** How did the regents treat Ivan IV?
   A. They were kind to him.   **C.** They obeyed his commands.
   B. They educated him.   **D.** They neglected and tortured him.

_____ **26.** Ivan IV became famous for ____.
   A. his wise leadership
   B. torture and murder
   C. his respect toward members of the Russian Orthodox Church
   D. his heirs, who led Russia for 60 years after Ivan IV's death

Directions: Essay On a separate sheet of paper, answer the question below. *(10 points)*

   27. Explain why traveling by automobile can be difficult in Russia.

SCORE

Directions: Matching Match each item in Column A with its description in Column B. Write the correct letters in the blanks. *(10 points each)*

Column A

A. Boris Yeltsin

B. Kaliningrad

C. Communist Party

D. St. Petersburg

E. Moscow

Column B

_____ **1.** ruled Russia when it was part of the Soviet Union

_____ **2.** area of Russia isolated from the main part

_____ **3.** first president of Russia

_____ **4.** political, economic, and transportation center of Russia

_____ **5.** major port, cultural center, and former capital of Russia

Directions: Short Answer Answer each question or statement below on the line provided. *(10 points each)*

6. What three regions in Russia are involved in manufacturing?

_____

7. What makes Russia a federation and a federal republic?

_____

8. What is privatization, and how have Russian consumers benefited from it?

_____

9. How have Russians been influenced by American and European ideas and culture?

_____

10. What is causing the sharp decline in life expectancy in Russia?

_____

Name_____ Date_____ Class_____

Directions: Matching Match each item in Column A with its description in Column B. Write the correct letters in the blanks. *(10 points each)*

Column A

A. decrees

B. regional rivalries

C. fight against global terrorism

D. separatist movements

E. confusion

Column B

_____ **1.** roadblock to democracy in Russia

_____ **2.** give the Russian president strong power

_____ **3.** campaigns to break away from the national government to form independent countries

_____ **4.** resentments that have made Russian unity difficult

_____ **5.** strengthened Russia's ties with western countries

Directions: Short Answer Answer each question or statement below on the line provided. *(10 points each)*

6. Why did Boris Yeltsin stop the region of Chechnya from separating from Russia?

_____

7. What did Vladimir Putin do to strengthen his control over Russia's regions?

_____

8. What problems do Russians face in trying to change the way their government works?

_____

9. Why might it be difficult for Russian courts to control oligarchs?

_____

10. How do banks contribute to job growth? What has the Russian government done to encourage bank deposits?

_____

SCORE

Directions: Matching Match each item in Column A with its description in Column B. Write the correct letters in the blanks. *(3 points each)*

Column A

A. Siberia

B. market

C. 1994

D. heavy industry

E. command

F. pensioners

G. decree

H. 2002

I. light industry

J. Kaliningrad

Column B

_____ **1.** production of consumer goods

_____ **2.** ruling with the power of law but do not need legislative approval

_____ **3.** holds valuable mineral deposits and timber

_____ **4.** people who receive regular payments from the government

_____ **5.** economy driven by the central government

_____ **6.** year that Russian forces were sent into Chechnya

_____ **7.** production of machinery, mining equipment, and steel

_____ **8.** economy driven by competition and consumer needs

_____ **9.** year that Russia joined NATO in fighting global terrorism

_____ **10.** major Russian port along the Baltic Sea

Directions: Multiple Choice In the blank at the left, write the letter of the choice that best completes the statement or answers the question. *(3 points each)*

_____ **11.** Monthly incomes are much higher in _____ than in other cities and regions.

    A. Kaliningrad   **C.** St. Petersburg

    B. Yekaterinburg   **D.** Moscow

_____ **12.** How has Vladimir Putin limited the power of some of Russia's oligarchs?

    A. by putting them in jail

    B. by strengthening government authority

    C. by taking their businesses from them

    D. by encouraging other business start-ups

_____ 13. Why is the division of governmental power in Russia less clear than it is in the United States?

   A. The new Russian government is still developing.

   B. The Communist Party wants to keep the divisions of authority less clear.

   C. Russia's economic problems impact the division of governmental power.

   D. Elections are held too often for the divisions to become clearly defined.

_____ 14. Which city is the political center of Russia?

   A. St. Petersburg   **C.** Moscow

   B. Volga   **D.** Omsk

_____ 15. How many districts does Russia have?

   A. four   **C.** six

   B. five   **D.** seven

_____ 16. After the end of Communist rule, the government _____.

   A. loosened its control on society   **C.** closed Russia's borders

   B. fell apart   **D.** declared bankruptcy

_____ 17. The life expectancy of Russian men has declined because _____.

   A. ethnic groups left Russia to escape hardships

   B. of the arrival of new immigrants

   C. of poor nutrition, alcoholism, and drug abuse

   D. of low birthrates

_____ 18. What happened in Russia when communism fell?

   A. The communist government stayed in place, but new officials were elected.

   B. Russians had to build a new government and economy.

   C. Russia became less democratic.

   D. Russian citizens still had no voice in choosing their leaders.

_____ 19. Which Russian city is known for its palaces and churches?

   A. Moscow   **C.** Volga

   B. Kaliningrad   **D.** St. Petersburg

_____ 20. Russia views the war in Chechnya as _____.

   A. a struggle against terrorism

   B. a struggle to return communism to the government

   C. an attempt to overthrow the government

   D. a threat against NATO

Applying Skills: Reading a Chart Use the chart below to answer the questions that follow. *(5 points each)*

Life Expectancies: Russia and Europe		
Country	**Average Life Expectancy**	
	Men	**Women**
Sweden	78	83
Italy	77	83
France	76	84
Germany	76	82
Poland	71	79
Russia	60	74

Source: *CIA World Factbook,* 2006.

_____ **21.** Which country has the lowest life expectancy for men?
   A. Russia   **C.** Italy
   B. Poland   **D.** Germany

_____ **22.** Life expectancies for men are the same in ____.
   A. Italy and France   **C.** France and Germany
   B. Poland and Russia   **D.** Germany and Poland

_____ **23.** Life expectancies for women are the same in which two countries?
   A. Germany and France   **C.** Poland and Russia
   B. France and Italy   **D.** Sweden and Italy

Directions: Document-Based Questions Use the document below to answer the questions that follow. *(5 points each)*

> The Volga River, the longest river in Europe, is approximately 2,300 miles long. The river lies entirely within Russia and is often called "Mother Volga" by the Russians. More than 40 percent of the Russian people live near the Volga and its tributaries. Over half of Russia's industry is located within its system. Because of the building of dams for hydroelectric power, the Volga is navigable for most of its length. The Volga carries nearly half of Russia's river traffic.
>
> The Volga River empties into the Caspian Sea and is an important source of water for the sea and for the famous sturgeon fisheries. By the time the water enters the Caspian Sea, it has supplied water and power for industry and farming along its length.
>
> **Source:** "The Volga River," Center for Global Environmental Education, Hamline University. cgee.hamline.edu/rivers/Resources/river_profiles/Volga.html.

_____ **24.** The Volga River carries approximately how much of Russia's river traffic?

    A. 50 percent   **C.** 75 percent

    B. 30 percent   **D.** 80 percent

_____ **25.** Why were dams built on the Volga River?

    A. to make the river navigable   **C.** to provide hydroelectric power

    B. to control flooding   **D.** to assist the fishing industry

_____ **26.** Why are sturgeon important to the Caspian Sea?

    A. They provide fertilizer.   **C.** They attract foreign investors.

    B. Many Russians eat them.   **D.** They provide caviar.

Directions: Essay On a separate sheet of paper, answer the question below. *(10 points)*

    27. What actions of Vladimir Putin concerned the United States and other countries?

SCORE

Directions: Matching Match each item in Column A with its description in Column B. Write the correct letters in the blanks. *(3 points each)*

Column A

A. Ural Mountains

B. deposit insurance

C. Russian Federation

D. middle class

E. separatist movements

F. 1991

G. Chechnya

H. 1993

I. drug abuse

J. federal republic

Column B

_____ **1.** emerged along with Russia's new economy

_____ **2.** one of the leading causes of reduced life expectancy in Russia

_____ **3.** Russia's form of government

_____ **4.** year when communism fell in Russia

_____ **5.** Muslim region in southern Russia

_____ **6.** year that Russian voters approved a new constitution

_____ **7.** encourages Russians to save

_____ **8.** emerged when the Soviet Union fell

_____ **9.** major source for Russia's natural resources

_____ **10.** official name of Russia

Directions: Multiple Choice In the blank at the left, write the letter of the choice that best completes the statement or answers the question. *(3 points each)*

_____ **11.** What has assisted Russia in the shift to a market economy?

    A. weakening government authority

    B. increases in wealth for the people

    C. higher prices for its oil and gas

    D. better health for Russian citizens

_____ **12.** Which Russian president gave the Chechens more self-rule?

    A. Vladimir Putin   **C.** Mikhail Gorbachev

    B. Boris Yeltsin   **D.** Joseph Stalin

_____ **13.** Who was Russia's leader when it was a Soviet republic?

    A. Mikhail Gorbachev   **C.** Boris Yeltsin

    B. Vladimir Putin   **D.** Joseph Stalin

_____ **14.** Approximately how many ethnic Russians chose to return to Russia after the Soviet republics became independent?

    A. 2 million   **C.** 4 million

    B. 3 million   **D.** 5 million

_____ **15.** Why has Russia's banking system been unable to fully contribute to economic growth?

    A. Many Russians do not trust the country's banks.

    B. Those running the banking system have made some unwise investments.

    C. Inflation is causing the worth of Russia's currency to drop.

    D. Russia has many banks, and they do not always follow the same banking practices.

_____ **16.** Since becoming president, Vladimir Putin has _____.

    A. taken control of Russia's newspapers

    B. allowed television news stations to operate with no government control

    C. done away with issuing decrees

    D. strengthened presidential powers

_____ **17.** With the end of Communist rule, _____.

    A. Russians were still not allowed to criticize their leaders

    B. many different political parties were able to organize

    C. the government still controlled the content of books and magazines

    D. consumerism in Russia declined

_____ **18.** In what kind of economy does the central government make all the economic decisions?

    A. market economy   **C.** command economy

    B. welfare economy   **D.** free market economy

_____ **19.** What was the outcome of the struggle between the Chechens and the Russian government?

    A. It is unresolved.

    B. The government was victorious.

    C. The Chechens won their independence.

    D. A truce was declared.

_____ **20.** As a result of Russia's new economic system, _____.

    A. government price controls have been added

    B. privatization is being discouraged

    C. Russia's central government is making all the economic decisions

    D. Russian companies have begun to advertise to attract customers

Applying Skills: Reading a Map Use the map below to answer the questions that follow. *(5 points each)*

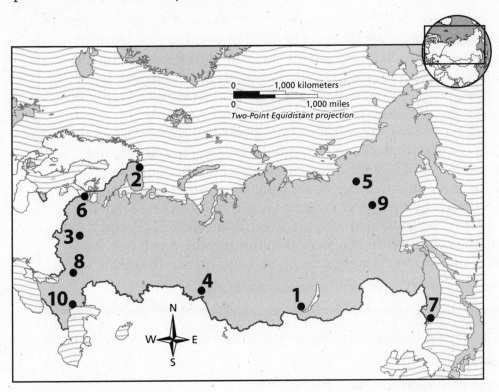

0   1,000 kilometers
0   1,000 miles
Two-Point Equidistant projection

____ **21.** Which city is represented by the number *3*?

   A. Omsk   **C.** St. Petersburg

   B. Moscow   **D.** Vladivostok

____ **22.** Which city is represented by the number *7*?

   A. Volgograd   **C.** Vladivostok

   B. Moscow   **D.** St. Petersburg

____ **23.** Which city is represented by the number *6*?

   A. St. Petersburg   **C.** Irkutsk

   B. Verkhoyansk   **D.** Vladivostok

Directions: Document-Based Questions Use the document below to answer the questions that follow. *(5 points each)*

> After the fall of the Soviet Union, a handful of wealthy businessmen grabbed the spoils—the state-owned oil, metal, and transport companies. But the future of Russia is being wrestled away by a growing group of young businesspeople—the new army in Russia's economic revolution who started with little more than an education and a dream.
>
> Some have business degrees from Yale, Harvard, and (increasingly) Russian schools. They have lived through the fall of communism and the rise of capitalism. This new breed of Russian entrepreneur means that more Russians are speaking the language of western business.
>
> Before the young entrepreneurs, there were the oligarchs—a small group of wealthy businessmen who made great fortunes. The good news for Russia: The next time the economy is in trouble, there will be a lot more skilled and educated entrepreneurs on hand to help the country.
>
> **Source:** "A Changing Business Climate." www.msnbc.msn.com/id/6090140.

_____ **24.** Who made great fortunes immediately after the fall of the Soviet Union?
   A. oligarchs
   B. people who taught in business schools
   C. entrepreneurs
   D. the army

_____ **25.** What does it mean to "speak the language of western business"?
   A. Russian students are being taught to speak English.
   B. Entrepreneurs are learning vocabulary words that are needed to run a business.
   C. Entrepreneurs are learning the language of business so that they can participate in international business meetings.
   D. Entrepreneurs are learning more about capitalism and how to run successful businesses.

_____ **26.** What were the "spoils" after the fall of the Soviet Union?
   A. business schools   **C.** government-owned businesses
   B. educated entrepreneurs   **D.** a group of wealthy businessmen

Directions: Essay On a separate sheet of paper, answer the question below. *(10 points)*

27. What natural resources are found in Siberia? Why is it difficult to take advantage of these resources?

SCORE

Directions: Matching Match each item in Column A with its description in Column B. Write the correct letters in the blanks. *(5 points each)*

Column A

A. Ivan IV

B. Hermitage

C. perestroika

D. subarctic zone

E. serfs

F. Vladimir Lenin

G. privatization

H. permafrost

I. Vladimir Putin

J. Kamchatka

Column B

_____ **1.** transfer of ownership of businesses from the government to individuals

_____ **2.** first czar of Russia

_____ **3.** farm laborers who are bought and sold

_____ **4.** permanently frozen layer of soil beneath the surface

_____ **5.** Russia's largest climate area

_____ **6.** area of Russia where tectonic plates cause the area to be unstable

_____ **7.** supported a pro-Russian candidate in Ukraine's 2004 presidential election

_____ **8.** established a communist state

_____ **9.** home to one of the most famous art collections in the world

_____ **10.** policy of rebuilding the Soviet economy

Directions: Multiple Choice Write the letter of the choice that best completes the statement or answers the question. *(5 points each)*

_____ **11.** The northern and eastern areas of Russia have ____.

    A. very long summers   **C.** short, snowy winters

    B. long, snowy winters   **D.** a humid continental climate

_____ **12.** Which of Russia's economic regions is developing technology and electronics industries?

    A. Moscow   **C.** Baltic

    B. St. Petersburg   **D.** Urals

_____ **13.** Which of the following leaders is most associated with the policy of glasnost?

    A. Vladimir Putin   **C.** Boris Yeltsin

    B. Karl Marx   **D.** Mikhail Gorbachev

_____ **14.** How is the Russian government encouraging its citizens to
save their money?

　A. by creating a deposit insurance system

　B. by rewarding citizens each time they deposit money in the bank

　C. by encouraging businesses to counsel their employees about savings

　D. by giving tax breaks to citizens who save one-fifth of their monthly
　income

_____ **15.** In what year did Russia join France and Britain in fighting
Germany and Austria in World War I?

　A. 1940　　　　　　　　　**C.** 1914

　B. 1921　　　　　　　　　**D.** 1925

Applying Skills: Reading a Chart Use the chart below to answer the
questions that follow. *(5 points each)*

_____ **16.** Which country had the highest
GNP per capita in 1999?

　A. Russia

　B. Germany

　C. the United States

　D. France

_____ **17.** In what year was Russia's
GNP per capita at its highest?

　A. 2001

　B. 1991

　C. 2000

　D. 1995

_____ **18.** In 2001, which country had the
third-highest GNP per capita?

　A. France

　B. Russia

　C. Germany

　D. the United States

GNP Per Capita in U.S. Dollars

Year(s)	Russia	United States	France	Germany
1991	$3,470	$22,340	$20,460	$20,510
1992	$2,820	$23,830	$22,300	$23,360
1993	$2,350	$24,750	$22,360	$23,560
1994	$2,650	$25,860	$23,470	$25,580
1995	$2,240	$26,980	$24,990	$27,510
1996	$2,410	$28,020	$26,270	$28,870
1997	$2,680	$29,080	$26,300	$28,280
1998	$2,260	$29,240	$24,210	$26,570
1999	$2,250	$31,910	$24,170	$26,620
2000	$1,660	$34,100	$24,090	$25,120
2001	$1,750	$34,280	$22,730	$23,560

GNP per capita is the dollar value of a country's final
output of goods and services in a year (its GNP), divided
by its population. It reflects the average income of a
country's citizens.

Source: http://world.britannica.com/analyst/chrono/table.

Directions: Essay On a separate sheet of paper, answer the question
below. *(10 points)*

　19. What steps have Russians taken to clean up their pollution problems?

SCORE

Unit 6 Pretest

Directions: Matching Match each item in Column A with its description in Column B. Write the correct letters in the blanks. *(5 points each)*

Column A

A. Suez Canal

B. oases

C. Islam

D. bedouin

E. Sunni

F. hieroglyphics

G. Istanbul

H. clan

I. al-Qaeda

J. Mesopotamia

Column B

_____ **1.** desert nomad

_____ **2.** Muslim terrorist group

_____ **3.** city in Turkey

_____ **4.** links Mediterranean and Red Seas

_____ **5.** Muslim religious group

_____ **6.** early Egyptian writing

_____ **7.** area of desert springs or wells

_____ **8.** between the Tigris and Euphrates

_____ **9.** monotheistic religion

_____ **10.** related family group

Directions: Multiple Choice Write the letter of the choice that best completes the statement or answers the question. *(7 points each)*

_____ **11.** In which of these areas is the Sahara located?

    A. Central Asia   **C.** North Africa

    B. Southwest Asia   **D.** Africa South of the Sahara

_____ **12.** What is a reason for desalinization and rationing in Southwest Asia?

    A. Oil is abundant.   **C.** Water is scarce.

    B. Food is scarce.   **D.** Some people are poor.

_____ **13.** Which of the following groups seeks its own nation in Southwest Asia?

    A. Kurds   **C.** Iranians

    B. bedouins   **D.** Muslims

_____ **14.** Which of these is a holy city of Islam?

    A. Istanbul   **C.** Beirut

    B. Makkah   **D.** Cairo

_____ **15.** What is the main reason that most Egyptians live within 20 miles of the Nile River?

    A. The Nile provides easy transportation.

    B. The Nile is considered a sacred river.

    C. Most of Egypt is a vast desert.

    D. The Nile provides safety from invaders.

Applying Skills: Reading a Chart Use the chart below to answer the questions that follow. *(5 points each)*

Selected Southwest Asian Countries			
Country	Literacy Rate (percentage of people over 15 who can read and write)	Television Sets (per 1,000 people)	GDP Per Capita ($ value of goods and services produced per person in one year)
Egypt	57.5	170	$4,200
Iran	79.4	154	$7,700
Israel	95.4	328	$20,800
Saudi Arabia	78.8	263	$12,000
Syria	76.9	68	$3,400

Source: *CIA World Factbook*, 2005.

_____ **16.** Which of the countries on the table has the lowest literacy rate?

    A. Egypt   **C.** Iran

    B. Syria   **D.** Saudi Arabia

_____ **17.** Which of the countries has the highest GDP per capita?

    A. Saudi Arabia   **C.** Israel

    B. Iran   **D.** Egypt

_____ **18.** Which country has the lowest rate of television sets and the lowest GDP per capita?

    A. Iran   **C.** Israel

    B. Syria   **D.** Saudi Arabia

SCORE

Physical Features

Quiz 16-1

Directions: Matching Match each item in Column A with its description in Column B. Write the correct letters in the blanks. *(10 points each)*

Column A

A. Persian Gulf

B. Suez Canal

C. Strait of Hormuz

D. Strait of Gibraltar

E. Aral Sea

Column B

_____ **1.** used by oil tankers to enter and leave the Persian Gulf

_____ **2.** used to pass from the Mediterranean Sea to the Red Sea

_____ **3.** contains largest reserves of petroleum and natural gas

_____ **4.** body of water that borders both Kazakhstan and Uzbekistan

_____ **5.** used to pass from the Mediterranean Sea to the Atlantic Ocean

Directions: Short Answer Answer each question or statement below on the line provided. *(10 points each)*

6. How has the Aswān High Dam affected the use of fertilizers by farmers along the Nile?

_____

7. How have oil revenues brought divisions to the region of North Africa, Southwest Asia, and Central Asia?

_____

8. Why is Lebanon's forest industry unique?

_____

9. Describe how the fishing industries of the Caspian Sea and Aral Sea have been hurt.

_____

10. What do the Strait of Gibraltar and the Khyber Pass have in common?

_____

SCORE

Directions: Matching Match each item in Column A with its description in Column B. Write the correct letters in the blanks. *(10 points each)*

Column A

A. desalinization

B. ergs

C. Empty Quarter

D. Sahara

E. dry farming

Column B

_____ **1.** world's largest desert

_____ **2.** creates drinkable water from seawater

_____ **3.** large sand dunes

_____ **4.** desert on the Arabian Peninsula

_____ **5.** stores moisture in unplanted land

Directions: Short Answer Answer each question or statement below on the line provided. *(10 points each)*

6. What air masses blow over North Africa, Southwest Asia, and Central Asia? How have they affected the land?

_____

7. How do Libya and Syria differ in the way they are dealing with water shortages?

_____

8. How does the climate of Turkey's coastal areas differ from that of its steppes?

_____

9. Why have villages, towns, and cities grown around many Saharan oases?

_____

10. What has formed the Kara-Kum and the Kyzyl Kum in Central Asia?

_____

SCORE

Physical Geography of North Africa, Southwest Asia, and Central Asia

Chapter 16 Test Form A

Directions: Matching Match each item in Column A with its description in Column B. Write the correct letters in the blanks. *(3 points each)*

Column A

A. wadi

B. steppes

C. nomads

D. aquifer

E. Bosporus Strait

F. sedimentary rock

G. silt

H. Khyber Pass

I. phosphates

J. poaching

Column B

_____ **1.** people who travel across steppes to find food and water

_____ **2.** mineral salts used to make fertilizer

_____ **3.** dry riverbed

_____ **4.** small particles of rich soil

_____ **5.** grassy plains

_____ **6.** narrow gap in the Hindu Kush

_____ **7.** links the Mediterranean and Black Seas

_____ **8.** layers of material hardened by intense weight

_____ **9.** illegal fishing or hunting

_____ **10.** underground rock layers through which water flows

Directions: Multiple Choice In the blank at the left, write the letter of the choice that best completes the statement or answers the question. *(3 points each)*

_____ **11.** Which of the following separates Africa from Europe?

    A. Suez Canal   **C.** Strait of Gibraltar

    B. Strait of Hormuz   **D.** Black Sea

_____ **12.** Rain shadow areas have formed deserts in ____.

    A. Central Asia   **C.** North Africa

    B. Southwest Asia   **D.** Turkey

_____ **13.** People in this region have been unable to manage which resource effectively?

    A. oil   **C.** coal

    B. timber   **D.** water

_____ **14.** When irrigation water evaporates rapidly, it leaves behind
_____.

   A. salt   **C.** sand

   B. rich soil   **D.** gravel

_____ **15.** Which physical feature covers much of North Africa?

   A. Carpathians   **C.** Atlantic coastal plain

   B. Sahara   **D.** Nile River valley

_____ **16.** Which of these regions is nearly covered by deserts?

   A. Arabian Peninsula   **C.** eastern Mediterranean

   B. Turkey   **D.** coastal North Africa

_____ **17.** About 20 percent of the Sahara is covered by _____.

   A. wadis   **C.** steppes

   B. oases   **D.** ergs

_____ **18.** What did Turkey build that caused problems for Iraq
and Syria?

   A. a dam   **C.** desalinization plants

   B. an aquifer   **D.** oil wells

_____ **19.** Which of these regions has enough rainfall to support
farming and a large population?

   A. the mountains of Saudi Arabia   **C.** southeastern Egypt

   B. central Iran   **D.** coastal North Africa

_____ **20.** An expensive water-management system used by oil-rich
countries is _____.

   A. aquifers   **C.** irrigation

   B. desalinization   **D.** rationing

Applying Skills: Reading a Map Use the map below to answer the questions that follow. *(5 points each)*

Known Oil Reserves by Region

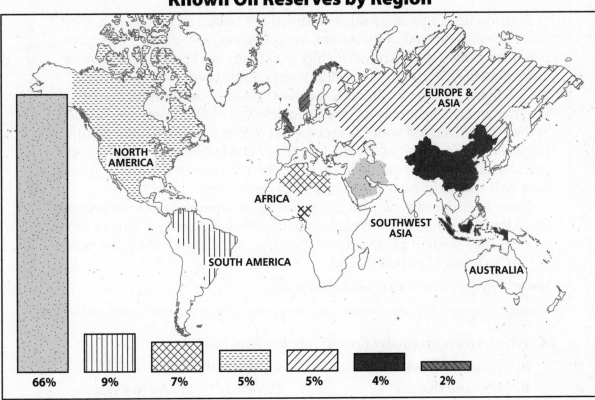

Source: www.pbs.org/.../colombia/images/map04.gif.

_____ **21.** What percentage of the world's known oil reserves are in North Africa and Southwest Asia?

　　A. less than 50 percent 　　　**C.** more than 70 percent

　　B. about 46 percent 　　　　　**D.** nearly 90 percent

_____ **22.** Which region has the fewest oil reserves?

　　A. North America 　　　　　　**C.** Asia and Oceania

　　B. Western Europe 　　　　　　**D.** Eastern Europe

_____ **23.** The oil-rich nations of Southwest Asia have about _____ times as many oil reserves as the rest of the world combined.

　　A. two 　　　　　　　　　　　　**C.** four

　　B. three 　　　　　　　　　　　**D.** five

Directions: Document-Based Questions Use the document below to answer the questions that follow. *(5 points each)*

> Four decades ago, the Aral Sea offered a constant supply of fish. Two dozen species thrived in its waters, including caviar-rich sturgeon, pike perch, and silver carp, known locally as fat tongue. The sea spread over more than 26,000 square miles, and ships could travel 250 miles from the northern port of Aralsk, in Kazakhstan, to the southern harbor of Muynak in Uzbekistan. But Soviet-sponsored irrigation projects, begun in the 1950s, diverted water from two rivers that fed the sea: the Amu Darya and the Syr Darya. By the late '90s, the Aral Sea was known as the world's fastest-disappearing body of water. It had then shrunk by more than half and lost nearly three-fourths of its volume.
>
> Now, after decades of grim losses, the news from the Aral Sea is good: Since the Kok-Aral Dam's completion, the smaller, northern part of the Aral Sea has swelled by 30 percent, flooding more than 300 square miles of parched, sun-bleached seabed.
>
> **Source:** "Return of the Aral Sea," *Discover*, September 2006.

_____ 24. Which rivers originally flowed into the Aral Sea?

    A. Tigris and Euphrates   **C.** Volga and Tiber

    B. Nile and Thames   **D.** Amu Darya and Syr Darya

_____ 25. Why did the Soviet Union divert the rivers?

    A. to supply freshwater to Moscow

    B. to cool nuclear power plants

    C. for irrigation projects

    D. to force Kazakhs to move

_____ 26. Which two countries share the Aral Sea?

    A. Kazakhstan and Uzbekistan   **C.** Kazakhstan and Russia

    B. Turkmenistan and Tajikistan   **D.** Uzbekistan and Kyrgyzstan

Directions: Essay On a separate sheet of paper, answer the question below. *(10 points)*

    27. The lack of water is an important concern for most countries in Southwest Asia. What have countries in this region done to deal with this issue?

Name_____ Date_____ Class_____

Directions: Matching Match each item in Column A with its description in Column B. Write the correct letters in the blanks. *(3 points each)*

Column A

A. Rub' al Khali

B. Saudi Arabia

C. coastal plains

D. dry farming

E. Aswān High Dam

F. refineries

G. Pamirs

H. Kara-Kum

I. ancient Egyptians

J. Suez Canal

Column B

_____ **1.** controls water so farmers can grow food

_____ **2.** human-made waterway between Mediterranean and Red Seas

_____ **3.** mountains in Central Asia

_____ **4.** desert on the Arabian Peninsula

_____ **5.** relied on Nile's flooding

_____ **6.** land is left unplanted to store moisture

_____ **7.** fertile land for the region's grain farmers

_____ **8.** where most of the world's oil is found

_____ **9.** facilities that turn petroleum into gasoline

_____ **10.** large desert in Central Asia

Directions: Multiple Choice In the blank at the left, write the letter of the choice that best completes the statement or answers the question. *(3 points each)*

_____ **11.** Which of the following makes land more fertile?

    A. ergs   **C.** silt

    B. wadis   **D.** steppes

_____ **12.** Libya draws water from _____.

    A. oases   **C.** steppes

    B. wadis   **D.** aquifers

_____ **13.** Which mountains stretch through Turkey and Iran?

    A. Hindu Kush   **C.** Atlas

    B. Zagros   **D.** Ahaggar

_____ **14.** Oil was formed in the Persian Gulf area when heat and pressure affected ____.

    A. sedimentary rock   **C.** minerals and salts

    B. sea animals and plants   **D.** air and water

_____ **15.** An alluvial plain is located _____.

    A. near the Aral Sea

    B. between the Kyzyl Kum and Kara-Kum

    C. in the Empty Quarter

    D. between the Tigris and Euphrates Rivers

_____ **16.** Which of the following countries supports a lumber industry?

    A. Syria   **C.** Lebanon

    B. Iran   **D.** Egypt

_____ **17.** Why must farmers in the Nile valley use expensive fertilizers?

    A. The Nile River's annual floods wash away fertilizers.

    B. Farmers there are growing more rice.

    C. The Aswān High Dam blocks the flow of silt down the river.

    D. The Nile River is drying up.

_____ **18.** What implement helps people in Southwest Asia obtain underground water?

    A. shadoof   **C.** desalinization

    B. aquifer   **D.** oil-well drill

_____ **19.** Which two seas have been damaged by poaching and irrigation projects?

    A. Black and Mediterranean   **C.** Aral and Caspian

    B. Caspian and Red   **D.** Baltic and Black

_____ **20.** Which of these are dry riverbeds that fill with water when rain falls?

    A. aquifers   **C.** creeks

    B. wadis   **D.** silts

Applying Skills: Reading a Map Use the map below to answer the questions that follow. *(5 points each)*

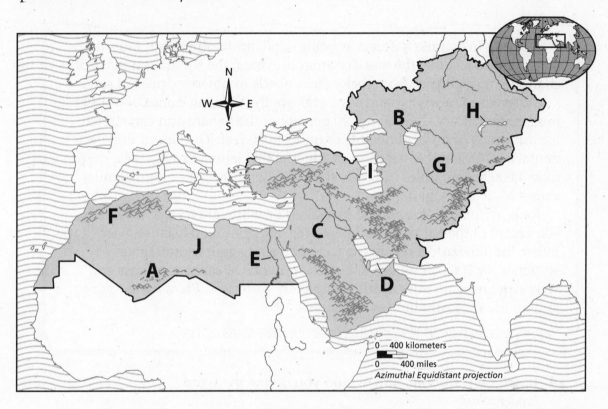

_____ **21.** Which physical feature is labeled *D* on the map?

A. Red Sea	**C.** Persian Gulf
B. Strait of Hormuz	**D.** Arabian Sea

_____ **22.** Which physical feature is labeled *F* on the map?

A. Atlas Mountains	**C.** Taurus Mountains
B. Sahara	**D.** Ahaggar Mountains

_____ **23.** Which letter on the map signifies the Euphrates River?

A. B	**C.** E
B. C	**D.** G

Physical Geography of North Africa, Southwest Asia, and Central Asia

Chapter 16 Test Form B (continued)

Directions: Document-Based Questions Use the document below to answer the questions that follow. *(5 points each)*

It's easy to dismiss a desert as being sand, and nothing but mountains of sand. But, just like the less dry areas of Africa, the Sahara is a place of changing topography, from rocky streambeds to powdery piles of sand.

Otherwise known as sand seas, ergs are the Saharan dunes of popular imagination. They cover about 20 percent of the Sahara and can stretch for hundreds of miles at heights of up to 1,000 feet. The Grand Erg Occidental and Oriental cover most of Algeria; the Selima Erg blankets more than 3,000 square miles in Libya; the Erg Cherch stretches for 600 miles across Mali and Algeria. . . .

Regs are plains of sand and black, red or white gravel that make up 70 percent of the Sahara. The Libyan reg stretches for 340,000 square miles; the Tanezrouft reg, to the west of the Ahaggar Mountains, stretches for 200,000 square miles. The remains of prehistoric seas and rivers, the regs are now nearly completely waterless. Plant life is sparse; animal life is mostly limited to rodents.

Source: www.pbs.org/wnet/africa/explore/sahara/sahara_topography_lo.html.

_____ **24.** Based on the quote, how would you define the word *topography?*
    A. waterways   **C.** landscapes
    B. sand dunes   **D.** climate

_____ **25.** What are ergs?
    A. unusual sand formations   **C.** black, red, and white gravel
    B. rocky streambeds   **D.** common sand dunes

_____ **26.** What did regs used to be?
    A. gravelly plains   **C.** towering sand dunes
    B. seas and rivers   **D.** ocean floor

Directions: Essay On a separate sheet of paper, answer the question below. *(10 points)*

    27. Compare the climates of the Sahara, steppes, and coastal regions of North Africa, Southwest Asia, and Central Asia.

SCORE

Directions: Matching Match each item in Column A with its description in Column B. Write the correct letters in the blanks. *(10 points each)*

Column A

A. Abraham

B. Sumerians

C. Muhammad

D. pharaohs

E. Jesus

Column B

_____ **1.** prophet of Islam

_____ **2.** a Jew who taught that God loved all people

_____ **3.** the first people known to use the wheel and the plow

_____ **4.** Jews believe they are descended from this Mesopotamian herder

_____ **5.** viewed as gods and rulers

Directions: Short Answer Answer each question or statement below on the line provided. *(10 points each)*

6. What form of writing did the Sumerians invent? How did it differ from hieroglyphics?

_____

7. How do Judaism, Christianity, and Islam differ from the religions of the Sumerians and Egyptians?

_____

8. What effect did Muslim merchants have on the Arab Empire from the A.D. 700s to the 1400s?

_____

9. What present-day country is in the same location as the ancient civilization of Mesopotamia?

_____

10. What is terrorism, and what is the goal of al-Qaeda?

_____

Name_____ Date_____ Class_____

Directions: Matching Match each item in Column A with its description in Column B. Write the correct letters in the blanks. *(10 points each)*

Column A

A. Yom Kippur

B. dietary laws

C. Arabic

D. Makkah

E. fast

Column B

_____ **1.** what Muslims must do during Ramadan

_____ **2.** state that Jews and Muslims cannot eat pork

_____ **3.** holy city of Islam

_____ **4.** major language of the region

_____ **5.** holiest day for Jewish people

Directions: Short Answer Answer each question or statement below on the line provided. *(10 points each)*

6. How do the economies of Qatar and Afghanistan differ?

_____

7. What challenges face Istanbul, Cairo, Tehran, and Baghdad?

_____

8. Describe at least three expectations of women in many countries of this region.

_____

9. What has enabled Saudi Arabia to raise the standard of living of its people? Name two services that are free to Saudis.

_____

10. Into what two major groups is Islam divided? What do these two groups share, and how do they differ?

_____

Directions: Matching Match each item in Column A with its description in Column B. Write the correct letters in the blanks. *(3 points each)*

Column A

A. cuneiform

B. hajj

C. saints

D. Abraham

E. Five Pillars of Islam

F. caliphs

G. hieroglyphics

H. David

I. Muhammad

J. revenue

Column B

_____ **1.** Muslim acts of worship

_____ **2.** holy journey to Makkah

_____ **3.** Christian holy people

_____ **4.** early Sumerian writing

_____ **5.** made a covenant with God

_____ **6.** created first Israelite kingdom

_____ **7.** government income

_____ **8.** Muslim leaders

_____ **9.** greatest prophet of Islam

_____ **10.** early Egyptian writing

Directions: Multiple Choice In the blank at the left, write the letter of the choice that best completes the statement or answers the question. *(3 points each)*

_____ **11.** What did Hammurabi's Code provide for Mesopotamians?

    A. a religious tradition   **C.** a legal system

    B. an economic system   **D.** a writing system

_____ **12.** Which of the following did ancient Egypt have in common with Sumer?

    A. Both were theocracies.

    B. Both depended on the desert for protection.

    C. Both used hieroglyphics.

    D. Both used a 60-minute hour and 60-second minute.

_____ **13.** Judaism, Christianity, and Islam all have what in common?

    A. All were polytheistic.

    B. None became a dominant religion of an entire continent.

    C. All began before 1000 B.C.

    D. All were monotheistic.

_____ **14.** Which prophet led the Israelites out of Egypt and received the Ten Commandments?
   A. Moses
   B. Muhammad
   C. Hammurabi
   D. Jesus

_____ **15.** What is the holy book of Islam?
   A. the Ramayana
   B. the Makkah
   C. the Quran
   D. the Tanakh

_____ **16.** Which ethnic group is often angry with the United States for its support of Israel?
   A. Kurds
   B. Arabs
   C. Berbers
   D. Turks

_____ **17.** Which country's 1979 revolution overthrew the shah and set up an Islamic republic?
   A. Syria
   B. Jordan
   C. Iraq
   D. Iran

_____ **18.** Who attacked the United States in 2001?
   A. al-Qaeda
   B. Palestinians
   C. Zionists
   D. Kurds

_____ **19.** Which phrase best describes the lifestyles of people in Southwest Asia and North Africa?
   A. mostly rural with poor living conditions
   B. wealthy and poor; mostly urban
   C. mostly wealthy and city dwellers
   D. wealthy farm communities

_____ **20.** Which of the following reflects life during the Arab Empire?
   A. *The Thousand and One Nights*
   B. *The Tale of Two Cities*
   C. *The Ramayana*
   D. *Lawrence of Arabia*

Applying Skills: Reading a Map Use the map below to answer the questions that follow. *(5 points each)*

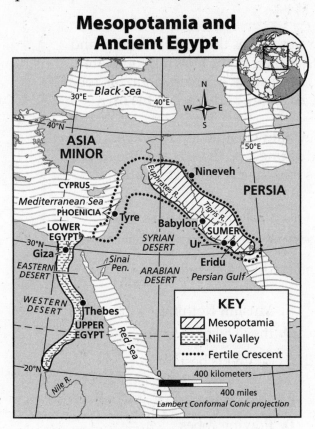

Mesopotamia and Ancient Egypt

_____ **21.** Sumer was located in _____.

    A. the Fertile Crescent   **C.** the Arabian Desert

    B. Phoenicia   **D.** Persia

_____ **22.** Where is the city of Giza located?

    A. Southern Egypt   **C.** Lower Egypt

    B. Sinai Peninsula   **D.** Upper Egypt

_____ **23.** The city of Babylon was located _____.

    A. on the Tigris River   **C.** on the Persian Gulf

    B. on the Euphrates River   **D.** near the Mediterranean Sea

Directions: Document-Based Questions Use the document below to answer the questions that follow. *(5 points each)*

> . . . Respectable men and women wear clothes that appear formal and dignified. They need to cover all parts of their body. Flowing robes are probably the best method to do so. To see a sheik or ayatollah in his robes is to see a person of dignity, learning, authority and grace in his own society.
>
> Loose clothes are worn because they allow people to say prayers which would include . . . bending and sitting. . . . There is also the force of tradition. People often wear clothes that the previous generation has worn before them.
>
> **Source:** Akbar S. Ahamed, *Living Islam.*

_____ **24.** The author believes that dignity and tradition are reflected in ____.

    A. Muslim homes   **C.** Muslim clothing

    B. Muslim work   **D.** the level of income

_____ **25.** According to the author, what kind of clothing is best for Muslims to wear?

    A. priest's robes   **C.** casual clothes

    B. fashionable clothes   **D.** flowing robes

_____ **26.** What do the robes of a sheik or an ayatollah express?

    A. position or rank   **C.** good taste

    B. dignity, learning, and grace   **D.** keen fashion sense

Directions: Essay On a separate sheet of paper, answer the question below. *(10 points)*

    27. What beliefs do Judaism, Christianity, and Islam have in common?

SCORE

History and Cultures of North Africa, Southwest Asia, and Central Asia

Chapter 17 Test Form B

Directions: Matching Match each item in Column A with its description in Column B. Write the correct letters in the blanks. *(3 points each)*

Column A

A. Phoenicians

B. Zionists

C. Muslim architecture

D. Ramadan

E. Diaspora

F. Mesopotamia

G. Egypt

H. pyramids

I. Mount Sinai

J. bazaar

Column B

_____ **1.** scattering of Jews all over the world

_____ **2.** where Moses received the Ten Commandments

_____ **3.** created Jewish state of Israel

_____ **4.** a traditional marketplace

_____ **5.** great trading empire

_____ **6.** tombs of the pharaohs

_____ **7.** protected by desert, the sea, and the Nile's waterfalls

_____ **8.** large interiors and brilliant colors

_____ **9.** located along the Tigris and Euphrates Rivers

_____ **10.** Muslim holy month

Directions: Multiple Choice In the blank at the left, write the letter of the choice that best completes the statement or answers the question. *(3 points each)*

_____ **11.** A government led by religious leaders is called a _____.

    A. polytheism

    B. monotheism

    C. theocracy

    D. covenant

_____ **12.** Wedge-shaped writing made with reeds on clay tablets is called _____.

    A. cuneiform

    B. hieroglyphics

    C. calligraphy

    D. picture writing

_____ **13.** Islam expanded into Asia, North Africa, and parts of Europe under _____.

    A. Muhammad

    B. the caliphs

    C. Mongol invaders

    D. the Ottoman Kurds

_____ 14. Muslim merchants developed _____.

    A. astronomy   **C.** banking

    B. calligraphy   **D.** Arabic numerals

_____ 15. What is the oldest major religion?

    A. Christianity   **C.** Judaism

    B. Islam   **D.** Muslim

_____ 16. The holy book of Judaism is the _____.

    A. Tanakh   **C.** Epic

    B. New Testament   **D.** Quran

_____ 17. Which of these religions spread first to Europe and then around the world?

    A. Judaism   **C.** Islam

    B. Buddhism   **D.** Christianity

_____ 18. What caused the breakup of the Ottoman Empire?

    A. the spread of Christianity   **C.** its defeat in World War I

    B. the rise of Islam   **D.** the Romans

_____ 19. In 1948 Jews set up Israel in their part of _____.

    A. Iraq   **C.** Turkey

    B. Saudi Arabia   **D.** Palestine

_____ 20. The main language of Southwest Asia is _____.

    A. Farsi   **C.** Arabic

    B. Hebrew   **D.** English

Applying Skills: Reading a Chart Use the chart below to answer the questions that follow. *(5 points each)*

Comparative Ethnic Populations	
Israel	European/American: 32% Israeli: 21% African: 14.5% Asian: 12.5% non-Jewish Arab: 20%
Egypt	Eastern Hamitic: 99% (Egyptian, Bedouin, Berber) Other European: 1%
Iraq	Arab: 75–80% Kurdish: 15–20% Turkoman, Assyrian, other: 5%
Lebanon	Arab: 95% Armenian: 4% Other: 1%

Source: PBS online.

_____ 21. Which of these countries has the least varied population?

    A. Egypt   **C.** Israel

    B. Lebanon   **D.** Iraq

_____ 22. Which of these countries has the most varied population?

    A. Iraq   **C.** Lebanon

    B. Egypt   **D.** Israel

_____ 23. Which is the smallest ethnic group among the four countries?

    A. Europeans   **C.** Arabs

    B. Armenians   **D.** Kurds

Directions: Document-Based Questions Use the document below to answer the questions that follow. *(5 points each)*

> If any one brings an accusation against a man, and the accused goes to the river and leaps into the river, if he sinks in the river his accuser shall take possession of his house. But if the river proves that the accused is not guilty, and he escapes unhurt, then he who had brought the accusation shall be put to death, while he who leaped into the river shall take possession of the house that had belonged to his accuser.
>
> **Source:** Code of Hammurabi.

_____ **24.** According to the Code, what will happen to a guilty man who jumps into the river?

    A. He will swim away.   **C.** He will drown.

    B. He will float.   **D.** He will receive mercy.

_____ **25.** If a man is accused and NOT found guilty, the person who made the accusation is ____.

    A. forced to apologize   **C.** banished from town

    B. put to death   **D.** required to pay a fine

_____ **26.** What was this section of the Code concerned with?

    A. punishment for stealing   **C.** seriousness of accusations

    B. rules of inheritance   **D.** justice for accident victims

Directions: Essay On a separate sheet of paper, answer the question below. *(10 points)*

    27. How have urban women's roles changed in North Africa, Southwest Asia, and Central Asia over the past 50 years?

SCORE

Directions: Matching Match each item in Column A with its description in Column B. Write the correct letters in the blanks. *(10 points each)*

Column A

A. Tunisia

B. casbah

C. Algeria

D. fellahin

E. Maghreb

Column B

_____ **1.** older section of Algiers with narrow streets and bazaars

_____ **2.** Egyptian peasant farmers

_____ **3.** large North African country that experienced civil war in the 1990s

_____ **4.** another name for the region that includes Tunisia, Algeria, and Morocco

_____ **5.** small North African country whose women enjoy many rights

Directions: Short Answer Answer each question or statement below on the line provided. *(10 points each)*

6. How are the Egyptian farmers able to grow crops more than once per year?

_____

7. How do Casablanca and Marrakesh benefit Morocco's economy?

_____

8. Which North African countries have economies based in part on oil?

_____

9. How did Algeria win its independence?

_____

10. Who is Muammar al-Qaddafi? Compare his power to the power held by the king of Morocco.

_____

SCORE

Directions: Matching Match each item in Column A with its description in Column B. Write the correct letters in the blanks. *(10 points each)*

Column A

A. Beirut

B. trade embargo

C. Istanbul

D. Law of Return

E. Aden

Column B

_____ **1.** allows Jews anywhere in the world to become Israeli citizens

_____ **2.** major port for ships traveling between the Arabian Sea and the Red Sea

_____ **3.** major economic and cultural center at the entrance of the Black Sea

_____ **4.** placed on Iraq after the Persian Gulf War

_____ **5.** capital and major port of Lebanon

Directions: Short Answer Answer each question or statement below on the line provided. *(10 points each)*

6. What steps is Saudi Arabia taking to change its dependence on oil?

_____

7. How does the Turkish republic differ from the Iranian republic?

_____

8. What problems do the democratic governments of Iraq and Afghanistan face?

_____

9. How is the lifestyle of Jordan's bedouins different from that of people living in Amman?

_____

10. What farming technique do Syria, Jordan, and Israel use to grow crops?

_____

SCORE

Directions: Matching Match each item in Column A with its description in Column B. Write the correct letters in the blanks. *(10 points each)*

Column A

A. Tashkent

B. Kyrgyzstan

C. Yerevan

D. Dushanbe

E. Turkmenistan

Column B

_____ **1.** one of the world's oldest cities and capital of Armenia

_____ **2.** Uzbekistan's capital and Central Asia's largest city and industrial center

_____ **3.** most of this country is part of the huge Kara-Kum desert

_____ **4.** country with valuable mercury and gold deposits but little industry

_____ **5.** largest city, industrial center, and capital of Tajikistan

Directions: Short Answer Answer each question or statement below on the line provided. *(10 points each)*

6. What are the two regions of Central Asia? What countries are included in each region?

_____

7. How do most people in Azerbaijan differ from the Armenians and Georgians in regard to religion?

_____

8. How does the collision of tectonic plates affect Georgia and Armenia?

_____

9. What do Kazakhstan and Kyrgyzstan seek from foreigners to help improve their economies?

_____

10. What occurred in Armenia during World War I? What dispute is Armenia involved in today?

_____

SCORE

North Africa, Southwest Asia, and Central Asia Today

Chapter 18 Test Form A

Directions: Matching Match each item in Column A with its description in Column B. Write the correct letters in the blanks. *(3 points each)*

Column A

A. Beirut

B. Riyadh

C. Tajiks and Uzbeks

D. Nile River valley

E. secular

F. Shia, Sunnis, and Kurds

G. Casablanca

H. Dubai

I. trade sanctions

J. Israel

Column B

_____ **1.** ethnic groups in Tajikistan

_____ **2.** used to punish Libya for supporting terrorism

_____ **3.** capital of Lebanon

_____ **4.** large port on the Persian Gulf

_____ **5.** ethnic groups in Iraq

_____ **6.** Saudi Arabian city on an oasis

_____ **7.** city in Morocco

_____ **8.** an independent Jewish republic

_____ **9.** a nonreligious society

_____ **10.** where most Egyptians live

Directions: Multiple Choice In the blank at the left, write the letter of the choice that best completes the statement or answers the question. *(3 points each)*

_____ **11.** Which of the following makes up almost 25 percent of Egypt's export trade?

A. cotton and cotton products

B. phosphates

C. processed foods

D. citrus fruits

_____ **12.** Which group settled in North Africa before the arrival of the Muslim Arabs?

A. Bantu

B. Kurds

C. Moors

D. Berbers

_____ **13.** Who set up a dictatorship in Libya?

A. Saddam Hussein

B. Ayatollah Khomeini

C. Muammar al-Qaddafi

D. Hezbollah

_____ **14.** The largest of the Central Asian Republics is _____.
   A. Kazakhstan
   B. Tajikistan
   C. Kyrgyzstan
   D. Turkmenistan

_____ **15.** What do all Maghreb countries in North Africa have in common?
   A. the Islamic religion
   B. tourism as the main economic activity
   C. rugged mountain ranges
   D. constitutional monarchies

_____ **16.** Which countries make up the Caucasus Republics?
   A. Turkey, Iran, and Iraq
   B. Kazakhstan and Uzbekistan
   C. Lebanon, Jordan, and Syria
   D. Georgia, Armenia, and Azerbaijan

_____ **17.** One of the oldest continuously inhabited cities in the world is _____.
   A. Cairo
   B. Beirut
   C. Tehran
   D. Damascus

_____ **18.** Why does Armenia experience so many serious earthquakes?
   A. It is landlocked.
   B. It sits on top of many faults.
   C. It contains many mineral deposits.
   D. It is near the Caspian Sea.

_____ **19.** What did the Persian Gulf countries use to build prosperous economies?
   A. money from the ruling families
   B. timber profits
   C. oil profits
   D. loans from other countries

_____ **20.** The Tigris and Euphrates Rivers are the major geographic features of which country?
   A. Iran
   B. Iraq
   C. Turkey
   D. Syria

Name_____ Date_____ Class_____

Applying Skills: Reading a Map Use the map below to answer the questions that follow. *(5 points each)*

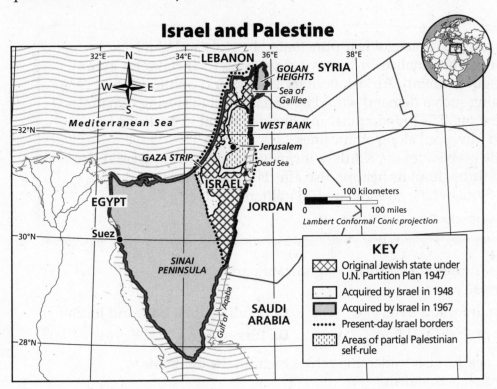

Israel and Palestine

KEY
- Original Jewish state under U.N. Partition Plan 1947
- Acquired by Israel in 1948
- Acquired by Israel in 1967
- Present-day Israel borders
- Areas of partial Palestinian self-rule

_____ **21.** Which nation was created from lands provided by the United Nations?

A. Egypt   **C.** Lebanon

B. Palestine   **D.** Israel

_____ **22.** Which area is home to many Palestinians with partial self-rule?

A. Sinai Peninsula   **C.** Syria

B. West Bank   **D.** Golan Heights

_____ **23.** During which year did Israel acquire the most land?

A. 1947   **C.** 1967

B. 1948   **D.** 1993

Directions: Document-Based Questions Use the document below to answer the questions that follow. *(5 points each)*

> "In a growing climate of fear punctuated by riots and bomb explosions, Kurdish nationalists in Turkey are pressing their claim for autonomy [self-government]. Turkish military leaders and politicians feel that granting such a demand would be tantamount to storing dynamite under the republic's foundations, and likely to result in Turkey's fragmentation [division] along ethnic lines.
>
> ". . . The problem of the Kurds, a tormented nation-tribe deprived of statehood throughout its history, also affects Turkey's neighbors Iran, Iraq, and Syria, where an estimated 10 million Kurds live."
>
> **Source:** *The Washington Times*, April 19, 2006.

_____ **24.** Besides Turkey, Kurds form a significant part of which countries?

   A. Iran, Iraq, and Syria

   B. Egypt, Iran, and Iraq

   C. Saudi Arabia, Iran, and Jordan

   D. Turkey, Syria, and Egypt

_____ **25.** Why does Turkish leadership refuse to grant the demands of Kurdish nationalists?

   A. Kurds have not resorted to violence.

   B. Kurds do not receive support from other countries.

   C. Granting the demands would divide Turkey along ethnic lines.

   D. Kurds will use dynamite against the Turkish government.

_____ **26.** What do Turkish Kurds want?

   A. independence from Turkish rule

   B. to merge with Iraq

   C. to move to Syria or Iraq

   D. to form an Islamic republic

Directions: Essay On a separate sheet of paper, answer the question below. *(10 points)*

27. How did cotton farming have a negative impact on the environment and economy of Uzbekistan?

SCORE

North Africa, Southwest Asia, and Central Asia Today

Chapter 18 Test Form B

Directions: Matching Match each item in Column A with its description in Column B. Write the correct letters in the blanks. *(3 points each)*

Column A

A. Kemal Atatürk

B. fellahin

C. genocide

D. enclave

E. Western Sahara

F. Maghreb

G. King Hussein I

H. kibbutz

I. Uzbekistan

J. Algeria

Column B

_____ **1.** farming settlement in Israel

_____ **2.** Turkey's first president

_____ **3.** Egyptian peasant farmer

_____ **4.** North Africa's largest country

_____ **5.** claimed by Morocco

_____ **6.** a small territory surrounded by a larger territory

_____ **7.** Jordanian ruler

_____ **8.** relies on cotton as its cash crop

_____ **9.** deliberate killing of an ethnic group

_____ **10.** "the land farthest west"

Directions: Multiple Choice In the blank at the left, write the letter of the choice that best completes the statement or answers the question. *(3 points each)*

_____ **11.** Nearly 11 million people live in Egypt's capital, ____.

  A. Alexandria   **C.** Aswān

  B. Cairo   **D.** Suez

_____ **12.** Which country straddles Europe and Asia?

  A. Armenia   **C.** Jordan

  B. Yemen   **D.** Turkey

_____ **13.** In 2001 the United States invaded and overthrew ____.

  A. Israel's David Ben-Gurion   **C.** Iraq's Saddam Hussein

  B. Palestine's Arabs   **D.** Afghanistan's Taliban government

_____ **14.** Who established a monarchy in Saudi Arabia in 1932?

    A. the Hamas family   **C.** the Riyadh clan

    B. the Saud family   **D.** Muhammad

_____ **15.** Israel's economy is based mainly on which of the following?

    A. tourism, oil, and natural gas

    B. agriculture and mining

    C. high-tech equipment, clothing, chemicals, and machinery

    D. dairy farming, tourism, and steel

_____ **16.** What are oil-rich countries doing to prepare for the future?

    A. digging in new places for oil

    B. investing in new industries

    C. building new refineries

    D. using dams for hydroelectric power

_____ **17.** Which group of countries was once part of the Soviet Union?

    A. the Maghreb   **C.** the Caucasus Republics

    B. the Persian Gulf countries   **D.** the Tian Shan Republics

_____ **18.** Which country was the first to make Christianity its official religion?

    A. Georgia   **C.** Turkmenistan

    B. Azerbaijan   **D.** Armenia

_____ **19.** Which country's people are mostly nomads who live in oases of the Kara-Kum desert?

    A. Turkmenistan

    B. Kyrgyzstan

    C. Tajikistan

    D. Kazakhstan

_____ **20.** Libya's infrastructure was developed with money from ____.

    A. agriculture   **C.** mercury

    B. phosphates   **D.** oil

Applying Skills: Reading a Map Use the map below to answer the questions that follow. *(5 points each)*

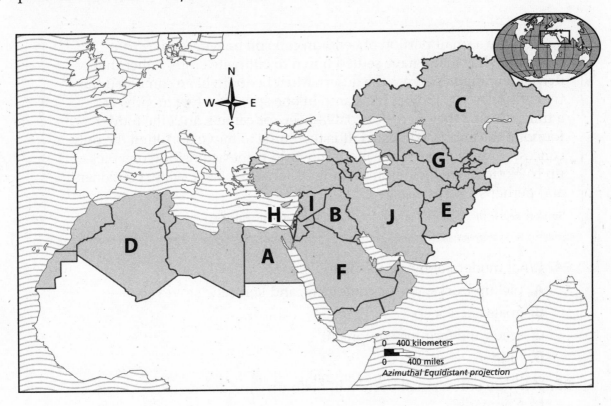

_____ **21.** Which country is signified by the letter *D?*

    A. Morocco   **C.** Algeria

    B. Tunisia   **D.** Libya

_____ **22.** Which letter shows the location of Syria?

    A. B   **C.** J

    B. H   **D.** I

_____ **23.** Which country is signified by the letter *C?*

    A. Afghanistan   **C.** Uzbekistan

    B. Tajikistan   **D.** Kazakhstan

North Africa, Southwest Asia, and Central Asia Today

Chapter 18 Test Form B (continued)

Directions: Document-Based Questions Use the document below to answer the questions that follow. *(5 points each)*

> . . . Only a small portion of bedouin can still be regarded as true nomads, while many have settled down to cultivate crops rather than drive their animals across the desert. Most Bedouin have combined the two lifestyles . . . . [Some] will camp in one spot for a few months at a time, grazing their herds of goats, sheep, or camels until the fodder found in the area is exhausted. It is then time to move on. Often the only concession they make to the modern world is the acquisition of a pick-up truck (to move their animals long distances), plastic water containers, and perhaps a kerosene stove.
>
> **Source:** *Keys to the Kingdom: The People of Jordan,* www.kinghussein.gov.jo.

_____ **24.** What modern items do the bedouin use?

    A. pickup trucks, plastic containers, and kerosene stoves

    B. goats and sheep

    C. seeds and farming equipment

    D. fodder

_____ **25.** Why are only a small portion of bedouin considered true nomads?

    A. They all use modern conveniences.

    B. Many have settled down to farm.

    C. Some camp in one spot for a few months before moving on.

    D. They graze goats, sheep, and camels.

_____ **26.** Most bedouin ____.

    A. are farmers only   **C.** are true nomads

    B. raise livestock only   **D.** combine farming and raising livestock

Directions: Essay On a separate sheet of paper, answer the question below. *(10 points)*

    27. Describe at least three physical or human features that the countries of North Africa have in common.

Directions: Matching Match each item in Column A with its description in Column B. Write the correct letters in the blanks. *(5 points each)*

Column A

A. sedimentary

B. Sumer

C. Abraham

D. moshav

E. casbah

F. Beirut

G. Madinah

H. Kurds

I. phosphates

J. Hindu Kush

Column B

_____ **1.** ethnic group in Turkey

_____ **2.** mineral salts used as fertilizer

_____ **3.** old section of a city in North Africa

_____ **4.** rock layers that may contain oil

_____ **5.** mountain range in Afghanistan

_____ **6.** farming settlement in Israel

_____ **7.** Jewish ancestor

_____ **8.** holy city of Islam

_____ **9.** capital of Lebanon

_____ **10.** region in ancient Mesopotamia

Directions: Multiple Choice Write the letter of the choice that best completes the statement or answers the question. *(5 points each)*

_____ **11.** What is this region's most valuable resource?

    A. farmland

    B. gold

    C. wood

    D. oil

_____ **12.** Which is a scarce and sometimes misused resource in this region?

    A. natural gas

    B. salt

    C. water

    D. phosphates

_____ **13.** The oldest monotheistic religion in the world is _____.

    A. Buddhism

    B. Islam

    C. Christianity

    D. Judaism

_____ **14.** The predominant physical feature of North Africa is the _____.

    A. Nile River

    B. Sahara

    C. Arabian Desert

    D. alluvial plain

_____ **15.** What do Kazakhstan, Turkmenistan, Uzbekistan, and Kyrgyzstan have in common?

    A. All are mountainous.

    B. All are Islamic countries that were part of the Soviet Union.

    C. All are Southwest Asian nations rich in oil and minerals.

    D. All have large deserts.

Applying Skills: Reading a Map Use the map below to answer the questions that follow. *(5 points each)*

Jerusalem

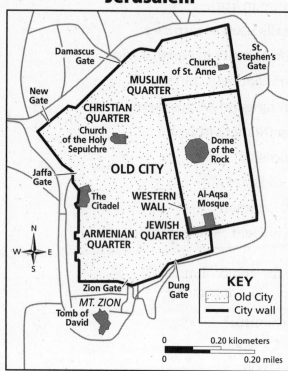

_____ **16.** Where is the Tomb of David located?

    A. outside the Old City   **C.** in the Armenian Quarter

    B. in the Christian Quarter   **D.** near the Dome of the Rock

_____ **17.** Where is the Jaffa Gate located?

    A. on the north side of the Old City   **C.** on the west side of the Old City

    B. on the south side of the Old City   **D.** on the east side of the Old City

_____ **18.** Which of these is a Jewish landmark?

    A. Church of the Holy Sepulchre   **C.** Dome of the Rock

    B. Western Wall   **D.** Church of St. Anne

Directions: Essay On a separate sheet of paper, answer the question below. *(10 points)*

    19. What are the Five Pillars of Islam?

SCORE

Directions: Matching Match each item in Column A with its description in Column B. Write the correct letters in the blanks. *(5 points each)*

Column A

A. urbanization

B. Kush

C. rain forest

D. Lake Victoria

E. Nigeria

F. Lake Chad

G. escarpments

H. rural areas

I. Democratic Republic of the Congo

J. Bantu

Column B

_____ **1.** steep, jagged cliffs

_____ **2.** major oil-producing country

_____ **3.** has a tall canopy

_____ **4.** changes in size from dry to rainy season

_____ **5.** movement of people to cities

_____ **6.** early ancestors of Africans

_____ **7.** country that is a major source of copper, tin, and industrial diamonds

_____ **8.** where about 70 percent of Africans live

_____ **9.** ancient kingdom along the Nile River

_____ **10.** source of the White Nile

Directions: Multiple Choice Write the letter of the choice that best completes the statement or answers the question. *(7 points each)*

_____ **11.** The Great Rift Valley was created from ____.
   A. erosion over millions of years   **C.** shifting tectonic plates
   B. the Nile River   **D.** high winds and sandstorms

_____ **12.** Which of the following are major causes of deforestation in Central and West Africa?
   A. cutting trees for lumber and clearing land for farming
   B. overgrazing by cattle and poor soil
   C. large fires and heavy rains
   D. tourists taking home wood and uprooting saplings

_____ **13.** The earliest trading empire was ____.
   A. Mali   **C.** Axum
   B. Songhai   **D.** Ghana

_____ **14.** The population in Africa south of the Sahara is ____.
   A. growing slowly   **C.** decreasing slowly
   B. growing rapidly   **D.** staying the same

_____ **15.** Until 1990 this policy prevented South Africans from working together as a nation.

    A. deforestation   **C.** apartheid

    B. communism   **D.** tribal religions

Applying Skills: Reading a Map Use the map below to answer the questions that follow. *(5 points each)*

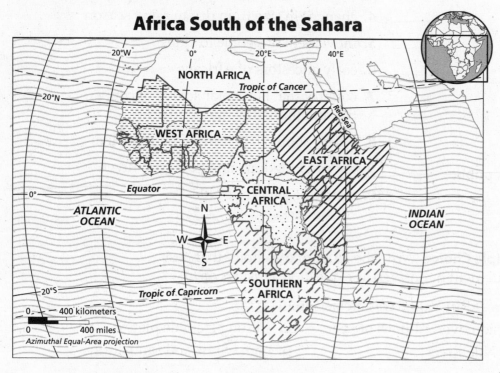

Africa South of the Sahara

_____ **16.** Madagascar is part of which region?

    A. Central   **C.** Southern

    B. West   **D.** East

_____ **17.** Which region of Africa borders both the Indian and Atlantic Oceans?

    A. Southern   **C.** West

    B. East   **D.** Central

_____ **18.** The distance from the westernmost part of West Africa to the Horn of Africa is approximately how many miles?

    A. 2,000 miles   **C.** 1,000 miles

    B. 1,500 miles   **D.** 500 miles

SCORE

Directions: Matching Match each item in Column A with its description in Column B. Write the correct letters in the blanks. *(10 points each)*

Column A

A. uranium

B. escarpment

C. Lake Chad

D. Kilimanjaro

E. plateaus

Column B

_____ **1.** means "shining mountain" in Swahili

_____ **2.** changes dramatically in size

_____ **3.** gives Africa south of the Sahara its high elevation

_____ **4.** mineral used to produce nuclear power

_____ **5.** steep, jagged cliff

Directions: Short Answer Answer each question or statement below on the line provided. *(10 points each)*

6. What resources do Lake Victoria and Lake Volta provide?

_____

7. What hinders transportation on the Congo River?

_____

8. How has oil changed trade in Nigeria?

_____

9. In addition to jewelry, what are the diamonds of South Africa used for?

_____

10. How did tectonic activity form the Congo Basin and the Great Rift Valley?

_____

Directions: Matching Match each item in Column A with its description in Column B. Write the correct letters in the blanks. *(10 points each)*

Column A

A. canopy

B. higher altitude

C. ecotourism

D. national parks

E. ocean breezes

Column B

_____ **1.** land set aside to protect elephants on the African savanna

_____ **2.** increases revenue to local economies while preserving rain forests

_____ **3.** makes the Namib cooler than other African deserts

_____ **4.** umbrella-like covering in Africa's rain forests

_____ **5.** makes for cooler temperatures in parts of East Africa

Directions: Short Answer Answer each question or statement below on the line provided. *(10 points each)*

6. What is the main difference in climate between the tropical rain forest and the tropical savanna? Describe the plants each climate can support.

_____

7. What is the Kalahari? How do some trees survive in the Kalahari?

_____

8. How does climate change lead to desertification on the steppes?

_____

9. What areas of Africa south of the Sahara have a moderate climate?

_____

10. Why do farmers in the rain forest often clear more land?

_____

SCORE

Directions: Matching Match each item in Column A with its description in Column B. Write the correct letters in the blanks. *(3 points each)*

Column A

A. savanna

B. Zambezi

C. Kalahari

D. Kilimanjaro

E. Tanganyika

F. Madagascar

G. Great Rift Valley

H. Drakensberg

I. Namib

J. rain forest

Column B

_____ **1.** dense stand of trees that receives large amounts of precipitation

_____ **2.** largest island off the mainland

_____ **3.** natural wonder of East Africa

_____ **4.** grasslands with scattered woods

_____ **5.** sandy desert in Southern Africa

_____ **6.** desert made up of rocks and dunes along the southwestern coast

_____ **7.** highest mountain peak in Africa

_____ **8.** river that forms Victoria falls

_____ **9.** called the "barrier of pointed spears"

_____ **10.** longest freshwater lake in the world

Directions: Multiple Choice In the blank at the left, write the letter of the choice that best completes the statement or answers the question. *(3 points each)*

_____ **11.** Most of the land of Africa south of the Sahara consists of ____.

    A. rich, rolling plains   **C.** rugged mountains

    B. high plateaus   **D.** dry, flat desert

_____ **12.** Which physical feature is located in East Africa?

    A. Ethiopian Highlands   **C.** Cape of Good Hope

    B. Congo Basin   **D.** Sahara

_____ **13.** The Great Rift Valley was formed mainly by ____.

    A. shifting tectonic plates   **C.** Nile River flooding

    B. seawater erosion   **D.** a large meteor

_____ **14.** What creates waterfalls on many African rivers?
  A. earthquakes   **C.** escarpments
  B. volcanoes   **D.** terminal moraines

_____ **15.** The principal export in many Atlantic coastal countries is
  _____.
  A. cacao   **C.** oil
  B. bananas   **D.** chromium

_____ **16.** Which country has major gold and diamond deposits?
  A. South Africa   **C.** Zimbabwe
  B. Nigeria   **D.** Chad

_____ **17.** Why are many African countries promoting ecotourism?
  A. to allow tourists to distribute African plants
  B. to attract more industry and investment
  C. to encourage trade with other nations
  D. to help preserve the rain forests and boost economies

_____ **18.** In steppe areas, clearing trees or herding large amounts of
  livestock can cause _____.
  A. farmers to become angry   **C.** irrigation problems
  B. desertification   **D.** soil to become compacted

_____ **19.** Which type of climate is found in southwestern Africa?
  A. desert   **C.** highland
  B. Mediterranean   **D.** steppe

_____ **20.** Where in Africa are you most likely to find elephants, lions,
  and giraffes?
  A. in the steppes   **C.** in the rain forest
  B. in the mountains   **D.** in the savanna

Applying Skills: Reading a Map Use the map below to answer the questions that follow. *(5 points each)*

The Great Rift Valley

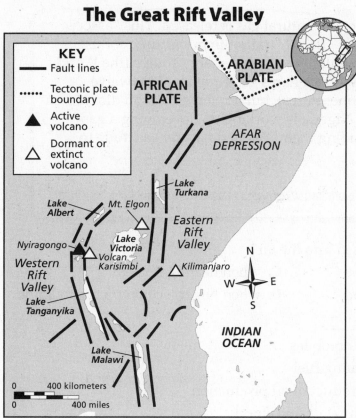

Source: Encarta.msn.com.

_____ **21.** Kilimanjaro is located in the ____.

    A. Western Rift Valley   **C.** Arabian Plate

    B. Afar Depression   **D.** Eastern Rift Valley

_____ **22.** Nyiragongo is ____.

    A. a dormant volcano   **C.** an active volcano

    B. an extinct volcano   **D.** a lake

_____ **23.** What do Lake Alberta, Lake Turkana, and Lake Malawi have in common?

    A. All three lie within fault lines.

    B. All three lie within plate boundaries.

    C. All three are the largest lakes in Africa.

    D. All three are next to active volcanoes.

Directions: Document-Based Questions Use the document below to answer the questions that follow. *(5 points each)*

> In the process of oil production, natural gas is released. This "associated" gas is often burned off, or "flared," rather than captured for use. Not only does this waste a potentially valuable energy source (the World Bank estimates that every day Africa flares gas equivalent to twelve times the energy that the continent uses), but it releases carbon dioxide directly into the atmosphere. Nigeria is working on developing a gas-to-liquids industry and expanding their liquefied natural gas trade to reduce flaring.
>
> **Source:** U.S. Department of Energy.
> www.eia.doe.gov/emeu/cabs/subafricaenv.htmlhttp://www.eia.doe.gov/emeu/cabs/subafricaenv.html.

_____ **24.** When is natural gas released into the air?

    A. when oil is produced   **C.** when heating homes

    B. when the weather is bad   **D.** when Nigeria converts gas to liquid

_____ **25.** Natural gas is "flared" to ____.

    A. convert it for use in automobiles

    B. convert it for home-heating fuel

    C. burn it off as a waste product of oil production

    D. develop a liquefied natural gas product

_____ **26.** Why is flaring of natural gas a problem?

    A. It wastes energy that Africa needs.

    B. It releases carbon dioxide into the atmosphere.

    C. It is inefficient.

    D. All of these.

Directions: Essay On a separate sheet of paper, answer the question below. *(10 points)*

    27. What threatens the rain forests of Central and West Africa today?

SCORE

Physical Geography of Africa South of the Sahara

Chapter 19 Test Form B

Directions: Matching Match each item in Column A with its description in Column B. Write the correct letters in the blanks. *(3 points each)*

Column A

A. gorges

B. savanna

C. droughts

D. Mediterranean

E. basins

F. succulents

G. Transvaal

H. highland

I. steppe

J. oil

Column B

_____ **1.** plants with thick, fleshy leaves

_____ **2.** region with a large gold deposit

_____ **3.** low, sunken areas formed from tectonic activity

_____ **4.** elephants, lions, and giraffes live here

_____ **5.** climate found in Southwestern Africa

_____ **6.** steep-sided valleys formed from rivers

_____ **7.** principal export in many Atlantic coastal countries

_____ **8.** climate found in East Africa

_____ **9.** periods of time with little or no rain

_____ **10.** vegetation includes trees, thick shrubs, and grasses

Directions: Multiple Choice In the blank at the left, write the letter of the choice that best completes the statement or answers the question. *(3 points each)*

_____ **11.** Which of the following is a break in the Earth's surface caused by shifting tectonic plates?
A. Kilimanjaro   **C.** escarpment
B. Great Rift Valley   **D.** Congo Basin

_____ **12.** Why are Africa's many rivers not used for shipping?
A. The rivers are polluted.
B. The rivers flow in the wrong direction.
C. The rivers all end in swamps.
D. The rivers flow over too many escarpments.

_____ **13.** What is the Drakensberg Range?
A. a high plateau in South Africa
B. a mountain range in southern Africa
C. grazing lands for wild animals in Central Africa
D. a series of mountains along the Equator

_____ **14.** Which of these lakes is the second-largest freshwater lake
in the world?

    A. Lake Tanganyika   **C.** Lake Tana

    B. Lake Victoria   **D.** Lake Superior

_____ **15.** Africa's major rivers include the Nile, Congo, Niger,
and ___.

    A. Elbe   **C.** Zambezi

    B. Orinoco   **D.** Volga

_____ **16.** An important source of hydroelectric power is the
Akosombo Dam in ____.

    A. Nigeria   **C.** Ghana

    B. the Democratic Republic   **D.** Sudan
       of the Congo

_____ **17.** Among its resources, South Africa is thought to have half
of the world's ____.

    A. oil   **C.** natural gas

    B. iron ore   **D.** gold

_____ **18.** Most of Africa south of the Sahara lies ____.

    A. along the Equator

    B. between the Tropic of Cancer and the Tropic of Capricorn

    C. along the Atlantic Ocean

    D. between the Tropic of Capricorn and the Antarctic Circle

_____ **19.** Where do most parrots, monkeys, and snakes live
in Africa?

    A. on the rain forest floor   **C.** in the rain forest canopy

    B. in the steppes   **D.** in the tropical savanna

_____ **20.** The Namib and the Kalahari are two of Africa's ____.

    A. deserts   **C.** highest mountains

    B. rain forests   **D.** savannas

Applying Skills: Reading a Map Use the map below to answer the questions that follow. *(5 points each)*

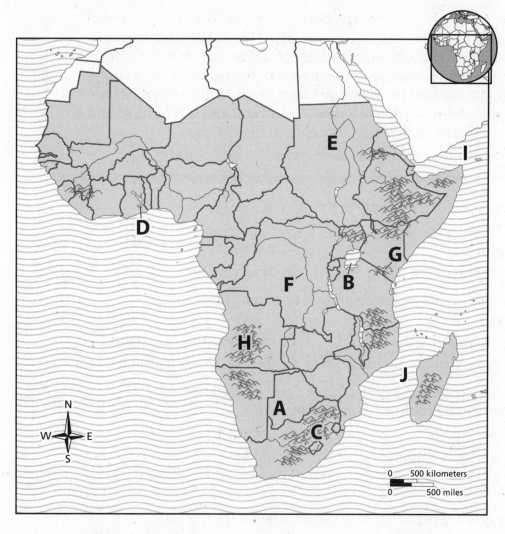

_____ **21.** Which physical feature is represented by the letter *F?*

    A. Niger River   **C.** Zambezi River

    B. Nile River   **D.** Congo River

_____ **22.** Which physical feature is represented by the letter *B?*

    A. Lake Albert   **C.** Lake Victoria

    B. Lake Tanganyika   **D.** Lake Volta

_____ **23.** Which landform is represented by the letter *A?*

    A. Namib   **C.** The Sahel

    B. Kalahari   **D.** Ethiopian Highlands

Directions: Document-Based Questions Use the document below to answer the questions that follow. *(5 points each)*

> Two-thirds of the people in Africa south of the Sahara live in rural areas and rely on agriculture and other natural resources for income. However, the environmental resource base of the region is shrinking rapidly. Environmental problems of Africa south of the Sahara include air and water pollution, deforestation, loss of soil and soil fertility, and a dramatic decline in biodiversity throughout the region.
>
> **Source:** U.S. Department of Energy. www.eia.doe.gov/emeu/cabs/subafricaenv.html.

_____ 24. What do most of the people in this region rely on for income?

    A. shipping   **C.** trade

    B. agriculture   **D.** biodiversity

_____ 25. The people in this region could face economic problems because _____.

    A. they have few cities   **C.** their resources are dwindling

    B. the governments are unstable   **D.** they receive little foreign aid

_____ 26. According to the passage, which of these is a serious environmental problem facing the region?

    A. deforestation   **C.** acid rain

    B. depletion of natural resources   **D.** increase in biodiversity

Directions: Essay On a separate sheet of paper, answer the question below. *(10 points)*

    27. How do the climates and vegetation of the savanna, steppe, and desert regions of Africa south of the Sahara differ?

SCORE

Directions: Matching Match each item in Column A with its description in Column B. Write the correct letters in the blanks. *(10 points each)*

Column A

A. apartheid

B. nationalism

C. King Ezana

D. Mansa Musa

E. discrimination

Column B

_____ **1.** unfair and unequal treatment of a group

_____ **2.** separated ethnic groups and limited the rights of black South Africans

_____ **3.** a people's desire to rule themselves and have their own independent country

_____ **4.** ruler who accepted Christianity and made Axum a major power

_____ **5.** made Timbuktu a center of trade, education, and Islamic culture

Directions: Short Answer Answer each question or statement below on the line provided. *(10 points each)*

6. From where did the Bantu originate and spread? What skills did they spread?

_____

7. What brought wealth to the Axum and Great Zimbabwe kingdoms?

_____

8. Why did the slave trade increase in the 1500s? What effects did the slave trade have on Africans?

_____

9. In what ways did European colonists discriminate against Africans?

_____

10. Why did European colonialism later result in civil wars?

_____

SCORE

Directions: Matching Match each item in Column A with its description in Column B. Write the correct letters in the blanks. *(10 points each)*

Column A

A. extended families

B. clan

C. urbanization

D. lineage

E. malnutrition

Column B

_____ **1.** the movement of people from rural areas to cities

_____ **2.** large group of people united by a common ancestor in the far past

_____ **3.** poor health from not eating the right foods or not eating enough food

_____ **4.** large family group with close blood ties

_____ **5.** households made up of several generations

Directions: Short Answer Answer each question or statement below on the line provided. *(10 points each)*

6. How is AIDS affecting the life expectancy in some southern African countries?

_____

7. Why are many Africans south of the Sahara malnourished even though most are farmers?

_____

8. How are African family structures changing as rural Africans move to cities?

_____

9. Describe Arab and European influences on the language and religion of Africans south of the Sahara.

_____

10. How have the griots of West Africa maintained traditions?

_____

SCORE

Directions: Matching Match each item in Column A with its description in Column B. Write the correct letters in the blanks. *(3 points each)*

Column A

A. hunter-gatherers

B. griots

C. missionaries

D. discrimination

E. malnutrition

F. Mansa Musa

G. rural villages

H. Great Zimbabwe

I. nationalism

J. rites of passage

Column B

_____ **1.** famous ruler of Mali

_____ **2.** a people's desire to rule themselves

_____ **3.** storytellers

_____ **4.** empire in southern Africa

_____ **5.** people who moved from place to place in search of food

_____ **6.** special ceremonies that mark life stages

_____ **7.** unfair and unequal treatment of a group

_____ **8.** group who wanted to convert Africans to Christianity

_____ **9.** poor health due to not eating the right foods

_____ **10.** where most people south of the Sahara live

Directions: Multiple Choice In the blank at the left, write the letter of the choice that best completes the statement or answers the question. *(3 points each)*

_____ **11.** Which ancient people migrated west and south from Nigeria?

    A. Kush   **C.** Great Zimbabwe

    B. Arab Muslims   **D.** Bantu

_____ **12.** Which ancient kingdom, in present-day Ethiopia, was a center of African Christianity?

    A. Chad   **C.** Nok

    B. Axum   **D.** Zambezi

_____ **13.** When Europeans began trading with African societies, the African slave trade _____.

    A. grew   **C.** diminished

    B. began   **D.** was abolished

_____ 14. Why did European countries carve Africa into colonies
in the 1800s?

A. to promote the slave trade

B. for profit and political advantage

C. to spread Islamic beliefs

D. to develop African economies

_____ 15. What is one reason the death rate in Africa south of the
Sahara is so high?

A. heart disease

B. obesity

C. tuberculosis

D. lack of clean water

_____ 16. Which is the most widely spoken language in Africa south
of the Sahara?

A. Swahili

B. Hausa

C. Yoruba

D. English

_____ 17. What is the most serious problem related to population
growth in Africa south of the Sahara?

A. racial conflict

B. too many people in villages

C. not enough food

D. too many immigrants

_____ 18. The first African country to regain its independence after
World War II was _____.

A. Nigeria

B. Ethiopia

C. Sudan

D. Ghana

_____ 19. In Africa, a person's ethnic group is most closely associated
with which of these?

A. nationality

B. language

C. region

D. religion

_____ 20. What is the most common expression of community life,
social status, and rites of passage in Africa?

A. painting

B. sculpture

C. dance

D. theater

Applying Skills: Reading a Map Use the map below to answer the questions that follow. *(5 points each)*

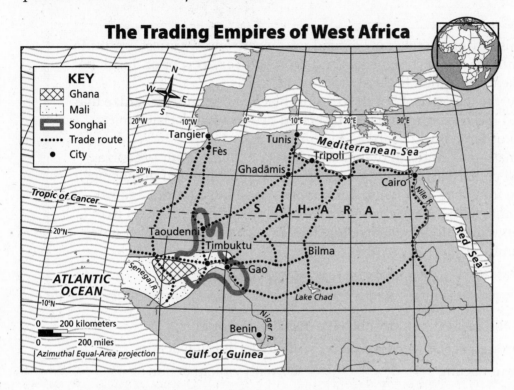

The Trading Empires of West Africa

_____ **21.** Most trade routes connect _____.

    A. rivers   **C.** cities

    B. countries   **D.** mountains

_____ **22.** Through which region did most of the trade routes go?

    A. Central Africa   **C.** the Atlantic coast

    B. the Sahara   **D.** Africa south of the Sahara

_____ **23.** Which trading empire bordered the Atlantic Ocean?

    A. Mali   **C.** Songhai

    B. Ghana   **D.** Benin

Directions: Document-Based Questions Use the document below to answer the questions that follow. *(5 points each)*

> On this day of my release, I extend my sincere and warmest gratitude to the millions of my compatriots and those in every corner of the globe who have campaigned tirelessly for my release. . . .
>
> Today, the majority of South Africans, black and white, recognize that apartheid has no future. It has to be ended by our own decisive mass action in order to build peace and security. . . .
>
> The mass campaigns of defiance and other actions of our organizations and people can only culminate in the establishment of democracy.
>
> I have fought against white domination, and I have fought against black domination. I have cherished the ideal of a democratic and free society in which all persons live together in harmony and with equal opportunity.
>
> **Source:** Nelson Mandela, 1990. www.fordham.edu/halsall/mod/1990MANDELA.html.

_____ 24. How did Nelson Mandela believe apartheid should end?

A. through decisive mass action **C.** by individual action

B. by not acting **D.** with violent action

_____ 25. At the time of Mandela's release, most South Africans believed apartheid ____.

A. was just beginning **C.** was justified

B. had to end **D.** was needed to keep order

_____ 26. Nelson Mandela expressed his desire that South Africa become ____.

A. a black African nation **C.** a rising economic power

B. a democratic free society **D.** a white African nation

Directions: Essay On a separate sheet of paper, answer the question below. *(10 points)*

27. Describe the ethnic diversity of Africa, and explain the importance of the extended family and clan.

SCORE

Directions: Matching Match each item in Column A with its description in Column B. Write the correct letters in the blanks. *(3 points each)*

Column A

A. nuclear family

B. kente

C. 1957

D. compound

E. Kwame Nkrumah

F. Chinua Achebe

G. clan

H. 1994

I. malaria

J. King Ezana

Column B

_____ **1.** large group of people united by a common ancestor

_____ **2.** group of houses surrounded by walls

_____ **3.** widespread disease in Africa south of the Sahara

_____ **4.** husband, wife, and their children

_____ **5.** African writer

_____ **6.** year of South Africa's first democratic election for both races

_____ **7.** brightly colored cloth

_____ **8.** year that Ghana gained its independence

_____ **9.** led independence movement

_____ **10.** accepted Christianity in the A.D. 300s

Directions: Multiple Choice In the blank at the left, write the letter of the choice that best completes the statement or answers the question. *(3 points each)*

_____ **11.** What do the ancient empires of Mali and Ghana have in common?

    A. Both were founded by Muslims. **C.** They traded gold and salt.

    B. They share a common ancestor. **D.** Their wealth came from the sea.

_____ **12.** Between 1500 and 1800, about how many Africans were captured and sent to the Americas?

    A. 10,000   **C.** one million

    B. 200,000   **D.** 12 million

_____ **13.** By 1914, which of the following was true of Africa?

    A. Almost all of Africa was independent.

    B. Nearly every African colony was in revolt.

    C. European nations controlled almost all of Africa.

    D. Cities dominated nearly every region.

_____ 14. What conditions prevailed in many African nations soon
after they won independence?

   A. Ethnic divisions led to civil wars.

   B. Drought produced widespread famine.

   C. Europeans seized control of the new governments.

   D. Democracy was established, and economic goals were reached.

_____ 15. How did many countries respond to South Africa's policy
of apartheid?

   A. They sent troops into South Africa.

   B. They supported the white government.

   C. They cut off trade with South Africa.

   D. They bombed Johannesburg.

_____ 16. Compared to the rest of the world, the rate of population
growth in Africa south of the Sahara is _____.

   A. one of the slowest   **C.** about the same

   B. one of the fastest   **D.** slightly slower

_____ 17. Where do most people in Africa south of the Sahara live?

   A. in the highlands of South Africa

   B. along the edges of the Sahara

   C. in rural regions of the steppe

   D. along the West African coast

_____ 18. In Africa, dance is an expression of _____.

   A. individual feelings   **C.** celebration

   B. African music   **D.** a community's life

_____ 19. Which statement best describes religion in Africa south
of the Sahara?

   A. Most people follow traditional African religions.

   B. Muslim, Christian, and traditional African religions predominate.

   C. Buddhism, Islam, and traditional religions predominate.

   D. Religion is controlled by the governments.

_____ 20. What are the main crops grown on Africa's commercial farms?

   A. rice, beans, wheat, and corn

   B. fruits such as pineapple and oranges

   C. cacao, coffee, bananas, tea, and cotton

   D. milk, cheese, and other dairy products

Applying Skills: Reading a Chart Use the chart below to answer the questions that follow. *(5 points each)*

African Independence		
Country	**Year of Independence**	**Colonial Power**
Angola	1975	Portugal
Chad	1960	France
Democratic Republic of the Congo	1960	Belgium
Gambia	1965	United Kingdom
Kenya	1963	United Kingdom
Liberia		
Mauritania	1960	France
Mozambique	1975	Portugal
Nigeria	1960	United Kingdom
Rwanda	1962	Belgium
Senegal	1960	France
Somalia	1960	Italy
South Africa	1910	United Kingdom
Uganda	1962	Italy

_____ **21.** Of the countries listed, which one achieved independence first?

A. Nigeria **C.** South Africa

B. Senegal **D.** Angola

_____ **22.** Most African nations achieved independence in which decade?

A. 1960s **C.** 1980s

B. 1970s **D.** 1990s

_____ **23.** Which African nation was not colonized and controlled by a European power?

A. South Africa **C.** Liberia

B. Tanzania **D.** Angola

Directions: Document-Based Questions Use the document below to answer the questions that follow. *(5 points each)*

> There are more than 34 million orphans in the region today and some 11 million of them are orphaned by AIDS. Eight out of every 10 children in the world whose parents have died of AIDS live in sub-Saharan Africa. During the last decade, the proportion of children who are orphaned as a result of AIDS rose from 3.5% to 32% and will continue to increase exponentially as the disease spreads unchecked. As a result, the disease is, in effect, making orphans of a whole generation of children, jeopardizing their health, their rights, their well being and sometimes their very survival, not to mention the overall development prospects of their countries.
>
> **Source:** United Nations. www.un.org/events/tenstories/story.asp?storyID=400.

_____ **24.** The United Nations expects the number of children who are orphaned from AIDS to ____.

    A. fall dramatically   **C.** rise at a fast rate

    B. rise at a slow rate   **D.** stay the same

_____ **25.** What percentage of the world's children whose parents have died of AIDS live in sub-Saharan Africa?

    A. 20 percent   **C.** 60 percent

    B. 40 percent   **D.** 80 percent

_____ **26.** Besides affecting many children, what additional concern does the United Nations have about the AIDS epidemic in the region?

    A. It will affect the development of many countries.

    B. It will spread to other regions.

    C. It will cause other diseases to spread.

    D. It will cause a trade imbalance.

Directions: Essay On a separate sheet of paper, answer the question below. *(10 points)*

    27. Describe life for a rural farming family in Africa south of the Sahara.

SCORE

Directions: Matching Match each item in Column A with its description in Column B. Write the correct letters in the blanks. *(10 points each)*

Column A

A. Arabic

B. Lagos

C. Abidjan

D. Abuja

E. English

Column B

_____ **1.** where people of Côte d'Ivoire go to find work

_____ **2.** largest city in Nigeria

_____ **3.** language spoken by most people of the Sahel countries

_____ **4.** language spoken when people do business in Nigeria

_____ **5.** capital of Nigeria

Directions: Short Answer Answer each question or statement below on the line provided. *(10 points each)*

6. Why does Nigeria have to import food?

_____

7. How do Chad and Nigeria differ in their revenues from valuable oil deposits?

_____

8. What effect does livestock herding have on the land of the Sahel?

_____

9. What countries make up the Sahel?

_____

10. Describe the climate of coastal West Africa.

_____

Directions: Matching Match each item in Column A with its description in Column B. Write the correct letters in the blanks. *(10 points each)*

Column A

A. Amharic

B. Djibouti

C. Idi Amin

D. Kikuyu

E. Tutsis

Column B

_____ **1.** cruel dictator of Uganda in the 1970s

_____ **2.** the most stable country in the Horn of Africa

_____ **3.** ethnic group in Kenya

_____ **4.** Ethiopia's official language

_____ **5.** ethnic group targeted by the Hutu-led government in Rwanda

Directions: Short Answer Answer each question or statement below on the line provided. *(10 points each)*

6. Why has Djibouti profited from its location on the Red Sea, whereas Somalia has not?

_____

7. Name three landlocked countries in East Africa.

_____

8. What are ecotourists?

_____

9. Why is the Congo River important to the economy of the Democratic Republic of the Congo?

_____

10. Why did Sudan and Ethiopia each lose more than a million people in the last century?

_____

Directions: Matching Match each item in Column A with its description in Column B. Write the correct letters in the blanks. *(10 points each)*

Column A

A. people of Botswana

B. people of Angola and Namibia

C. Afrikaners

D. people of Zimbabwe

E. black South Africans

Column B

_____ **1.** descendants of Dutch, German, and French settlers in South Africa

_____ **2.** live in poverty despite the mineral wealth of their country

_____ **3.** enjoy one of the strongest democracies in Africa

_____ **4.** set up the African National Congress in hopes of gaining power

_____ **5.** have protested against the strong-handed rule of President Robert Mugabe

Directions: Short Answer Answer each question or statement below on the line provided. *(10 points each)*

6. What did South Africa do in the 1990s to ensure equality for all of its people?

_____

7. What are South Africa's major exports?

_____

8. How does inland southern Africa depend on South Africa for jobs?

_____

9. How are the people of East Africa's island nations different from those living in the rest of Africa?

_____

10. Despite rich farmland, why has Zimbabwe had recent food shortages?

_____

SCORE

Directions: Matching Match each item in Column A with its description in Column B. Write the correct letters in the blanks. *(3 points each)*

Column A

A. Ghana

B. Sudan

C. sisal

D. cassava

E. Tutsi

F. Kinshasa

G. Burkina Faso

H. Djibouti

I. Lagos

J. Swahili

Column B

_____ **1.** landlocked country in the Sahel

_____ **2.** once a center of Kush civilization

_____ **3.** governing minority of Rwanda

_____ **4.** largest city in Nigeria

_____ **5.** plant used to make rope

_____ **6.** country in West Africa that has a stable democracy

_____ **7.** language of Tanzania

_____ **8.** capital of the Democratic Republic of the Congo

_____ **9.** plant with roots that make porridge

_____ **10.** stable country in the Horn of Africa

Directions: Multiple Choice In the blank at the left, write the letter of the choice that best completes the statement or answers the question. *(3 points each)*

_____ **11.** Which of these best describes Nigeria's population?

    A. more than 250 ethnic groups   **C.** four ethnic groups

    B. mostly Muslim city dwellers   **D.** mostly English and Hausa

_____ **12.** Which statement best describes the Sahel?

    A. dry area with grasses and few trees

    B. wet Mediterranean climate

    C. coastal region

    D. mostly desert

_____ **13.** Which of these nations has one of the world's largest rain forests?

    A. Mauritania   **C.** Democratic Republic of the Congo

    B. Nigeria   **D.** Chad

_____ **14.** The Swahili language, Serengeti National Park, and Zanzibar are features of _____.

    A. the Central Africa Republic   **C.** Kenya

    B. Ghana   **D.** Tanzania

_____ **15.** Djibouti is strategically located at a narrow water passage that links the Red Sea and the _____.

    A. Persian Gulf   **C.** Suez Canal

    B. Gulf of Aqaba   **D.** Gulf of Aden

_____ **16.** From 1983 to 2004, this country experienced a civil war between the north and south.

    A. Tanzania   **C.** Sudan

    B. Uganda   **D.** Madagascar

_____ **17.** Which of the following events brought worldwide attention to Ethiopia in 1980?

    A. the breaking away of Eritrea

    B. founding the capital at Addis Ababa

    C. European attempts at control

    D. drought and famine

_____ **18.** Which is the major business center for all of East Africa?

    A. Nairobi   **C.** Johannesburg

    B. Mombasa   **D.** Khartoum

_____ **19.** Which of these countries was ruled by white Afrikaners until the 1990s?

    A. Democratic Republic of the Congo

    B. Union of South Africa

    C. Ethiopia

    D. Angola

_____ **20.** Which of the following recently caused disorder and violence in Zimbabwe?

    A. The government tried to turn farmland over to Africans.

    B. Factories closed, causing unemployment.

    C. Drought caused food shortages.

    D. Afrikaners tried to take over the government.

Applying Skills: Reading a Graph Use the graph below to answer the questions that follow. *(5 points each)*

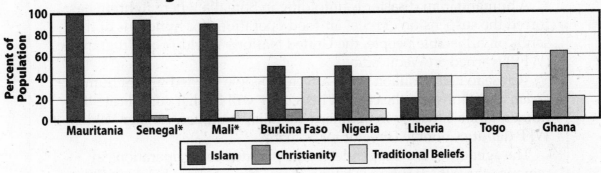

Religion in Selected Countries of West Africa

Islam   Christianity   Traditional Beliefs

Source: *CIA World Factbook, 2006.*

***Note:** 1 percent of Senegal's population practices traditional beliefs; 1 percent of Mali's population practices Christianity*

_____ **21.** In which of these countries is Christianity the main religion?

    A. Senegal   **C.** Togo

    B. Liberia   **D.** Ghana

_____ **22.** Which of these countries is entirely Muslim?

    A. Mauritania   **C.** Togo

    B. Nigeria   **D.** Liberia

_____ **23.** Which Sahel country has the most people who practice traditional religions?

    A. Mali   **C.** Burkina Faso

    B. Togo   **D.** Liberia

Directions: Document-Based Questions Use the document below to answer the questions that follow. *(5 points each)*

> A humanitarian disaster is unfolding in Somalia where fighting has forced the suspension of relief air food operations for hundreds of thousands of vulnerable people, the United Nations World Food Programme (WFP) warned on Wednesday.
>
> "Close to half a million flood-affected people needed urgent humanitarian assistance and the current insecurity will further complicate the humanitarian situation in Southern Somalia," said Leo van der Velden, WFP deputy Country Director for Somalia.
>
> The agency . . . has suspended some planned relief operations in regions where the fighting is taking place. The fighting, between Ethiopian-backed forces of the Transitional Federal Government (TFG) and the Union of Islamic Courts (UIC), entered its second week on Wednesday.
>
> **Source:** United Nations. www.irinnews.org/report.aspx?reportid=62911.

_____ 24. In which country was a humanitarian disaster developing as a result of flooding?

A. Ethiopia   **C.** Eritrea

B. Somalia   **D.** Kenya

_____ 25. Why did the United Nations suspend some planned relief operations?

A. flooding   **C.** fighting in the region

B. lack of funds   **D.** no cooperation from the government

_____ 26. According to this report, what difficulty faces the United Nations or other countries and agencies that try to aid some African countries?

A. internal conflict among ethnic and religious groups

B. lack of support from volunteers

C. lack of resources to meet the need

D. failure of some African governments to appeal for rescue workers

Directions: Essay On a separate sheet of paper, answer the question below. *(10 points)*

27. Describe three challenges facing the governments of countries of Africa south of the Sahara.

SCORE

Africa South of the Sahara Today

Chapter 21 Test Form B

Directions: Matching Match each item in Column A with its description in Column B. Write the correct letters in the blanks. *(3 points each)*

Column A

A. landlocked

B. Hutu and Tutsi

C. enclave

D. cacao

E. Mombasa

F. habitat

G. genocide

H. Ibo and Fulani

I. Afrikaner

J. Nairobi

Column B

_____ **1.** deliberate murder of a group of people because of their race or culture

_____ **2.** ethnic groups in Nigeria

_____ **3.** where a particular animal lives

_____ **4.** free market city of Kenya

_____ **5.** descendant of Dutch, German, or French

_____ **6.** people who fought a civil war in the 1990s

_____ **7.** country without a sea or an ocean border

_____ **8.** small territory inside a larger country

_____ **9.** tropical tree that produces chocolate

_____ **10.** a busy seaport in Kenya

Directions: Multiple Choice In the blank at the left, write the letter of the choice that best completes the statement or answers the question. *(3 points each)*

_____ **11.** Which of the following has the greatest direct effect on the economy of Nigeria?

A. the amount of rain that falls   **C.** the number of people moving to cities

B. a change in world oil prices   **D.** the decisions of its government

_____ **12.** What happened in Nigeria two years after it became independent in 1960?

A. Two million people died in a civil war.

B. Widespread famine struck the country.

C. The economy improved dramatically.

D. A president was elected.

_____ **13.** Coastal West Africa is an area of _____.

A. large deserts and small villages   **C.** grasslands and agriculture

B. forest preserves and tourism   **D.** growing cities and deforestation

_____ **14.** Which of these is the main reason for the growth of tourism in Tanzania?

    A. Serengeti National Park   **C.** large cities

    B. Lake Victoria   **D.** remains of ancient civilizations

_____ **15.** The largest country in Africa is _____.

    A. Nigeria   **C.** Somalia

    B. Sudan   **D.** Kenya

_____ **16.** Which name has been given to the northern part of East Africa?

    A. Swaziland   **C.** the Horn of Africa

    B. Afrikaner   **D.** the Sahel

_____ **17.** Which of these is the oldest independent nation in Africa and also where the ancient Christian kingdom of Axum existed?

    A. Liberia   **C.** Eritrea

    B. Ethiopia   **D.** Sudan

_____ **18.** Which country has the most highly developed economy in Africa?

    A. Somalia   **C.** Angola

    B. Madagascar   **D.** South Africa

_____ **19.** Which two countries are enclaves within South Africa?

    A. Lesotho and Swaziland   **C.** Malawi and Niger

    B. Zimbabwe and Zambia   **D.** Botswana and Togo

_____ **20.** Which of these is an island country?

    A. Malawi   **C.** Namibia

    B. Mauritius   **D.** Angola

Applying Skills: Reading a Map Use the map below to answer the questions that follow. *(5 points each)*

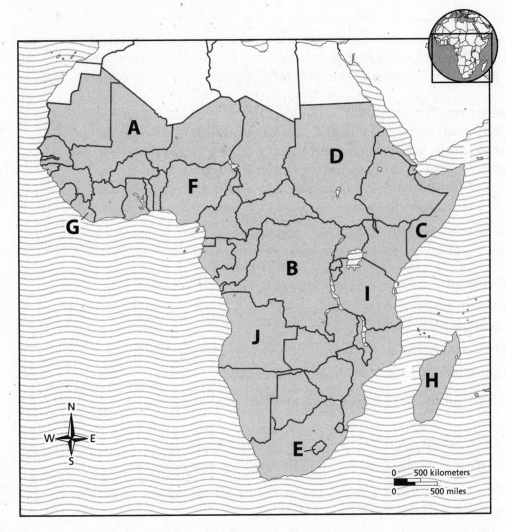

_____ **21.** Which country is signified by the letter *J*?

    A. Angola   **C.** Equatorial Guinea

    B. Namibia   **D.** Gabon

_____ **22.** Which country is signified by the letter *F*?

    A. Ghana   **C.** Nigeria

    B. Cameroon   **D.** Senegal

_____ **23.** Which country is signified by the letter *A*?

    A. Mali   **C.** Burkina Faso

    B. Mauritania   **D.** Niger

Directions: Document-Based Questions Use the document below to answer the questions that follow. *(5 points each)*

> The Maasai, or Masai, are a nomadic tribe who roam the land which covers the borders of Kenya and Tanzania. They live in temporary settlements called *kraals*, which house several families and their prize cattle herds.
>
> The Maasai are the equivalent of the lower classes in Kenya and are looked down upon by the inland and coastal populations. Their lifestyle is hard; for example, young men from the age of 14 upwards are sent out into the plains to live in solitude for eight months to two years. These years are spent building the courage, strength, and fighting skills that Maasai warriors are famous for.
>
> **Source:** www.bbc.co.uk/dna/h2g2/A517132.

_____ **24.** What is a kraal?

  A. a Maasai village

  B. a corral for prize cattle

  C. a permanent home in which families live with their cattle

  D. a temporary settlement for families and cattle

_____ **25.** The majority of the people in Kenya feel that the Maasai are _____.

  A. proud warriors   **C.** a lower class

  B. equal members of society   **D.** an untapped resource

_____ **26.** How does a young man, around the age of 14, spend up to two years of his life?

  A. in solitude   **C.** being educated in a city in Kenya

  B. raising cattle   **D.** roaming the land

Directions: Essay On a separate sheet of paper, answer the question below. *(10 points)*

  27. What are the main reasons for unrest in Rwanda and Burundi and for stability in Kenya and Tanzania?

SCORE

Directions: Matching Match each item in Column A with its description in Column B. Write the correct letters in the blanks. *(5 points each)*

Column A

A. apartheid

B. plateaus

C. Eritrea

D. 250

E. Kenya

F. life expectancy

G. 2,000–3,000

H. basins

I. Timbuktu

J. Akosombo Dam

Column B

_____ **1.** covers most of Africa south of the Sahara

_____ **2.** number of years people can expect to live

_____ **3.** has a democracy with free markets

_____ **4.** number of ethnic groups in Nigeria

_____ **5.** laws that limited rights of blacks

_____ **6.** low, sunken areas

_____ **7.** small Muslim country

_____ **8.** supplies hydroelectric power

_____ **9.** number of languages spoken in this region

_____ **10.** early Islamic center of trade

Directions: Multiple Choice Write the letter of the choice that best completes the statement or answers the question. *(5 points each)*

_____ **11.** Which was a chief goal of European colonial rule in Africa?

    A. to build strong economies   **C.** to provide slaves for Europe

    B. to unite ethnic groups   **D.** to get raw materials

_____ **12.** For Africans, this is one of the main expressions of a community's life.

    A. kente cloth   **C.** wealth

    B. dance   **D.** food

_____ **13.** Which is a natural wonder of East Africa?

    A. Great Rift Valley   **C.** Drakensberg Range

    B. Congo rain forest   **D.** Sphinx

_____ **14.** Which is the main cause of desertification in the Sahel?

    A. misuse of river water   **C.** overgrazing of livestock

    B. deforestation   **D.** grassfires

_____ **15.** Which of these has replaced agricultural products as the main export of many countries south of the Sahara?

    A. iron ore   **C.** oil

    B. silver   **D.** ivory

Applying Skills: Reading a Graph Use the graph below to answer the questions that follow. *(5 points each)*

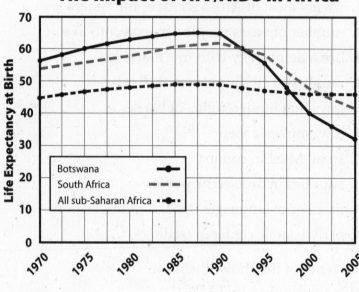

The Impact of HIV/AIDS in Africa

Source: World Health Organization. www.who.int/whr/2004/en/charts_en.pdf.

_____ **16.** Life expectancy in Botswana is _____ than the rest of Africa south of the Sahara.

    A. more than 10 years less   **C.** about the same

    B. slightly better   **D.** much better

_____ **17.** In about what year did the life expectancy of South Africa dip below that of the rest of the region?

    A. 2002   **C.** 1990

    B. 1995   **D.** 1980

_____ **18.** Since 1970, life expectancy for Africa south of the Sahara has _____.

    A. dropped by about 10 years   **C.** risen by about 15 years

    B. dropped by about 20 years   **D.** remained about the same

Directions: Essay On a separate sheet of paper, answer the question below. *(10 points)*

    19. Why does the death rate in Africa south of the Sahara remain high compared to other world regions?

SCORE

Directions: Matching Match each item in Column A with its description in Column B. Write the correct letters in the blanks. *(5 points each)*

Column A

A. India

B. Karakoram

C. Khyber Pass

D. highland

E. Everest

F. caste

G. Maldives

H. tropical wet

I. yak

J. Kashmir

Column B

_____ **1.** tallest mountain in the world

_____ **2.** climate along South Asia's northern edge

_____ **3.** valued animal in Tibet

_____ **4.** source of tension between Pakistan and India

_____ **5.** mountain system in South Asia

_____ **6.** social division in India

_____ **7.** global warming poses a particular danger here

_____ **8.** passageway used for centuries by caravans and conquering armies

_____ **9.** climate in Bangladesh and Sri Lanka

_____ **10.** country where farming is an important economic activity

Directions: Multiple Choice Write the letter of the choice that best completes the statement or answers the question. *(7 points each)*

_____ **11.** Which of the following did the people of South Asia accomplish thousands of years ago?

A. built two major cities, although the cities had no sewers or plumbing

B. developed two of the world's major religions

C. established the permanent Indus Valley civilization

D. created civilizations that had no concept of status

_____ **12.** Which major problem does Bangladesh face today?

A. drought

B. too few workers

C. severe poverty

D. dictatorship

_____ **13.** What form of government does India have?

A. military dictatorship

B. monarchy

C. oligarchy

D. federal republic

_____ **14.** Which problem is created by South Asia's growing population?

A. The universities are too crowded.

B. Not enough high-rise apartments have been built.

C. Land is used inefficiently.

D. The demand for food and fuel threatens the environment.

_____ **15.** India has shifted from a largely government-run economy toward a _____.

    A. free market economy   **C.** social economy

    B. capitalist system   **D.** communist system

Applying Skills: Reading a Map Use the map below to answer the questions that follow. *(5 points each)*

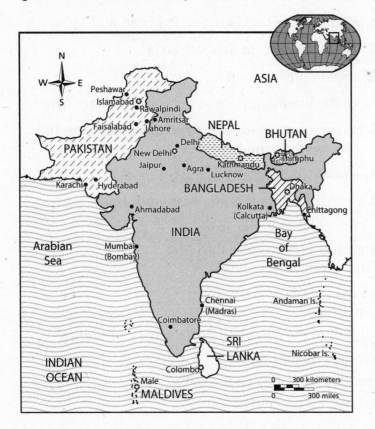

_____ **16.** The capital of Bhutan is _____.

    A. Faisalabad   **C.** Dhaka

    B. Delhi   **D.** Thimphu

_____ **17.** Which of the following is a union territory of India?

    A. Maldives   **C.** Nicobar

    B. Sri Lanka   **D.** Chennai

_____ **18.** Which city do you think hires many people for ship breaking?

    A. Chittagong   **C.** Agra

    B. Colombo   **D.** Male

SCORE

Directions: Matching Match each item in Column A with its description in Column B. Write the correct letters in the blanks. *(10 points each)*

Column A

A. salt water

B. tectonic plate movements

C. atolls

D. delta

E. air pollution

Column B

_____ **1.** soil deposits at the mouth of a river

_____ **2.** damaging the aquifers of Dhaka and Karachi

_____ **3.** many of Maldives's 1,300 islands

_____ **4.** cause of a brown cloud over the Indian Ocean

_____ **5.** causes the mountains of South Asia to grow taller every year

Directions: Short Answer Answer each question or statement below on the line provided. *(10 points each)*

6. How were the Hindu Kush, the Himalaya, and the Karakoram formed?

_____

7. In what three ways have South Asians depended on the Ganges, the Indus, and the Brahmaputra?

_____

8. How do the Western Ghats affect the climates of the Deccan Plateau and the Karnataka Plateau?

_____

9. What do most countries of South Asia rely on to meet their energy needs?

_____

10. What fuel do the people of Nepal rely on for heating and cooking? What does this fuel do to the land and air?

_____

Directions: Matching Match each item in Column A with its description in Column B. Write the correct letters in the blanks. *(10 points each)*

Column A

A. steppes

B. highlands

C. humid subtropical

D. cyclones

E. monsoons

Column B

_____ **1.** causes devastating floods in Bangladesh

_____ **2.** storms with high winds and heavy rains

_____ **3.** found along South Asia's northern edge

_____ **4.** surrounds the Thar Desert, except on the coast

_____ **5.** climate of the Ganges Plain

Directions: Short Answer Answer each question or statement below on the line provided. *(10 points each)*

6. What effect do the Himalaya have on monsoon winds during the wet season?

_____

7. How is Bangladesh's climate helpful and harmful to its crops?

_____

8. How do the tropical climates of south central India and southern Sri Lanka differ?

_____

9. How does the rainfall of eastern Pakistan compare with the rainfall of Bangladesh?

_____

10. Describe the temperature and vegetation above 16,000 feet.

_____

SCORE

Directions: Matching Match each item in Column A with its description in Column B. Write the correct letters in the blanks. *(3 points each)*

Column A

A. Himalaya

B. Africa

C. steppe

D. Deccan Plateau

E. limestone

F. chromite

G. Tibet

H. coral

I. Karnataka Plateau

J. Khyber Pass

Column B

_____ **1.** original location of Indian subcontinent

_____ **2.** blocks rain after it sweeps over the Ganges-Brahmaputra delta

_____ **3.** source of Indus River

_____ **4.** Western Ghats form a rain shadow in this area

_____ **5.** many of the Maldives are made of this

_____ **6.** surrounds the Thar Desert

_____ **7.** allowed people from the north to enter parts of South Asia

_____ **8.** mineral used in making steel

_____ **9.** elephants move through dense rain forests here

_____ **10.** ingredient for making cement

Directions: Multiple Choice In the blank at the left, write the letter of the choice that best completes the statement or answers the question. *(3 points each)*

_____ **11.** How many islands do people inhabit in the Maldives?

A. 1,300   **C.** 200

B. 700   **D.** 12

_____ **12.** To meet their energy needs, countries of South Asia rely heavily on ____.

A. imported coal   **C.** kerosene

B. hydroelectric power   **D.** imported oil

_____ **13.** All of the following are mountain systems along South Asia's northern border EXCEPT the ____.

A. Hindu Kush   **C.** Himalaya

B. Kunlan Shan   **D.** Karakoram

_____ **14.** The Khyber Pass is located between _____.

    A. Afghanistan and Pakistan   **C.** India and Sri Lanka

    B. Nepal and Bhutan   **D.** India and Nepal

_____ **15.** Which country has most of the region's mineral resources?

    A. Nepal   **C.** India

    B. Bangladesh   **D.** Sri Lanka

_____ **16.** Most of South Asia's forests were cut down _____.

    A. in the 1970s   **C.** centuries ago

    B. during British rule   **D.** in the 1980s

_____ **17.** How many seasons does much of South Asia experience?

    A. one   **C.** three

    B. two   **D.** four

_____ **18.** Which area of India has a tropical dry climate?

    A. south central   **C.** northwestern

    B. north central   **D.** southeastern

_____ **19.** The Deccan Plateau and western Pakistan _____.

    A. may receive little or no yearly rainfall

    B. may receive large amounts of rain

    C. lay inside the monsoon's path

    D. are vital to farmers in the region

_____ **20.** As one travels north to the Ganges Plain, the climate becomes _____.

    A. more dry

    B. less temperate

    C. humid and subtropical

    D. highland with little vegetation

Applying Skills: Reading a Chart Use the chart below to answer the questions that follow. *(5 points each)*

Environmental Concerns		
Water	**Deforestation**	**Air Pollution**
Supplies of freshwater are low because of the large number of people living in South Asia.	Only a small part of South Asia is forested.	Exhaust fumes from vehicles increase air pollution.
Farmers often use wasteful irrigation methods. In cities, water is wasted because __A__.	Forests are being cut down to provide building materials and __B__.	Many villagers cook and heat their homes by burning wood, kerosene, charcoal, or animal dung.
Water pollution caused by sewage, factory waste, and runoff from fertilizers is increasing.	Nepal and India have introduced programs at the local level to limit forest loss.	Air pollution from South Asia and Southeast Asia is so severe that a brown cloud has formed __C__.

_____ **21.** Which of the following best completes the statement labeled *B?*

    A. farming tools   **C.** more farmland

    B. prevent erosion   **D.** fuel

_____ **22.** Which of the following best completes statement *A?*

    A. animals consume large amounts of drinking water

    B. aquifers become polluted by salt water

    C. it is used for irrigation

    D. of old, leaky distribution pipes

_____ **23.** Which of the following best completes statement *C?*

    A. over the Indian Ocean

    B. and blocks 50 percent of sunlight

    C. over Nepal

    D. and made the region colder

Directions: Document-Based Questions Use the document below to answer the questions that follow. *(5 points each)*

> Three days after the cyclone hit southeast India, killing at least 1,000 people, the extent of the disaster was emerging. People cremated their loved ones in funeral pyres. . . . Survivors gathered wood and palm leaves to rebuild their homes. Navy helicopters spent a second day dropping rice, drinking water, medicine, and clothing to stranded people.
>
> The cyclone swirled in . . . from the Bay of Bengal with 112-mph winds and torrential rain, toppling mud dwellings and submerging roads and rails in 2 feet of water. . . . The government estimated more than 1,000 people died. A top state official said . . . that nearly 1,000 fishermen are missing at sea.
>
> **Source:** The Digital Kent State World View.
> dept.kent.edu/idl/digitalstater/Stories/111296w2k.html.

_____ 24. Approximately how many people are feared dead from this cyclone?

  A. 112   **C.** 10,000

  B. 1,000   **D.** 2,000

_____ 25. In which direction did the cyclone move?

  A. northwest   **C.** northeast

  B. southwest   **D.** southeast

_____ 26. What is a cyclone similar to?

  A. tornado   **C.** earthquake

  B. tsunami   **D.** hurricane

Directions: Essay On a separate sheet of paper, answer the question below. *(10 points)*

  27. How are monsoons both positive and negative in South Asia?

SCORE

Directions: Matching Match each item in Column A with its description in Column B. Write the correct letters in the blanks. *(3 points each)*

Column A

A. Ganges

B. hydroelectric plants

C. Eastern Ghats

D. Cherrapunji

E. brown cloud

F. cyclone

G. atoll

H. wood

I. Sri Lanka

J. Bangladesh

Column B

_____ **1.** formed from chemicals, ash, and dust

_____ **2.** source of 70 percent of Nepal's energy

_____ **3.** teardrop-shaped island

_____ **4.** struck India's northeast coast in 1999

_____ **5.** circular-shaped island

_____ **6.** helps control flooding in South Asia

_____ **7.** location of world's largest delta

_____ **8.** holy river in South Asia

_____ **9.** eroded coastal mountains

_____ **10.** one of the wettest spots on Earth

Directions: Multiple Choice In the blank at the left, write the letter of the choice that best completes the statement or answers the question. *(3 points each)*

_____ **11.** Which river flows through Pakistan?

    A. Ganges   **C.** Mekong

    B. Brahmaputra   **D.** Indus

_____ **12.** Approximately 60 million years ago, the South Asian subcontinent was part of ____.

    A. Africa   **C.** Europe

    B. South America   **D.** Central America

_____ **13.** South Asia is home to what percentage of the world's population?

    A. less than 15 percent   **C.** more than 20 percent

    B. more than 60 percent   **D.** less than 10 percent

_____ **14.** Where in South Asia is it possible to smell spices growing and see wild elephants?

    A. Hindu Kush   **C.** Maldives

    B. Karnataka Plateau   **D.** Khyber Pass

_____ **15.** About 40 percent of India's population lives _____.

    A. in the Ganges Plain   **C.** near the Eastern Ghats

    B. on the Deccan Plateau   **D.** in Kashmir

_____ **16.** Which major factor shapes the climate of South Asia?

    A. the Himalaya

    B. seasonal dry and wet winds

    C. currents in the Indian Ocean

    D. trade winds near the Tropic of Cancer

_____ **17.** During South Asia's cool season, monsoons blow _____.

    A. from the Bay of Bengal

    B. from the north and northeast

    C. from the Arabian Sea

    D. from the Persian Gulf

_____ **18.** Approximately how much rain does Bangladesh get per year?

    A. 25 inches   **C.** 100 inches

    B. 50 inches   **D.** 450 inches

_____ **19.** Where is the Thar Desert located?

    A. west of the Ganges River   **C.** west of the Indus River

    B. east of the Indus River   **D.** east of the Ganges River

_____ **20.** Which of the following features has a steppe climate?

    A. Ganges Plain   **C.** Kathmandu Valley

    B. Deccan Plateau   **D.** coast of Sri Lanka

Applying Skills: Reading a Map Use the map below to answer the questions that follow. *(5 points each)*

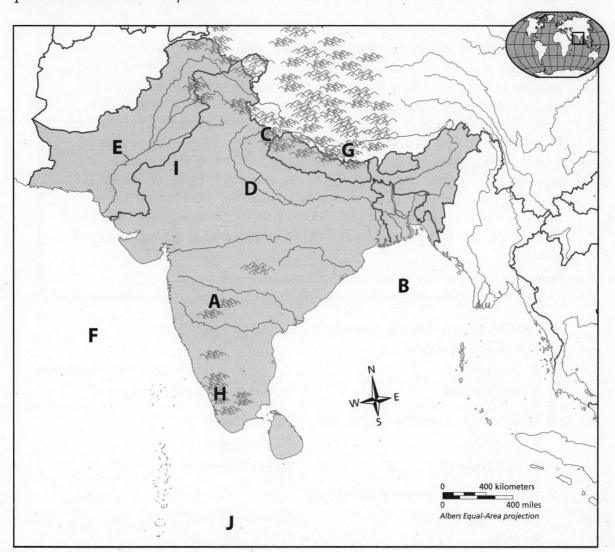

0 400 kilometers

0 400 miles

Albers Equal-Area projection

_____ **21.** Where is the letter *B* located?

    A. Arabian Sea   **C.** Strait of Malaysia

    B. Indian Ocean   **D.** Bay of Bengal

_____ **22.** What is the letter *D* pointing to?

    A. Ganges River   **C.** Indus River

    B. Brahmaputra River   **D.** Deccan River

_____ **23.** Which mountain range is signified by the letter *C?*

    A. Hindu Kush   **C.** Himalaya

    B. Karakoram   **D.** Eastern Ghats

Directions: Document-Based Questions Use the document below to answer the questions that follow. *(5 points each)*

> The Maldive Islands are a series of coral atolls built up from the crowns of a submerged ancient volcanic mountain range. All the islands are low-lying, none rising to more than 6 feet above sea level. Barrier reefs protect the islands from the destructive effects of monsoons. The rainy season, from May to August, is brought by the southwest monsoon. From December to March, the northeast monsoon brings dry and mild winds. The average temperature varies from 76° to 86°F. Rainfall averages about 84 inches per year. The atolls have sandy beaches, lagoons, and a luxuriant growth of coconut palms, together with breadfruit trees and tropical bushes. Fish abound in the reefs, lagoons, and seas adjoining the islands. Sea turtles are caught for food and for their oil, a traditional medicine.
>
> **Source:** *Encyclopaedia Britannica*, www.britannica.com/eb/article4497.

_____ **24.** Which of the following protects the Maldives from the effects of monsoons?

    A. barrier reefs   **C.** coconut palms and breadfruit trees

    B. coral atolls   **D.** volcanic mountain ranges

_____ **25.** From which direction do the wet monsoons come?

    A. southeast   **C.** northeast

    B. southwest   **D.** northwest

_____ **26.** What supports the coral Maldives?

    A. sandy beaches   **C.** coconut palms

    B. reefs   **D.** ancient volcanoes

Directions: Essay On a separate sheet of paper, answer the question below. *(10 points)*

    27. What causes air pollution in urban and rural areas of South Asia?

SCORE

Directions: Matching Match each item in Column A with its description in Column B. Write the correct letters in the blanks. *(10 points each)*

Column A

A. Ganges River Valley

B. Sri Lanka

C. Aryans

D. Indus River Valley

E. Moguls

Column B

_____ **1.** location of Asia's first cities

_____ **2.** nomadic herders who settled parts of South Asia around 1500 B.C.

_____ **3.** large area conquered by Chandragupta Maurya

_____ **4.** came from the mountains north of India to create an empire in South Asia

_____ **5.** Tamil groups are engaged in a civil war with the government of this country

Directions: Short Answer Answer each question or statement below on the line provided. *(10 points each)*

6. Describe the core teachings of the Buddha.

_____

7. How did Mohandas Gandhi and his followers use British goods to gain independence for the region?

_____

8. How do Nepal and Sri Lanka differ in regard to European rule?

_____

9. What were the four varnas of Aryan society?

_____

10. What were some achievements of the people of Harappa and Mohenjo Daro?

_____

SCORE

Directions: Matching Match each item in Column A with its description in Column B. Write the correct letters in the blanks. *(10 points each)*

Column A

A. Mumbai

B. sari

C. sitar

D. Bangladesh

E. Sherpa

Column B

_____ **1.** South Asia's most densely populated nation

_____ **2.** Indian city formerly known as Bombay

_____ **3.** with ancestors from Tibet, one of the best-known ethnic groups in South Asia

_____ **4.** long-necked instrument that gives Indian music a distinctive sound

_____ **5.** a long, rectangular piece of cloth that is draped gracefully around the body

Directions: Short Answer Answer each question or statement below on the line provided. *(10 points each)*

6. In recent years, what technological advances have raised the living standards in Pakistan and India?

_____

7. How is family structure similar in India and Pakistan?

_____

8. What types of meats do Hindus, Muslims, and Jains avoid? Why?

_____

9. Why is Mumbai sometimes called Bollywood?

_____

10. How do the homes of upper- and middle-class people differ from those of poor people in South Asia?

_____

Directions: Matching Match each item in Column A with its description in Column B. Write the correct letters in the blanks. *(3 points each)*

Column A

A. Bengali

B. East India Company

C. Mumbai

D. Mohandas Gandhi

E. sari

F. *Mahabharata*

G. Akbar

H. Kashmir

I. Urdu

J. Jains

Column B

_____ **1.** traditional Indian garment

_____ **2.** area fought over by India and Pakistan

_____ **3.** greatest Mogul ruler

_____ **4.** long sacred text

_____ **5.** Pakistan's official language

_____ **6.** official language of Bangladesh

_____ **7.** followed a policy of nonviolent civil disobedience

_____ **8.** built trading posts in India during the 1600s

_____ **9.** "Bollywood"

_____ **10.** reject all violence and aim to protect every living creature

Directions: Multiple Choice In the blank at the left, write the letter of the choice that best completes the statement or answers the question. *(3 points each)*

_____ **11.** Why are some houses in South Asia built on stilts?

    A. to make theft more difficult for criminals

    B. to protect against flooding

    C. to guard against wild animals

    D. to save construction costs

_____ **12.** Which of the following were South Asia's first cities?

    A. Indus and Alladino

    B. Harappa and Mohenjo Daro

    C. Harappa and Lothan

    D. Alladino and Somnath

_____ **13.** Nomadic herders who settled parts of northern South Asia in the 1500s B.C. were the _____ .

    A. Moguls

    B. Mauryans

    C. Guptas

    D. Aryans

_____ **14.** Why did the death rate rise in South Asia during the late 1800s?

    A. severe famines   **C.** major wars and other armed conflicts

    B. flu epidemic   **D.** a drop in the birthrate

_____ **15.** In 1947 India was divided into which two independent countries?

    A. India and Pakistan   **C.** India and Nepal

    B. India and Bangladesh   **D.** India and Bhutan

_____ **16.** Approximately how many people live in South Asia?

    A. nearly 1.5 billion   **C.** 2.5 billion

    B. more than 2 billion   **D.** nearly 3.5 billion

_____ **17.** How many urban areas in South Asia have more than 12 million people?

    A. four   **C.** six

    B. five   **D.** seven

_____ **18.** Why are the Sherpa often hired to guide climbing expeditions or to carry supplies?

    A. They are a strong ethnic group.

    B. They know the mountains of Pakistan well.

    C. They work for low wages.

    D. They have remarkable endurance in high altitudes.

_____ **19.** Which religion is the most widely practiced in South Asia?

    A. Hinduism   **C.** Sikhism

    B. Islam   **D.** Buddhism

_____ **20.** In the Bhagavad Gita, what is the deity Krishna doing?

    A. bestowing blessings on those who believe in him

    B. preaching a sermon before a battle

    C. asking his followers to help the sick and less fortunate

    D. reminding his followers to believe in him so they will be reincarnated

Applying Skills: Reading a Map Use the map below to answer the questions that follow. *(5 points each)*

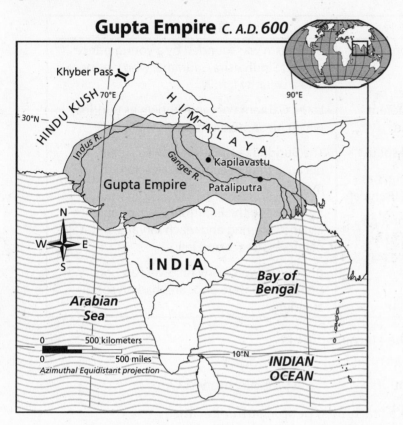

Gupta Empire C. A.D. 600

_____ **21.** The Gupta ruler chose the site of Pataliputra as his capital for all of the following reasons EXCEPT _____.

   A. it was easily defended in its Himalaya location

   B. most of the population lived near the Ganges River

   C. the ruler could easily control the empire from there

   D. it was located along a trade route for goods

_____ **22.** Natural barriers that protected the Gupta Empire's boundaries included _____.

   A. navigable rivers   **C.** the Bay of Bengal

   B. mountains and plateaus   **D.** the Arabian Sea

_____ **23.** During the Gupta Empire, mathematicians developed a system of abstract calculation that they eventually named *al-jabr w'al-muqabal-ah.* What do we call this system today?

   A. calculus   **C.** geometry

   B. trigonometry   **D.** algebra

Directions: Document-Based Questions Use the document below to answer the questions that follow. *(5 points each)*

Hinduism	Buddhism
• Hinduism is the third-largest religion in the world today. • Hindus worship thousands of deities, but they view these deities as being different parts of only one eternal spirit. • Brahman is the name of the eternal spirit. • Hindus believe that every living being has a soul that wants to be reunited with Brahman. • Hindus believe that a soul passes through many lives before it is pure enough to be reunited with Brahman. This is known as *reincarnation*.	• Buddhism was founded by a young prince named Siddhartha Gautama, who was born into a wealthy family. • Later, Gautama became known as Buddha, which means "Enlightened One." • The Buddha taught that people suffer because they become too attached to material things. • By following the Eightfold Path, people escape suffering and reach nirvana, a state of endless peace and joy. • Buddhism won many followers among people who were poor and had no social standing.

_____ **24.** Hindus believe that the eternal spirit is _____.

    A. Brahman   **C.** Buddha

    B. Gautama   **D.** "Enlightened One"

_____ **25.** According to Buddha's teachings, people suffer because _____.

    A. they are not wealthy   **C.** others are unkind to them

    B. they become too attached to material things   **D.** they do not hold high status in the community

_____ **26.** Why do Hindus believe that a soul reincarnates?

    A. A soul needs many lives to worship all of the deities in the Hindu religion.

    B. It takes time for some people to become aware of and learn about Hinduism.

    C. It takes many lives to follow the Eightfold Path.

    D. A soul needs to pass through many lives in order to become pure.

Directions: Essay On a separate sheet of paper, answer the question below. *(10 points)*

    27. How did Bangladesh become an independent country?

SCORE

Directions: Matching Match each item in Column A with its description in Column B. Write the correct letters in the blanks. *(3 points each)*

Column A

A. Aśoka

B. Brahman

C. Sikhism

D. Buddha

E. Mumbai

F. *jati*

G. sitar

H. Holi

I. Indus Valley

J. nirvana

Column B

_____ **1.** Indian festival during which people welcome the coming of spring

_____ **2.** common instrument in South Asia

_____ **3.** eternal spirit of Hinduism

_____ **4.** state of endless peace and joy

_____ **5.** teaches belief in one God

_____ **6.** South Asian word for caste

_____ **7.** Mauryan ruler dedicated to peace

_____ **8.** center of film industry in India

_____ **9.** location of South Asia's first cities

_____ **10.** Siddhartha Gautama

Directions: Multiple Choice In the blank at the left, write the letter of the choice that best completes the statement or answers the question. *(3 points each)*

_____ **11.** What is believed to have caused the downfall of Harappa and Mohenjo Daro?
  A. Earthquakes and floods damaged the cities.
  B. Many people left the area to form other, newer civilizations.
  C. Plumbing, sewers, and other technology stopped working.
  D. The civilizations were attacked and destroyed by enemies.

_____ **12.** The holy texts called the Vedas were written in ____.
  A. Latin   **C.** Urdu
  B. Bengali   **D.** Sanskrit

_____ **13.** By the mid-1800s, who was the dominant power in South Asia?
  A. Moguls   **C.** British
  B. Mauryans   **D.** Hindus

_____ **14.** Who practiced a nonviolent independence movement?

   A. Siddhartha Gautama   **C.** Mohandas Gandhi

   B. Chandragupta Maurya   **D.** Aśoka

_____ **15.** During colonial times, Sri Lanka was known as ____.

   A. Karachi   **C.** Kolkata

   B. Harappa   **D.** Ceylon

_____ **16.** Which South Asian nation is the most densely populated?

   A. Bangladesh   **C.** Pakistan

   B. India   **D.** Nepal

_____ **17.** Which technological advance has boosted farm incomes in Pakistan?

   A. more efficient farm machinery

   B. better fertilizers

   C. expanded irrigation system

   D. computers to better track crop sales

_____ **18.** How many major languages are spoken in South Asia?

   A. 15   **C.** 30

   B. 19   **D.** hundreds

_____ **19.** The Taj Mahal in Agra, India, was built by a Muslim ruler as ____.

   A. a gathering place for his people

   B. a monument to his reign

   C. a tomb for his beloved wife

   D. a place of worship

_____ **20.** Which country recently limited its monarchy's power?

   A. Nepal   **C.** Sri Lanka

   B. Bhutan   **D.** Tibet

Applying Skills: Reading a Chart Use the chart below to answer the questions that follow. *(5 points each)*

Early India's Social System

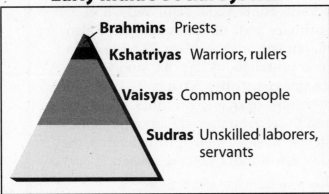

Brahmins Priests

Kshatriyas Warriors, rulers

Vaisyas Common people

Sudras Unskilled laborers, servants

_____ **21.** Which social group was made up of warriors and rulers?

    A. Kshatriyas   **C.** Brahmins

    B. Sudras   **D.** Vaisyas

_____ **22.** Which group had the largest number of people?

    A. Brahmins   **C.** Vaisyas

    B. Kshatriyas   **D.** Sudras

_____ **23.** What were these levels of society called?

    A. *varnas*   **C.** dharma

    B. *jati*   **D.** castes

Name_____ Date_____ Class_____

Directions: Document-Based Questions Use the document below to answer the questions that follow. *(5 points each)*

> There are four Vedas: the Rig Veda, Sama Veda, Yajur Veda, and Atharva Veda. The Vedas are the primary texts of Hinduism. They also had a vast influence on Buddhism, Jainism, and Sikhism. The Rig Veda, the oldest of the four Vedas, was composed about 1500 B.C. and was probably committed to writing at some point after 300 B.C.
>
> The Vedas contain hymns and rituals from ancient India. Along with the *Book of the Dead*, the *I Ching*, and the *Avesta*, they are among the most ancient religious texts still in existence. Besides their spiritual value, they also give a unique view of everyday life in India 4,000 years ago.
>
> **Source:** Adapted from *Internet Sacred Text Archive.* www.sacred-texts.com/hin/index.htm.

_____ **24.** Which of the Vedas is the oldest?

    A. Yajur Veda   **C.** Rig Veda

    B. Sama Veda   **D.** Atharva Veda

_____ **25.** The Vedas include ____.

    A. rituals and a description of daily life

    B. a method for preserving a body after death

    C. information on how to live a long life

    D. the *I Ching*

_____ **26.** Which of the following religions did the Vedas heavily influence?

    A. Buddhism   **C.** Protestantism

    B. Catholicism   **D.** Christianity

Directions: Essay On a separate sheet of paper, answer the question below. *(10 points)*

    27. What problems do people who live in urban areas in South Asia experience?

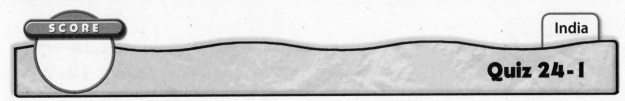

Directions: Matching Match each item in Column A with its description in Column B. Write the correct letters in the blanks. *(10 points each)*

Column A

A. green revolution

B. Council of States

C. cottage industries

D. People's Assembly

E. union territories

Column B

_____ **1.** seven small political areas directly under the control of the Indian government

_____ **2.** members of this group are directly elected by Indian voters

_____ **3.** members of this group are chosen by the prime minister or state legislatures

_____ **4.** set of changes that modernized agriculture and increased food production

_____ **5.** people working in their homes, using their own equipment to make goods

Directions: Short Answer Answer each question or statement below on the line provided. *(10 points each)*

6. Why do many American businesses outsource work to India?

_____

7. How is India's government based on the separation of powers?

_____

8. How is India's economy today different from its economy in the 1970s? What brought about this change?

_____

9. How did India modernize its agriculture?

_____

10. What natural resources support India's economy?

_____

SCORE

Directions: Matching Match each item in Column A with its description in Column B. Write the correct letters in the blanks. *(10 points each)*

Column A

A. Afghanistan

B. Pakistan

C. cotton cloth and clothing

D. clothing and ship breaking

E. Bangladesh

Column B

_____ **1.** two of Pakistan's major exports

_____ **2.** country surrounded on three sides by India

_____ **3.** Pakistan helped the United States overthrow this country's government

_____ **4.** about half of this country's people are farmers

_____ **5.** two profitable industries in Bangladesh

Directions: Short Answer Answer each question or statement below on the line provided. *(10 points each)*

6. What issues do Bangladesh and Pakistan dispute with India?

_____

7. Why is it difficult for Bangladesh to build a successful nation?

_____

8. Why, despite favorable growing conditions, is Bangladesh unable to feed its growing population?

_____

9. How do millions of Pakistani workers escape poverty?

_____

10. What occurrences in Pakistan show that the country has a limited democracy?

_____

Mountain Kingdoms, Island Republics

Quiz 24-3

Directions: Matching Match each item in Column A with its description in Column B. Write the correct letters in the blanks. *(10 points each)*

Column A

A. Bhutan

B. tourism

C. Kathmandu

D. farming

E. Colombo

Column B

_____ **1.** capital and only major city of Nepal

_____ **2.** major part of Nepal's economy

_____ **3.** the Himalaya are this country's major landform

_____ **4.** largest city in Sri Lanka

_____ **5.** largest industry in Maldives

Directions: Short Answer Answer each question or statement below on the line provided. *(10 points each)*

6. Why is Bhutan's tourist industry limited by the government?

_____

7. In Bhutan, what is the conflict between the Bhutia and the Nepali?

_____

8. How does the major religion of Maldives differ from the religions of Nepal, Bhutan, and Sri Lanka?

_____

9. Why might some people in the Maldives be worried about global warming?

_____

10. What two groups have fought a civil war in Sri Lanka since 1983? Why are they fighting?

_____

SCORE

Directions: Matching Match each item in Column A with its description in Column B. Write the correct letters in the blanks. *(3 points each)*

Column A

A. Jawaharlal Nehru

B. Council of States

C. Dhaka

D. People's Assembly

E. Indira Gandhi

F. Sinhalese

G. state governments

H. Bhutan

I. Kathmandu

J. Bengaluru

Column B

_____ **1.** form about 74 percent of Sri Lanka's population

_____ **2.** first prime minister of India

_____ **3.** capital of Nepal

_____ **4.** capital of Bangladesh

_____ **5.** city that provides outsourced computer software services

_____ **6.** prime minister of India until assassination in 1984

_____ **7.** government limits tourists here

_____ **8.** smaller house of India's legislature

_____ **9.** larger house of India's legislature

_____ **10.** carries out energy policies in India

Directions: Multiple Choice In the blank at the left, write the letter of the choice that best completes the statement or answers the question. *(3 points each)*

_____ **11.** Pakistan is a long, wide country wedged among ____.

    A. Iran, India, and Nepal

    B. Bhutan, Nepal, and Bangladesh

    C. Sri Lanka, India, and Nepal

    D. Afghanistan, Iran, and India

_____ **12.** Which of the following is the world's largest democracy?

    A. Pakistan   **C.** Bangladesh

    B. Nepal   **D.** India

_____ **13.** When was the country of Bangladesh established?

    A. 1968   **C.** 1970

    B. 1969   **D.** 1971

_____ **14.** Nepal faces all of these challenges EXCEPT _____.

    A. floods   **C.** declining tourism industry

    B. political conflict   **D.** lack of roads and airports

_____ **15.** How many states does India have?

    A. 28   **C.** 7

    B. 32   **D.** 29

_____ **16.** The executive power in India's government lies with the _____.

    A. president   **C.** Council of States

    B. prime minister   **D.** Supreme Court

_____ **17.** In contrast to the U.S. Bill of Rights, India's constitution includes the right to _____.

    A. free speech   **C.** practice any religion

    B. preserve local languages   **D.** vote

_____ **18.** When did the "green revolution" begin?

    A. in the 1940s   **C.** in the 1970s

    B. in the 1950s   **D.** in the 1980s

_____ **19.** In 2001 what did General Pervez Musharraf do?

    A. He survived two assassination attempts.

    B. He forced elected leaders out of office in Pakistan.

    C. He helped the United States overthrow the Taliban in Afghanistan.

    D. He helped the United States strengthen relations with India.

_____ **20.** Which country is a main supplier of forces for United Nations peacekeeping missions?

    A. Nepal   **C.** Pakistan

    B. India   **D.** Bangladesh

Applying Skills: Reading a Graph Use the graph below to answer the questions that follow. *(5 points each)*

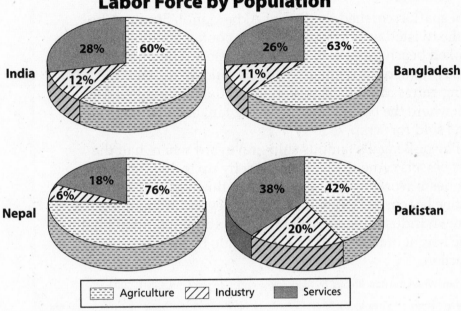

Labor Force by Population

India: 28%, 60%, 12%
Bangladesh: 26%, 63%, 11%
Nepal: 18%, 76%, 6%
Pakistan: 38%, 42%, 20%

Agriculture   Industry   Services

_____ **21.** Which country has the least manufacturing?

    A. India   **C.** Nepal

    B. Bangladesh   **D.** Pakistan

_____ **22.** About 60 percent of India's income is derived from services. What percentage of India's people are employed in service industries?

    A. 28 percent   **C.** 60 percent

    B. 76 percent   **D.** 12 percent

_____ **23.** Pakistan's population is about 163 million. About how many people work in industry in Pakistan?

    A. 16 million   **C.** 42 million

    B. 32 million   **D.** 63 million

Directions: Document-Based Questions Use the document below to answer the questions that follow. *(5 points each)*

> A shower of sparks scorched the face of Akbar Jamil. Stunned, he slipped from the twisted wreckage of the huge container ship onto the smoke-choked beach more than six metres below. The 19-year-old checked his body for serious damage. Then he quickly rejoined the chanting cutting gangs at his workstation in Chittagong's colossal ship-breaking yard, where the bodies of oceangoing tankers and liners are dismantled and sold for scrap.
>
> This is the Bay of Bengal's famous ship graveyard where half the world's largest vessels come to die, torn apart by up to 100,000 impoverished Bangladeshi workers. Just 15 years ago, this was a 20-kilometre stretch of pristine beach, but today it is scarred beyond recognition; an oily, debris-strewn industrial zone where almost 100 ships—potential death traps the height of tower blocks—stand side by side in progressive stages of dissection.
>
> **Source:** Adapted from "When the Bow Breaks" by Mark Townsend. *Geographical,* July 1, 2002.

_____ **24.** Where do the activities described in the excerpt take place?

    A. Bangladesh   **C.** Pakistan

    B. India   **D.** Sri Lanka

_____ **25.** Approximately how many workers break up ships in this shipyard?

    A. 19   **C.** 100

    B. 20   **D.** 100,000

_____ **26.** What sorts of ships are brought to Chittagong to be dismantled?

    A. container ships   **C.** private schooners

    B. sailing vessels   **D.** tugboats

Directions: Essay On a separate sheet of paper, answer the question below. *(10 points)*

    27. Why do American businesses outsource jobs to India? What types of jobs are outsourced to Indian workers?

SCORE

Directions: Matching Match each item in Column A with its description in Column B. Write the correct letters in the blanks. *(3 points each)*

Column A

A. Maldives

B. jute

C. Bangladesh

D. Pakistan

E. Nepal

F. New Delhi

G. Bhutia

H. Sri Lanka

I. India

J. malnutrition

Column B

_____ **1.** plant fiber used to make rope and carpet backing

_____ **2.** exports sapphires, rubies, and other gemstones

_____ **3.** tensions are high between this group and the smaller Nepali group

_____ **4.** problem affecting many people in Bangladesh

_____ **5.** landscape includes 8 of the world's 10 highest mountains

_____ **6.** diamonds are mined here

_____ **7.** its beaches and coral formations attract many tourists

_____ **8.** capital of India

_____ **9.** government here maintains control of banks, hospitals, and transportation

_____ **10.** large reserves of natural gas were recently discovered here

Directions: Multiple Choice In the blank at the left, write the letter of the choice that best completes the statement or answers the question. *(3 points each)*

_____ **11.** Along its border with India, Bhutan's physical geography includes ____.

    A. the Himalaya   **C.** plains and river valleys

    B. the Karakoram   **D.** thick forests

_____ **12.** India is a federal republic, which means power is shared between ____.

    A. the national government and state governments

    B. the executive, legislative, and judicial branches

    C. city governments and state governments

    D. the executive branch and the legislature

_____ **13.** Which of these is a thriving industry in Bangladesh?

    A. clothing   **C.** coal mining

    B. deep-sea fishing   **D.** food processing

_____ **14.** India has seven small political areas that are directly under the control of the national government. What are these areas called?

    A. united territories   **C.** union territories

    B. state territories   **D.** city territories

_____ **15.** Which is a famous export from Sri Lanka?

    A. rubber   **C.** cement

    B. tea   **D.** coconut oil

_____ **16.** Why did Indira Gandhi, who was prime minister of India for many years, leave office?

    A. She turned the office over to her father, Jawaharlal Nehru.

    C. She turned the office over to her daughter.

    B. She lost the election.

    D. She was assassinated.

_____ **17.** Which country could be said to form a steep stairway to the Himalaya?

    A. Bhutan   **C.** Sri Lanka

    B. Nepal   **D.** Pakistan

_____ **18.** Although India's economy is growing, why do many of its citizens remain very poor?

    A. Many people in India choose to farm.

    B. The government controls the economy and wages.

    C. Much of the economy depends on the fishing industry.

    D. India has a large population with too few jobs.

_____ **19.** As part of the "green revolution,"_____.

    A. new strains of wheat and rice were developed

    B. farming became a secondary industry to deep-sea fishing

    C. businesses were told to restore the land after coal mining

    D. dams were removed so that farmlands could be irrigated more efficiently

_____ **20.** Why, in the past, has Pakistan had trouble with India?

    A. Both Pakistan and India claim the territory of Kashmir.

    B. Neither country wants responsibility for the territory of Kashmir.

    C. Pakistan and India have fought over nuclear technology.

    D. Sikh extremists from Pakistan have attacked India.

Applying Skills: Reading a Map Use the map below to answer the questions that follow. *(5 points each)*

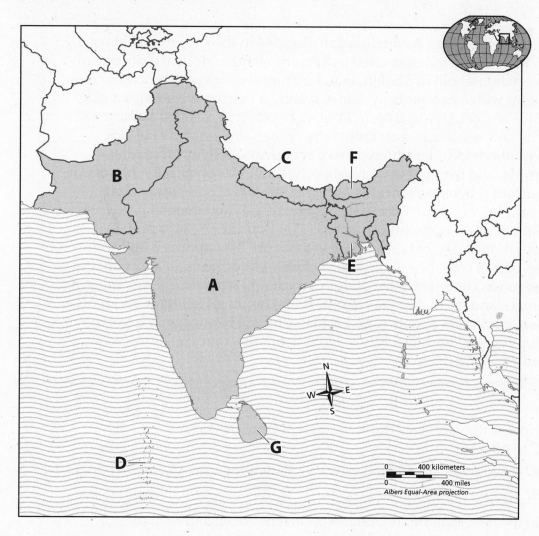

0 400 kilometers
0 400 miles
Albers Equal-Area projection

_____ **21.** Which country is signified by the letter *B*?
    A. Nepal   **C.** Kashmir
    B. Bangladesh   **D.** Pakistan

_____ **22.** In which lettered country were more than 30,000 people killed by a tsunami in 2004?
    A. A   **C.** D
    B. G   **D.** E

_____ **23.** Which lettered country is home to Mount Everest?
    A. A   **C.** C
    B. B   **D.** F

Directions: **Document-Based Questions** Use the document below to answer the questions that follow. *(5 points each)*

> Bhutan is a South Asian monarchy located in the eastern Himalaya. In 2005 King Wangchuk instituted a dramatic change. He sent a document to every household in Bhutan. In it, he proposed a new, democratic constitution with a two-party system. Creating a new constitution is a risky step for any country to take. In Bhutan, however, it is revolutionary.
>
> The new constitution insures many of the same rights as the U.S. Constitution: life, liberty, freedom of speech and religion, freedom of the press, and the right to own property. Bhutan's constitution has one significant difference, however. Whereas the U.S. Constitution demands a separation of "church and state," many of the fundamental principles of Bhutan's new constitution are based on Buddhist beliefs. Bhutan's constitution states that its purpose is to secure the happiness and well-being of everyone, one of the basic beliefs of Buddhism. In addition, the constitution comprises a list of duties for its citizens, such as encouraging tolerance and mutual respect of others and helping victims of accidents. It also encourages people to be pacifists and not to engage in terrorism or corruption—all Buddhist ideals. No other democratic constitutions are based on such principles.

_____ **24.** How is Bhutan's constitution different from the U.S. Constitution?
   A. It separates church and state.   **C.** It allows people to own property.
   B. It ensures freedom of speech.   **D.** It is based on religion.

_____ **25.** In the new constitution, Bhutan's citizens are encouraged to _____.
   A. run for office   **C.** vote
   B. be pacifists   **D.** be happy

_____ **26.** What does the word *revolutionary* mean in this excerpt?
   A. risky   **C.** radical
   B. rebellious   **D.** violent

Directions: **Essay** On a separate sheet of paper, answer the question below. *(10 points)*

   27. What is life like for the people of Bangladesh?

Directions: Matching Match each item in Column A with its description in Column B. Write the correct letters in the blanks. *(5 points each)*

Column A

A. 1971

B. 1983

C. Hindi

D. 200

E. 70 percent

F. 869

G. "Song of the Lord"

H. Sanskrit

I. Bangladesh

J. 85 percent

Column B

_____ **1.** number of inhabited islands in Maldives

_____ **2.** number of people per square mile in India

_____ **3.** Bhagavad Gita

_____ **4.** the "youngster" of South Asia

_____ **5.** year that East Pakistan declared its independence

_____ **6.** language spoken by about half of India's people

_____ **7.** amount of energy used in Nepal that comes from burning wood

_____ **8.** spoken language developed by the Aryans

_____ **9.** percentage of Nepal's population that lives in rural villages

_____ **10.** year that civil war began in Sri Lanka

Directions: Multiple Choice Write the letter of the choice that best completes the statement or answers the question. *(5 points each)*

_____ **11.** In which year did Pakistan and India test nuclear weapons?

A. 2001

B. 2005

C. 1998

D. 2000

_____ **12.** Why do Hindus not eat beef?

A. Cows are scarce.

B. Cows are unclean.

C. Cows are sacred.

D. Hindus do not eat any meat.

_____ **13.** Where are monsoon rains heaviest?

A. eastern South Asia

B. western South Asia

C. northern South Asia

D. southern South Asia

_____ **14.** Most of India's industrial goods come from ____.

A. cottage industries

B. trade with other countries

C. imports

D. factories

_____ **15.** According to the Buddha, people suffer because they are ____.

A. basically evil

B. too attached to material things

C. frail

D. weak willed

Applying Skills: Reading a Graph Use the graph below to answer the questions that follow. *(5 points each)*

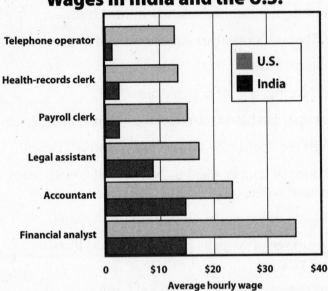

Wages in India and the U.S.

Telephone operator

Health-records clerk

Payroll clerk

Legal assistant

Accountant

Financial analyst

U.S.
India

0    $10 $20 $30 $40

Average hourly wage

Source: Fisher Center for Real Estate and Urban Economics, University of California, Berkeley.

_____ **16.** What is the average hourly wage of a financial analyst in the U.S.?

A. $15 per hour

B. $35 per hour

C. $21 per hour

D. $12 per hour

_____ **17.** For what two kinds of work are hourly wages approximately the same in India?

A. legal assistant and health-records clerk

B. telephone operator and payroll clerk

C. accountant and financial analyst

D. legal assistant and financial analyst

_____ **18.** Approximately how much more per hour does an American health-records clerk earn than an Indian health-records clerk?

A. $20 more per hour

B. $6 more per hour

C. $15 more per hour

D. $10 more per hour

Directions: Essay On a separate sheet of paper, answer the question below. *(10 points)*

19. What benefits did the Gupta Empire's Hindu rulers bring to South Asia and to the world?

Name_____ Date_____ Class_____

Directions: Matching Match each item in Column A with its description in Column B. Write the correct letters in the blanks. *(5 points each)*

Column A

A. loess

B. woodblock printing

C. Beijing

D. intensive agriculture

E. Manila

F. Asian Tiger

G. geisha

H. *dzud*

I. *anime*

J. Hong Kong

Column B

_____ **1.** Japanese style of animation

_____ **2.** Chinese invention

_____ **3.** country with a strong economy in East Asia

_____ **4.** capital of China

_____ **5.** soil carried by the Huang He

_____ **6.** dry summer followed by a harsh winter in Mongolia

_____ **7.** growing crops on all available land

_____ **8.** large city in the Philippines

_____ **9.** city that became part of China in the 1990s

_____ **10.** a symbol of Japan

Directions: Multiple Choice Write the letter of the choice that best completes the statement or answers the question. *(7 points each)*

_____ **11.** Southeast Asia is bordered by the _____.

A. Atlantic and Pacific Oceans
C. Mediterranean Sea and Bay of Bengal
B. Sea of Japan and Pacific Ocean
D. Indian and Pacific Oceans

_____ **12.** Most of Mongolia and northern China have which kind of climate?

A. steppe
C. highlands
B. humid subtropical
D. humid continental

_____ **13.** How many people live in China?

A. 1 billion
C. 1.6 billion
B. 1.3 billion
D. 1.9 billion

_____ **14.** Which of these countries has never had a Communist government?

A. North Korea
C. China
B. Japan
D. Vietnam

_____ **15.** Which is the major religion of Southeast Asia?

A. Hinduism
C. Buddhism
B. Daoism
D. Christianity

Applying Skills: Reading a Graph Use the graph below to answer the questions that follow. *(5 points each)*

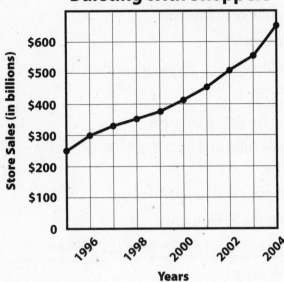

Bursting With Shoppers

Store Sales (in billions)

$600
$500
$400
$300
$200
$100
0

1996 1998 2000 2002 2004

Years

Source: Access Asia; TIME Research.

_____ **16.** How much money did people spend in Chinese retail stores in 2004?

    A. $200 billion   **C.** more than $600 billion

    B. almost $400 billion   **D.** more than $800 billion

_____ **17.** How does the amount spent in Chinese retail stores in 2004 compare to the amount spent in 1997?

    A. The amount doubled.   **C.** The amount quadrupled.

    B. The amount tripled.   **D.** The amount is the same.

_____ **18.** Which conclusion can you draw from the graph?

    A. Chinese incomes are decreasing.   **C.** Chinese imports are increasing.

    B. Chinese exports are increasing.   **D.** China's economy is improving.

Name_____ Date_____ Class_____

SCORE

Physical Features

Quiz 25-1

Directions: Matching Match each item in Column A with its description in Column B. Write the correct letters in the blanks. *(10 points each)*

Column A

A. Plateau of Tibet

B. Strait of Malacca

C. Chang Jiang

D. Ring of Fire

E. Huang He

Column B

_____ **1.** plate movements cause earthquakes and volcanic eruptions here

_____ **2.** northern China's main river system

_____ **3.** called the Roof of the World because of its high elevation

_____ **4.** makes Singapore one of the busiest shipping ports in the world

_____ **5.** important trade route in China

Directions: Short Answer Answer each question or statement below on the line provided. *(10 points each)*

6. How did Japan's physical features affect the development of its culture?

_____

7. What does the Mekong region in Vietnam provide for the country?

_____

8. How do Brunei and the Korean Peninsula differ in energy resources?

_____

9. Describe the location and landforms of the East Asia and Southeast Asia region.

_____

10. What are two uses for the teak harvested in Myanmar and mahogany from the Philippines?

_____

SCORE

Directions: Matching Match each item in Column A with its description in Column B. Write the correct letters in the blanks. *(10 points each)*

Column A

A. *dzud*

B. highland

C. humid continental

D. typhoons

E. Gobi

Column B

_____ **1.** Mongolian word meaning "place without water"

_____ **2.** hurricane-like storms that form in the Pacific and blow across coastal East Asia

_____ **3.** Mongolian word for a dry summer followed by a harsh winter

_____ **4.** climate zone of southwestern China and the Plateau of Tibet

_____ **5.** climate zone of northeastern China, the northern part of the Korean Peninsula, and northern Japan

Directions: Short Answer Answer each question or statement below on the line provided. *(10 points each)*

6. What brings harsh winters to Ulaanbaatar, Mongolia, and to Hokkaido, Japan?

_____

7. What keeps temperatures moderate in the tropical countries of Singapore and New Guinea?

_____

8. How does life on the Taklimakan in China differ from life in the rain forests of Indonesia?

_____

9. How does climate affect agriculture in Mongolia and Vietnam?

_____

10. What country in East Asia and Southeast Asia has the greatest variety of climates? Why?

_____

SCORE

Directions: Matching Match each item in Column A with its description in Column B. Write the correct letters in the blanks. *(3 points each)*

Column A

A. archipelago

B. tungsten

C. Gobi

D. humid continental

E. Mekong

F. mahogany

G. Singapore

H. Huang He

I. Chang Jiang

J. teak

Column B

_____ **1.** "place without water"

_____ **2.** where the Three Gorges Dam is built

_____ **3.** river that borders Laos and Thailand

_____ **4.** wood from the Philippines used to make furniture

_____ **5.** chain of islands

_____ **6.** climate of northern Japan

_____ **7.** Yellow River

_____ **8.** controls the Strait of Malacca

_____ **9.** wood from the region's rain forests used to make ships

_____ **10.** used to make rockets and lightbulbs

Directions: Multiple Choice In the blank at the left, write the letter of the choice that best completes the statement or answers the question. *(3 points each)*

_____ **11.** Which of these has been called the Roof of the World?
    A. Himalaya   **C.** Ring of Fire
    B. Huang He   **D.** Plateau of Tibet

_____ **12.** The Ring of Fire is an area where ____.
    A. lightning often strikes
    B. heat from the sun sets record temperatures
    C. plate movements cause volcanic eruptions
    D. deserts dominate the landscape

_____ **13.** East Asia and Southeast Asia touch which two oceans?
    A. Indian and Pacific   **C.** Indian and Atlantic
    B. Atlantic and Pacific   **D.** Arctic and Indian

_____ **14.** Because of frequent flooding, which river has been called "China's sorrow"?

A. Huang He

B. Chang Jiang

C. Mekong

D. Volga

_____ **15.** Indonesia, Malaysia, and China each have large deposits of which minerals?

A. gold and lead

B. iron ore and tin

C. aluminum and silver

D. copper and platinum

_____ **16.** Which of these nations has the lowest winter temperatures?

A. Myanmar

B. Japan

C. Malaysia

D. Mongolia

_____ **17.** Which of these countries has the greatest range of temperatures and landforms?

A. China

B. Japan

C. Tibet

D. North Korea

_____ **18.** Malaysia's rain forests contain about _____ species of flowering plants.

A. 400

B. 4,000

C. 14,000

D. 400,000

_____ **19.** Why has Singapore, which lies almost on the Equator, never had temperatures above 97°F (36°C)?

A. It is cooled by sea breezes.

B. It is located at a high elevation.

C. It receives a large amount of rainfall.

D. It is always cloudy.

_____ **20.** Which climate event is frequent in Indonesia?

A. month-long droughts

B. rainfall exceeding 20 inches in a day

C. tsunamis

D. hail

Applying Skills: Reading a Map Use the map below to answer the
questions that follow. *(5 points each)*

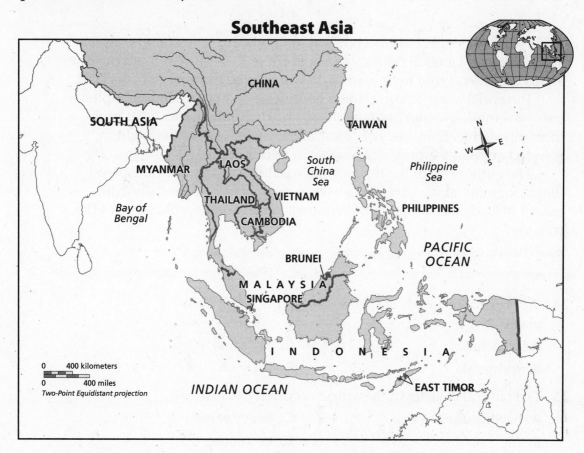

Southeast Asia

_____ **21.** Which of the following countries is landlocked?

    A. China   **C.** Thailand

    B. Vietnam   **D.** Laos

_____ **22.** Which of these countries is on a peninsula and an island?

    A. Japan   **C.** Indonesia

    B. Malaysia   **D.** Burma

_____ **23.** Which of the following countries is part of an archipelago?

    A. Malaysia   **C.** Cambodia

    B. the Philippines   **D.** China

Directions: Document-Based Questions Use the document below to answer the questions that follow. *(5 points each)*

> At least 12 people have been killed in floods that swept across six subdistricts of Langkat regency in the north of the island of Sumatra. The area's big rivers burst their banks and overflowed, putting homes at risk.
>
> Torrential rains pouring down on Indonesia since 21 December have created a mudflow that has made roads linking Sumatra to Aceh province impassable. Hundreds of commuters were stuck for the night in forested areas of the province, unable to return home.
>
> The authorities of the regency have publicly blamed "widespread illegal logging taking place in Leuser National Park." Syamsul Arifin, mayor of Langkat, said: "These criminals are the real perpetrators of this tragedy."
>
> **Source:** Asia News online. www.asianews.it/index.php?1=en&art=8075&size=A.

_____ **24.** Where did the flooding mentioned in this article take place?

    A. Jakarta   **C.** Malaysia

    B. Indonesia   **D.** Laos

_____ **25.** The natural disaster in the article occurred because of ____.

    A. earthquakes   **C.** heavy rains

    B. high winds   **D.** volcanoes

_____ **26.** According to some officials, what contributed to the disaster?

    A. unprepared government agencies

    B. illegal logging

    C. densely populated coasts

    D. lack of dams on the rivers

Directions: Essay On a separate sheet of paper, answer the question below. *(10 points)*

    27. Give two examples of how geography and climate affect where most people in East Asia and Southeast Asia choose to live.

SCORE

Directions: Matching Match each item in Column A with its description in Column B. Write the correct letters in the blanks. *(3 points each)*

Column A

A. Taklimakan

B. Manchurian Plain

C. tsunami

D. Hanoi

E. Hokkaido

F. steppe

G. Ring of Fire

H. Irrawaddy

I. typhoon

J. deforestation

Column B

_____ **1.** major river of Southeast Asia

_____ **2.** contributes to the problem of landslides

_____ **3.** capital of Vietnam

_____ **4.** huge tidal wave

_____ **5.** area of volcanoes and earthquakes

_____ **6.** northernmost island of Japan

_____ **7.** hurricane-like storm

_____ **8.** drier than the Gobi

_____ **9.** climate in much of Mongolia

_____ **10.** lowlands of East Asia

Directions: Multiple Choice In the blank at the left, write the letter of the choice that best completes the statement or answers the question. *(3 points each)*

_____ **11.** Which of these countries covers most of East Asia's landmass?

    A. China and Taiwan   **C.** China and Mongolia

    B. Japan and China   **D.** Tibet and Vietnam

_____ **12.** What do Indonesia, East Timor, Singapore, and Brunei have in common?

    A. They are located on peninsulas.

    B. They are located on the mainland of Southeast Asia.

    C. They are islands.

    D. They are archipelagoes.

_____ **13.** Which body of water, stretching from Taiwan to Southeast Asia, carries much of the world's shipping traffic?

    A. Indian Ocean   **C.** East China Sea

    B. Pacific Ocean   **D.** South China Sea

_____ **14.** Why is the Huang He also called the Yellow River?

    A. It carries loess, a yellow-brown soil.

    B. The factories on the river dump sulfur into it.

    C. The sun shines on the river most of the day.

    D. Yellow is China's national color.

_____ **15.** A disadvantage of the Three Gorges Dam is that it will ____.

    A. kill native plants and animals

    B. displace about a million people

    C. not provide enough power

    D. not control flooding

_____ **16.** What capital city has an average winter temperature of 15°F (−26°C)?

    A. Ulaanbaatar, Mongolia   **C.** Seoul, South Korea

    B. Bangkok, Thailand   **D.** Hanoi, Vietnam

_____ **17.** In which country are pearls harvested?

    A. Myanmar   **C.** Japan

    B. Thailand   **D.** Indonesia

_____ **18.** Which of these countries has the greatest variety of climates?

    A. Mongolia   **C.** Vietnam

    B. China   **D.** Japan

_____ **19.** What do the people of Mongolia call the pattern of a dry summer followed by a harsh winter?

    A. *dzud*   **C.** *dzong*

    B. *yuan*   **D.** *gobi*

_____ **20.** Which of these nations is relatively dry compared to the heavy rains of the other three?

    A. Malaysia   **C.** South Korea

    B. Thailand   **D.** Indonesia

Name_____ Date_____ Class_____

Applying Skills: Reading a Map Use the map below to answer the questions that follow. *(5 points each)*

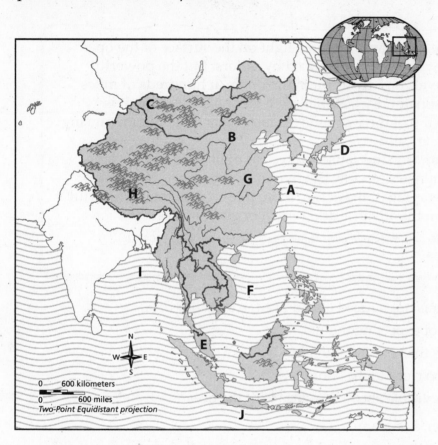

_____ **21.** Which physical feature is represented by the letter *B*?

    A. Huang He   **C.** Chang Jiang

    B. Mekong River   **D.** Irrawaddy River

_____ **22.** Which physical feature is represented by the letter *H*?

    A. Mount Fuji   **C.** Plateau of Tibet

    B. Gobi   **D.** Taklimakan

_____ **23.** Where is the letter *F* located?

    A. Sea of Japan   **C.** Bay of Bengal

    B. South China Sea   **D.** East China Sea

Directions: Document-Based Questions Use the document below to answer the questions that follow. *(5 points each)*

> Tsunamis can be less than a foot in height on the surface of the open ocean, which is why they are not noticed by sailors. But the powerful pulse of energy travels rapidly through the ocean at hundreds of miles per hour. Once a tsunami reaches shallow water near the coast, it is slowed down. The top of the wave moves faster than the bottom, causing the sea to rise dramatically.
>
> The Indian Ocean tsunami caused waves as high as 50 feet in some places, according to news reports. But in many other places, witnesses described a rapid surging of the ocean, more like an extremely powerful river or a flood than the advance and retreat of giant waves.
>
> **Source:** "The Deadliest Tsunami in History?" news.nationalgeographic.com/news/2004/12/ 1227_041226_tsunami.html.

_____ 24. Why are tsunamis not noticed ahead of time by sailors?

   A. Sailors are not expecting them.

   B. They are less than a foot in height.

   C. They start too close to the shore.

   D. They are not visible above the surface of the ocean.

_____ 25. In shallow water, a tsunami _____.

   A. slows down   **C.** remains the same

   B. speeds up   **D.** begins pulsing

_____ 26. How fast does tsunami energy travel through the ocean?

   A. one or two miles per hour

   B. about 10 miles per hour

   C. 50 miles per hour

   D. more than 100 miles per hour

Directions: Essay On a separate sheet of paper, answer the question below. *(10 points)*

   27. Describe three different climate zones in Southeast Asia and East Asia.

Directions: Matching Match each item in Column A with its description in Column B. Write the correct letters in the blanks. *(10 points each)*

Column A

A. samurai

B. census

C. dynasty

D. porcelain

E. shogun

Column B

_____ **1.** line of rulers from a single family

_____ **2.** fine clayware traded by China along the Silk Road

_____ **3.** the counting of people in order to collect taxes more accurately

_____ **4.** Japanese military leader

_____ **5.** land-owning warriors of Japan

Directions: Short Answer Answer each question or statement below on the line provided. *(10 points each)*

6. What three religions did traders from India, the Arab Empire, and Europe spread to Southeast Asia?

_____

7. Why did the Chinese and Japanese isolate themselves from the rest of the world? Who pressured them to end their isolation in the late 1800s?

_____

8. How did the Korean War help boost Japan's economy?

_____

9. Why are South Korea, Taiwan, Singapore, and Hong Kong known as the "Asian Tigers"?

_____

10. How has relaxed government control over factories and farms helped the Chinese economy?

_____

SCORE

Directions: Matching Match each item in Column A with its description in Column B. Write the correct letters in the blanks. *(10 points each)*

Column A

A. Islam

B. Java

C. calligraphy

D. Singapore

E. Buddhism

Column B

_____ **1.** majority of Indonesia's people live here

_____ **2.** art of beautiful writing

_____ **3.** smallest country in Southeast Asia with the greatest population density

_____ **4.** major religion of Thailand, Myanmar, Laos, Cambodia, and Vietnam

_____ **5.** major religion of Indonesia, Malaysia, and western China

Directions: Short Answer Answer each question or statement below on the line provided. *(10 points each)*

6. Identify the two main dialects of Han Chinese and where they are most widely spoken.

_____

7. How does the ethnic diversity of Japan differ from the ethnic diversity of Indonesia?

_____

8. How are the beliefs of Daoism and Shinto similar?

_____

9. Describe Mongolian yurts.

_____

10. Describe a pagoda and what it is used for.

_____

SCORE

Directions: Matching Match each item in Column A with its description in Column B. Write the correct letters in the blanks. *(3 points each)*

Column A

A. pagodas

B. Laozi

C. Angkor Wat

D. samurai

E. Minamoto Yoritomo

F. Siam

G. census

H. haiku

I. Chiang Kai-shek

J. Beijing

Column B

_____ **1.** Chinese Nationalist military leader

_____ **2.** taught harmony with nature

_____ **3.** helped shoguns govern Japan

_____ **4.** serve as temples

_____ **5.** known today as Thailand

_____ **6.** Japan's first shogun

_____ **7.** Japanese form of poetry

_____ **8.** built by the Khmer people

_____ **9.** location of the Forbidden City

_____ **10.** count of people by Ming rulers

Directions: Multiple Choice In the blank at the left, write the letter of the choice that best completes the statement or answers the question. *(3 points each)*

_____ **11.** Which of these describes the Chinese writing system?

    A. a large alphabet with 2,600 letters

    B. letters that stand for words

    C. characters that stand for words

    D. similar to the Egyptian alphabet

_____ **12.** Which of these best describes China's trade during the Han dynasty?

    A. All trade was within China.

    B. China traded with other nations via the Silk Road.

    C. The main trade route was through the Pacific Ocean.

    D. China traded with every continent.

_____ **13.** Which of these are early Chinese inventions?

    A. steel, gunpowder, printing   **C.** candy, glass, pottery

    B. alphabet, wheel, silk   **D.** paper, chess, haiku

_____ **14.** Which group invaded China from Central Asia in the 1200s?

    A. Mongols   **C.** Turks

    B. Berbers   **D.** Mandarins

_____ **15.** What happened to Hong Kong in 1997?

    A. It was returned to the United Kingdom.

    B. It became part of China as a special administrative region.

    C. Its economy was folded into China's communist rule.

    D. Portugal returned ownership of Hong Kong back to China.

_____ **16.** Which nation has the world's second-largest economy after the United States?

    A. South Korea   **C.** Japan

    B. China   **D.** Singapore

_____ **17.** Which ethnic group makes up 92 percent of China's population?

    A. Mandarin   **C.** Cantonese

    B. Han   **D.** Khalkha

_____ **18.** Which nation has the highest population density, with more than 18,000 people per square mile?

    A. Japan   **C.** China

    B. South Korea   **D.** Singapore

_____ **19.** Spanish is one of the main languages of ____.

    A. Singapore   **C.** Indonesia

    B. the Philippines   **D.** Borneo

_____ **20.** Which religion stresses that all parts of nature have their own spirits?

    A. Buddhism   **C.** Confucianism

    B. Shinto   **D.** Islam

Applying Skills: Reading a Chart Use the chart below to answer the questions that follow. *(5 points each)*

Events of the Korean War

June 1950	North Korea attacks South Korea.
June 1950	President Harry Truman commits U.S. forces to assist South Korea.
July 1950	United Nations command formed to fight for South Korea.
September 1950	UN forces land in Inchon, South Korea.
November 1950	Troops from China cross into North Korea to fight against the UN.
January 1951	Seoul, South Korea, falls to North Korea.
March 1951	Seoul retaken by UN troops.
July 1953	Final cease-fire ends the war.
August 1953	Sides begin to exchange prisoners of war.

_____ 21. In 1950 U.S. forces were sent to South Korea by ____.

    A. Seoul   **C.** China

    B. North Korea   **D.** President Truman

_____ 22. When did UN troops regain Seoul?

    A. July 1950   **C.** September 1950

    B. March 1951   **D.** January 1951

_____ 23. How long did it take UN forces to mobilize after North Korea invaded South Korea?

    A. three months   **C.** one year

    B. six months   **D.** three years

Directions: Document-Based Questions Use the document below to answer the questions that follow. *(5 points each)*

> The Forbidden City (Zijincheng), also known as the Imperial Palace (Gugong), and the Palace Museum are the largest and best-preserved collections of ancient buildings in China. This site is an image of China relayed throughout the world on national days and at public events. Today the Palace is filled with tourists, but under the emperors, these "commoners" would have been executed had they dared to enter the complex. Given the popularity of the site, the Chinese government has invested much time and money in the Palace. It is now a fantastic place to wander and dream of times gone by.
>
> **Source:** www.chinadaily.com.cn/english/livechina/2004-01/14/content_298859.htm.

_____ **24.** How is the Forbidden City being used today?

 A. for official visits of other governments

 B. as a city park

 C. for Chinese government offices

 D. as an attraction for tourists

_____ **25.** Which dynasty built the Forbidden City?

 A. Mongol **C.** Han

 B. Shang **D.** Ming

_____ **26.** Why did the Imperial Palace become known as the Forbidden City?

 A. People who lived there were not allowed to leave.

 B. Common people who dared to enter would be executed.

 C. China's emperors forbade anyone from looking directly at the palace.

 D. The government wanted to prevent people from harming China's ancient buildings.

Directions: Essay On a separate sheet of paper, answer the question below. *(10 points)*

 27. What is China's government doing to control population growth? How is it working?

SCORE

Directions: Matching Match each item in Column A with its description in Column B. Write the correct letters in the blanks. *(3 points each)*

Column A

A. China

B. Yamato

C. Buddhism

D. Singapore

E. Mandarin

F. Jakarta

G. Matthew C. Perry

H. Japan

I. megalopolis

J. Islam

Column B

_____ **1.** pressured Japan to end isolation

_____ **2.** major religion in Thailand, Laos, and Cambodia

_____ **3.** world's second-largest economy

_____ **4.** China's official language

_____ **5.** population passed 1.3 billion in 2005

_____ **6.** major religion in Malaysia and Indonesia

_____ **7.** capital of Indonesia

_____ **8.** super-sized city

_____ **9.** located at the tip of the Malay Peninsula

_____ **10.** dynasty that ruled Japan in the 1400s

Directions: Multiple Choice In the blank at the left, write the letter of the choice that best completes the statement or answers the question. *(3 points each)*

_____ **11.** Merchants traveled on the Silk Road from China to as far as ____.

    A. the Indian Ocean   **C.** Kazakhstan

    B. the Mediterranean region   **D.** Pakistan

_____ **12.** How did Marco Polo help many Europeans learn about China?

    A. He showed them artifacts from China.

    B. He introduced the Chinese printing press to Europeans.

    C. He smuggled silkworms out of China and into Europe.

    D. He wrote a book about China.

_____ **13.** These powerful people governed Japan until the 1800s.

    A. geishas   **C.** shoguns

    B. samurai   **D.** emperors

_____ **14.** By the 1890s, large areas of China were claimed as spheres of influence by _____.

    A. European governments and Japan   **C.** wealthy emperors

    B. Mongols   **D.** Korea and Russia

_____ **15.** Which Communist leader gained control of China in 1949?

    A. Chiang Kai-shek   **C.** Mao Zedong

    B. Ho Chi Minh   **D.** Minamoto Yoritomo

_____ **16.** About ___ of the world's population lives in East Asia and Southeast Asia.

    A. one-fourth   **C.** one-half

    B. one-third   **D.** two-thirds

_____ **17.** Which of the following is an accurate description of population change in East Asia?

    A. The entire region's population is growing rapidly.

    B. China is the only country with population growth.

    C. Wealthier countries like Japan and South Korea have declining growth rates.

    D. Poorer countries have declining population growth rates.

_____ **18.** Which of the following is true of East Asian and Southeast Asian cities?

    A. Some are among the world's largest.

    B. Most are declining in population.

    C. Few have modern buildings.

    D. Most are in Indonesia.

_____ **19.** Which statement best describes ethnic diversity in East Asia and Southeast Asia?

    A. Both regions have great ethnic diversity.

    B. Southeast Asia is more ethnically diverse.

    C. East Asia is more ethnically diverse.

    D. Most countries in the region have one dominant ethnic group.

_____ **20.** Which aspect of daily life has experienced the most change in East Asia?

    A. people's attitudes toward education

    B. young people's respect for their elders

    C. arranged marriages

    D. rural housing

Applying Skills: Reading a Map Use the map below to answer the questions that follow. *(5 points each)*

Southeast Asia: Colonialism and Independence

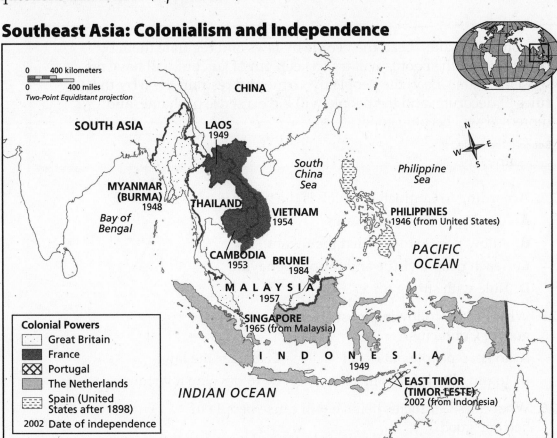

_____ **21.** Which of these countries first gained independence?

A. Vietnam   **C.** Philippines

B. Malaysia   **D.** Indonesia

_____ **22.** Which country has most recently become independent?

A. East Timor   **C.** Vietnam

B. Cambodia   **D.** Brunei

_____ **23.** What occurred in Vietnam soon after Communist forces defeated the French in 1954?

A. The United States helped the North Vietnamese fight the South Vietnamese.

B. Vietnam became a Communist country.

C. About 10 million North Vietnamese became refugees.

D. The United States helped the South Vietnamese fight the North Vietnamese.

Directions: Document-Based Questions Use the document below to answer the questions that follow. *(5 points each)*

> Confucius said: "Lead the people by laws and regulate them by penalties and the people will try to keep out of jail, but will have no sense of shame. Lead the people by virtue and restrain them by the rules of decorum, and the people will have a sense of shame, and moreover will become good."
>
> **Source:** The Analects.

_____ **24.** According to Confucius, which is the better way to rule?

    A. Teach and enforce the laws.

    B. Allow people to do what they want.

    C. Teach people virtue and proper behavior.

    D. Rule with strong force.

_____ **25.** Which of the following most correctly identifies a goal of Confucius?

    A. to keep people out of jail   **C.** to fear the law

    B. to put all criminals in jail   **D.** to develop a virtuous society

_____ **26.** What does Confucius believe will cause people to become good?

    A. cultivating shame

    B. having strong penalties for wrongdoing

    C. having laws that everyone likes

    D. leading by proper behavior

Directions: Essay On a separate sheet of paper, answer the question below. *(10 points)*

    27. What subject matter is common in the works of Chinese, Korean, and Japanese artists? How does this subject relate to religion?

Directions: Matching Match each item in Column A with its description in Column B. Write the correct letters in the blanks. *(10 points each)*

Column A

A. human rights

B. Tiananmen Square

C. Macao

D. Dalai Lama

E. exile

Column B

_____ **1.** site of student and worker protest for democratic reform

_____ **2.** Buddhist leader of Tibet

_____ **3.** basic freedoms such as freedom of speech and religion

_____ **4.** territory once controlled by Portugal

_____ **5.** forced to live somewhere other than your own country

Directions: Short Answer Answer each question or statement below on the line provided. *(10 points each)*

6. Has China seen more change in its economy or in its political system in recent years? Explain.

_____

7. Why do Chinese leaders believe Hong Kong and Macao will boost economic growth in the rest of the country?

_____

8. How does the standard of living in China differ between urban areas and rural areas?

_____

9. How has China's economic growth affected the environment?

_____

10. What do the governments of Taiwan and China both claim? Despite this conflict, what are Taiwanese businesses doing?

_____

Directions: Matching Match each item in Column A with its description in Column B. Write the correct letters in the blanks. *(10 points each)*

Column A

A. kimono

B. trade deficit

C. intensive agriculture

D. *anime*

E. tatami

Column B

_____ **1.** growing crops on every available piece of land

_____ **2.** Japanese style of animation

_____ **3.** straw mats that cover the wooden floors of traditional Japanese homes

_____ **4.** long, silken robe with an open neck and large sleeves

_____ **5.** occurs when one country buys more goods from another country than it sells to that country

Directions: Short Answer Answer each question or statement below on the line provided. *(10 points each)*

6. Why are Japan's long life expectancy and low birthrate a challenge for its economy?

_____

7. How does Japan's military might compare to its economic power?

_____

8. With few mineral resources of its own, how has Japan been able to grow its economy? What role do new technologies play?

_____

9. How do Bunraku and No differ in the way they tell stories?

_____

10. How have the Japanese adapted their homes to the crowded conditions of Tokyo?

_____

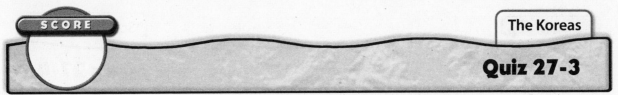

Directions: Matching Match each item in Column A with its description in Column B. Write the correct letters in the blanks. *(10 points each)*

Column A

A. tae kwon do

B. celadon

C. Kim Jong Il

D. Ban Ki-moon

E. hangul

Column B

_____ **1.** Korean writing system that uses only 28 symbols

_____ **2.** martial art emphasizing mental discipline as well as self-defense

_____ **3.** became Secretary General of the United Nations in 2006

_____ **4.** type of Chinese pottery modified by Koreans

_____ **5.** dictator of North Korea since 1994

Directions: Short Answer Answer each question or statement below on the line provided. *(10 points each)*

6. Describe the Korean Peninsula's relative location.

_____

7. Contrast the effect of foreign trade on the economies of South Korea and North Korea.

_____

8. How are South Korea's and North Korea's farms organized differently? Which are more productive?

_____

9. What happened to Korea after World War II?

_____

10. How has South Korea gained influence in world affairs?

_____

SCORE

Directions: Matching Match each item in Column A with its description in Column B. Write the correct letters in the blanks. *(10 points each)*

Column A

A. Kuala Lumpur

B. Angkor Wat

C. oil and gas reserves

D. Aung San Suu Kyi

E. cars and electronic goods

Column B

_____ **1.** won the Nobel Peace Prize for efforts to bring democracy to Myanmar

_____ **2.** capital of Malaysia

_____ **3.** basis of Brunei's wealthy economy

_____ **4.** growing portion of Malaysia's recent exports

_____ **5.** complex of temples and an architectural treasure in Cambodia

Directions: Short Answer Answer each question or statement below on the line provided. *(10 points each)*

6. Why does Indonesia's government have difficulty uniting the country?

_____

7. How does the standard of living in Singapore differ from the standard of living in Laos? Explain the difference.

_____

8. Who runs the economies of Myanmar and Vietnam?

_____

9. How has foreign rule influenced the culture of Thailand?

_____

10. Identify the major islands of Indonesia.

_____

SCORE

Directions: Matching Match each item in Column A with its description in Column B. Write the correct letters in the blanks. *(3 points each)*

Column A

A. Seoul

B. tatami

C. Dalai Lama

D. Diet

E. tae kwon do

F. Hong Kong

G. Singapore

H. Honshu

I. Thailand

J. kimono

Column B

_____ **1.** exiled Tibetan Buddhist leader

_____ **2.** once controlled by the United Kingdom

_____ **3.** island on which Tokyo is located

_____ **4.** Japanese representative assembly

_____ **5.** long silk robe

_____ **6.** capital of South Korea

_____ **7.** Southeast Asian country that has never been a European colony

_____ **8.** straw mat used in Japan

_____ **9.** city with a free port on the Malay Peninsula

_____ **10.** Korean martial art

Directions: Multiple Choice In the blank at the left, write the letter of the choice that best completes the statement or answers the question. *(3 points each)*

_____ **11.** Malaysia's cities, especially _____, are important centers of trade and industry.

    A. Manila

    B. Bangkok

    C. Kuala Lumpur

    D. Phnom Penh

_____ **12.** Southeast Asia's largest country is _____.

    A. Brunei

    B. East Timor

    C. the Philippines

    D. Indonesia

_____ **13.** In 2004 _____ caused a tsunami that killed hundreds of thousands of people in South Asia.

    A. a hurricane

    B. a cyclone

    C. an undersea earthquake

    D. a volcanic eruption

East Asia and Southeast Asia Today

Chapter 27 Test Form A (continued)

_____ 14. What promise did China make regarding Macao and Hong Kong when it took over these cities?

   A. to provide free public education

   B. to offer their people Chinese citizenship

   C. to lower taxes

   D. to maintain their economic and political freedoms

_____ 15. Which of these Chinese provinces is a democracy that was formed by Chinese people in 1949?

   A. Singapore   **C.** Macao

   B. Taiwan   **D.** Hong Kong

_____ 16. Japan's constitution prohibits ____.

   A. Japan from becoming a military power

   B. women from entering the workforce

   C. free markets

   D. Japan from taxing businesses

_____ 17. Which of these is a socialist country in which the government runs the economy?

   A. Myanmar   **C.** China

   B. Thailand   **D.** Laos

_____ 18. In 1910 Korea was conquered by ____.

   A. China   **C.** Japan

   B. the Soviet Union **D.** the United States

_____ 19. Both of Japan's main religions, Buddhism and Shinto, ____.

   A. teach respect for nature

   B. emphasize strong moral codes

   C. came from China

   D. teach belief in one God

_____ 20. Aung San Suu Kyi has struggled to bring democracy to ____.

   A. China   **C.** Laos

   B. Myanmar   **D.** Malaysia

Applying Skills: Reading a Graph Use the graph below to answer the questions that follow. *(5 points each)*

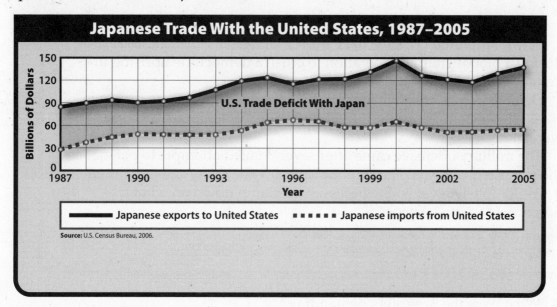

Japanese Trade With the United States, 1987–2005

U.S. Trade Deficit With Japan

Billions of Dollars

—— Japanese exports to United States   ▪▪▪▪▪ Japanese imports from United States

Source: U.S. Census Bureau, 2006.

_____ **21.** In which year was Japan's trade surplus the largest?
  A. 1987   **C.** 2004
  B. 2000   **D.** 1995

_____ **22.** Japan's imports from the United States were lowest
  in ____.
  A. 1990   **C.** 1987
  B. 1996   **D.** 2005

_____ **23.** Since 2002, the U.S. trade deficit has ____.
  A. gotten worse   **C.** remained the same
  B. gotten better   **D.** stabilized

Directions: Document-Based Questions Use the document below to answer the questions that follow. *(5 points each)*

> Several hundred civilians have been shot dead by the Chinese army during a bloody military operation to crush a democratic uprising in Peking's (Beijing) Tiananmen Square. . . .
>
> Demonstrators, mainly students, had occupied the square for seven weeks, refusing to move until their demands for democratic reform were met.
>
> The military offensive came after several failed attempts to persuade the protesters to leave. Throughout Saturday the government warned it would do whatever it saw necessary to clamp down on what it described as "social chaos."
>
> **Source:** "1989: Massacre in Tiananmen Square," BBC On This Day. news.bbc.co.uk/onthisday/hi/dates/stories/june/4/newsid_2496000/2496277.stm.

_____ **24.** What were the protesters demanding?

A. military reform **C.** democratic reform

B. social reform **D.** the right to protest

_____ **25.** Most demonstrators were _____.

A. soldiers **C.** the working class

B. students **D.** the unemployed

_____ **26.** The government saw the protests as _____.

A. social chaos **C.** the right of all citizens

B. treason **D.** a part of democracy

Directions: Essay On a separate sheet of paper, answer the question below. *(10 points)*

27. Describe the major economic changes that China has experienced in recent years.

Directions: Matching Match each item in Column A with its description in Column B. Write the correct letters in the blanks. *(3 points each)*

Column A

A. East Timor

B. kendo

C. emperor

D. Ban Ki-moon

E. demilitarized zone

F. Shinto

G. Kabuki

H. Kim Il Sung

I. Mongolia

J. celadon

Column B

_____ **1.** North Korea's first Communist ruler

_____ **2.** South Korea's Secretary General of the United Nations

_____ **3.** Chinese pottery

_____ **4.** Japanese martial art

_____ **5.** country known as the "Texas of Asia"

_____ **6.** stresses a respect for nature and cleanliness

_____ **7.** newest country in Southeast Asia

_____ **8.** type of theater that uses brilliantly colored costumes

_____ **9.** separates North Korea and South Korea

_____ **10.** head of state in Japan

Directions: Multiple Choice In the blank at the left, write the letter of the choice that best completes the statement or answers the question. *(3 points each)*

_____ **11.** How do people gain leadership positions in China's government?
  A. through carefully orchestrated elections
  B. through a lengthy process of passing civil service examinations
  C. through promotion and loyalty to the Communist Party
  D. by being born into the royal family

_____ **12.** Since 1949, the Communists and ____ have claimed to be the rulers of China.
  A. Nationalists of Taiwan   **C.** the Japanese Diet
  B. the Mongols   **D.** citizens of Hong Kong

_____ **13.** Which of these terms describes the government of Japan?
  A. a Communist republic   **C.** a direct democracy
  B. a constitutional monarchy   **D.** a military dictatorship

_____ 14. Which actions of China have been criticized by countries around the world?

A. China's harsh treatment of people who criticize it

B. taking control of Tibet

C. the killing of students at Tiananmen Square

D. All of these are true.

_____ 15. Which term identifies the Korean writing system?

A. tatami

B. *thanaka*

C. hangul

D. chuseok

_____ 16. This country has one of the world's highest rates of cell phone ownership.

A. China

B. Mongolia

C. North Korea

D. South Korea

_____ 17. Why must the nation of North Korea import much of its food?

A. The land is too poor for farming.

B. The collective farms are unproductive.

C. The population is growing too fast.

D. All of these are true.

_____ 18. Which of the following can be seen in Myanmar?

A. water buffalo pulling plows

B. the Petronas Towers skyscrapers

C. the temple complex of Angkor Wat

D. the beautiful beaches of Bali

_____ 19. Most Thais live in rural areas, but many look for jobs in ____, the capital.

A. Kuala Lumpur

B. Yangon

C. Rangoon

D. Bangkok

_____ 20. The culture of the Philippines blends Spanish, American, and ____ ways.

A. Vietnamese

B. Malay

C. Chinese

D. Japanese

Applying Skills: Reading a Map Use the map below to answer the questions that follow. *(5 points each)*

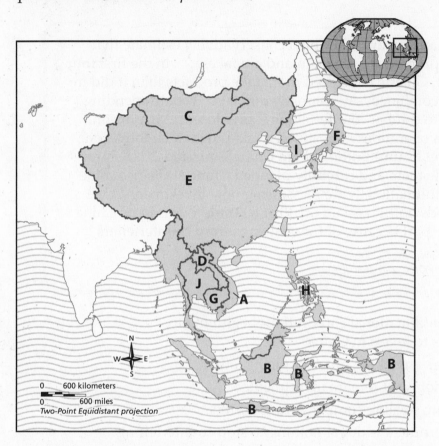

_____ **21.** Which country is represented by the letter *F*?

    A. China   **C.** Philippines

    B. Thailand   **D.** Japan

_____ **22.** Which country is represented by the letter *B*?

    A. Mongolia   **C.** Vietnam

    B. Indonesia   **D.** Philippines

_____ **23.** Which letter shows the location of Laos?

    A. A   **C.** J

    B. G   **D.** D

Directions: Document-Based Questions Use the document below to answer the questions that follow. *(5 points each)*

> Many foreign manufacturers in China conservatively estimate that 30 percent of their products in the mainland are fakes. . . . In the first four months of this year, Gillette has seized more fake products than it did in the past two years combined, say company officials. "We are spending millions of dollars to combat counterfeiting," says Joseph M. Johnson, president for China operations at Bestfoods Asia Ltd., which thinks one-quarter of its Skippy Peanut Butter sold in China is pirated. . . . As profits continue to elude them and carefully planned China strategies come unraveled, some multinationals are reassessing new investments. One U.S. consumer-goods outfit has laid off 35 of 800 employees in its China operations, in large part because of the challenge from counterfeiters.
>
> **Source:** Businessweek Online, June 5, 2000.
> www.businessweek.com/2000/00_23/b3684007.htm.

_____ **24.** Why are some multinational corporations beginning to reconsider plans to invest in China?

   A. Counterfeiters are taking much of their profits.

   B. China does not want foreign investment.

   C. Employees are stealing company trade secrets.

   D. China's government is doing nothing to stop counterfeiting.

_____ **25.** About what percent of foreign manufacturers' products being sold in China were thought to be fakes?

   A. 20 percent   **C.** 40 percent

   B. 30 percent   **D.** 50 percent

_____ **26.** How is Bestfoods Asia Ltd. dealing with counterfeiting?

   A. ignoring the problem

   B. moving operations out of China

   C. closing some operations

   D. spending millions of dollars to fight it

Directions: Essay On a separate sheet of paper, answer the question below. *(10 points)*

   27. What are four major challenges facing Japan today?

SCORE

East Asia and Southeast Asia

Unit 9 Posttest

Directions: Matching Match each item in Column A with its description in Column B. Write the correct letters in the blanks. *(5 points each)*

Column A

A. Mao Zedong

B. Republic of China

C. Nationalists

D. Boxers

E. Ulaanbaatar

F. United States

G. Silk Road

H. Beijing

I. Yuan

J. Confucius

Column B

_____ **1.** another name for Taiwan

_____ **2.** ancient overland trading route

_____ **3.** site of the Forbidden City

_____ **4.** Mongolia's capital

_____ **5.** wrote *Analects*

_____ **6.** led by Chiang Kai-shek

_____ **7.** Mongol dynasty in China

_____ **8.** first Communist leader of China

_____ **9.** rebelled against foreigners

_____ **10.** colonial power of the Philippines

Directions: Multiple Choice Write the letter of the choice that best completes the statement or answers the question. *(5 points each)*

_____ **11.** Which set of countries is made up entirely of islands?

    A. Myanmar, Thailand, and Vietnam

    B. Laos, Cambodia, and Malaysia

    C. Indonesia, Malaysia, and Singapore

    D. Myanmar, Cambodia, and Indonesia

_____ **12.** Why is the Huang He called the Yellow River?

    A. It spreads yellow fever.   **C.** It is polluted with sulfur.

    B. It carries yellow silt.   **D.** It causes much flooding.

_____ **13.** During the past 40 years, Thailand has lost nearly half of its ____.

    A. population   **C.** rain forests

    B. industry   **D.** birds

_____ **14.** Early Chinese civilizations invented steel, gunpowder, and ____.

    A. cloth   **C.** printing

    B. the steam engine   **D.** glass

_____ **15.** The Asian Tigers include South Korea, Taiwan, Singapore, and ____.

    A. Myanmar   **C.** Manila

    B. Hong Kong   **D.** Vietnam

Applying Skills: Reading a Map Use the map below to answer the questions that follow. *(5 points each)*

China's Defenses

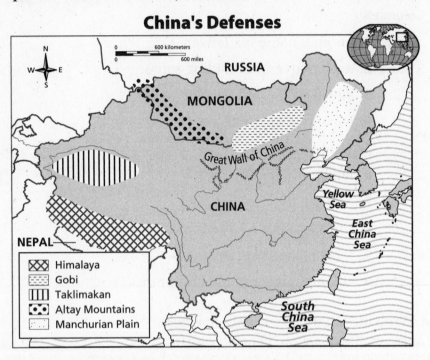

Himalaya
Gobi
Taklimakan
Altay Mountains
Manchurian Plain

_____ **16.** The Manchurian Plain is located _____.

    A. north of Nepal   **C.** in western Mongolia

    B. in northeastern China   **D.** near the South China Sea

_____ **17.** What is the Taklimakan?

    A. a mountain range in western China

    B. a plateau in western China

    C. a desert in western Mongolia

    D. a desert in western China

_____ **18.** Which of the following was effective in keeping the Mongols out of China?

    A. the Great Wall of China   **C.** the Altay Mountains

    B. the Gobi   **D.** none of these

Directions: Essay On a separate sheet of paper, answer the question below. *(10 points)*

    19. Describe the steppe, desert, and humid subtropical climate zones of China.

Name_____ Date_____ Class_____

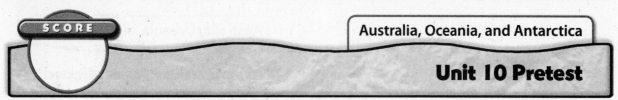
Directions: Matching Match each item in Column A with its description in Column B. Write the correct letters in the blanks. *(5 points each)*

Column A

A. Canberra

B. Wellington

C. wool

D. Australia

E. Antarctica

F. Marshall Islands

G. nickel

H. Europeans

I. krill

J. volcanic eruptions

Column B

_____ **1.** explored Australia from 1500 to 1800

_____ **2.** once belonged to the United States

_____ **3.** New Zealand's chief export

_____ **4.** country and continent

_____ **5.** how Tahiti was formed

_____ **6.** capital of Australia

_____ **7.** inhabited by scientists

_____ **8.** capital of New Zealand

_____ **9.** forms the diet of whales

_____ **10.** New Caledonia's chief export

Directions: Multiple Choice Write the letter of the choice that best completes the statement or answers the question. *(7 points each)*

_____ **11.** A vast area of plains and plateaus in Australia's interior is called the ____.

A. Canterbury Plains **C.** outback

B. Great Dividing Range **D.** Artesian Basin

_____ **12.** The low islands of Oceania were formed by ____.

A. sand from broken rocks **C.** shifting tectonic plates

B. skeletons of tiny sea animals **D.** volcanic eruptions

_____ **13.** Which of the following is the best description of New Zealand's climate?

A. moderate almost year-round **C.** hot almost year-round

B. hot in summer; cold in winter **D.** cold almost year-round

_____ **14.** The first European settlers in Australia were ____.

A. Spanish sailors looking for gold **C.** Irish farmers

B. convicts from British prisons **D.** French adventurers

_____ **15.** An Antarctic ice melt could endanger Oceania by ____.

A. weakening the ozone layer **C.** causing whales to become extinct

B. killing off krill that live on the ice **D.** raising sea levels and flooding the land

Applying Skills: Reading a Map Use the map below to answer the questions that follow. *(5 points each)*

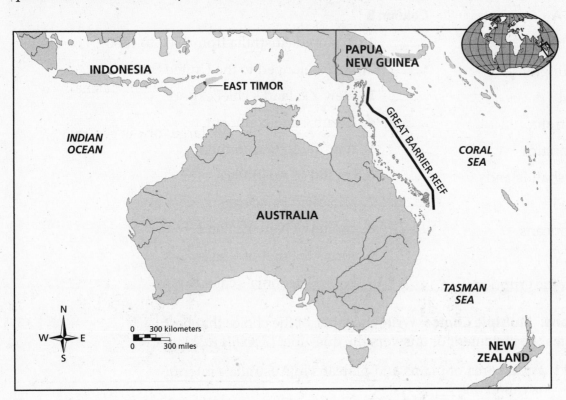

_____ **16.** Which is Australia's closest neighbor?

   A. New Zealand   **C.** Papua New Guinea

   B. Indonesia   **D.** East Timor

_____ **17.** What is the name of the island south of Australia?

   A. Great Barrier Reef   **C.** New Zealand

   B. Ayers Rock   **D.** Tasmania

_____ **18.** Approximately how many miles long is the
         Great Barrier Reef?

   A. 300 miles   **C.** 1,200 miles

   B. 600 miles   **D.** 2,000 miles

SCORE

Directions: Matching Match each item in Column A with its description in Column B. Write the correct letters in the blanks. *(10 points each)*

Column A

A. outback

B. Great Dividing Range

C. atolls

D. coral reef

E. Uluru

Column B

_____ **1.** a vast area of flat, dry plains and plateaus dotted with heavily eroded masses of rock

_____ **2.** structure formed by skeletons of small sea animals

_____ **3.** a heavily eroded, large rock in central Australia

_____ **4.** low-lying, ring-shaped islands surrounding shallow pools of water

_____ **5.** the rocky-faced escarpment of a plateau that plunges to lowland below

Directions: Short Answer Answer each question or statement below on the line provided. *(10 points each)*

6. What are the Canterbury Plains, and why are they important?

_____

7. Why does the North Island of New Zealand have many hot springs? What resource do these hot springs provide?

_____

8. How do Tahiti, the Marshall Islands, and New Guinea differ in the way they were formed?

_____

9. What two things prevent the tapping of Antarctica's minerals?

_____

10. Describe the distinguishing characteristics of a koala and a kiwi. Where are these animals found?

_____

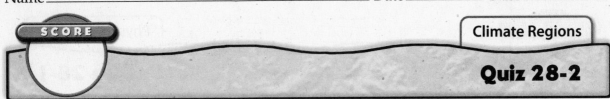

Directions: Matching Match each item in Column A with its description in Column B. Write the correct letters in the blanks. *(10 points each)*

Column A

A. breadfruit

B. marine west coast

C. Mediterranean

D. eucalyptus

E. lichens

Column B

_____ **1.** climate of southern and western Australia

_____ **2.** climate of New Zealand

_____ **3.** a starchy pod that can be cooked in several ways

_____ **4.** trees native to Australia and nearby islands

_____ **5.** plants that grow along the coasts of Antarctica

Directions: Short Answer Answer each question or statement below on the line provided. *(10 points each)*

6. How does elevation affect climate in Oceania?

_____

7. How do many New Zealanders make a living?

_____

8. What affects the climate of far northern Australia?

_____

9. Why is Antarctica so cold? How does the climate make the continent a desert?

_____

10. How do temperatures in the northern third of Australia differ from the rest of Australia?

_____

SCORE

Physical Geography of Australia, Oceania, and Antarctica

Chapter 28 Test Form A

Directions: Matching Match each item in Column A with its description in Column B. Write the correct letters in the blanks. *(3 points each)*

Column A

A. Oceania

B. lichens

C. Darling

D. Tahiti

E. outback

F. breadfruit

G. Great Barrier Reef

H. Tasmania

I. marsupial

J. Great Dividing Range

Column B

_____ **1.** 1,250 miles of coral

_____ **2.** a major river of Australia

_____ **3.** central plains and plateaus of Australia

_____ **4.** kangaroo

_____ **5.** huge group of islands in the Pacific Ocean

_____ **6.** escarpment in Australia

_____ **7.** tiny plants on the rocky coast of Antarctica

_____ **8.** starchy pod grown in Oceania

_____ **9.** island that belongs to Australia

_____ **10.** a high island of Oceania

Directions: Multiple Choice In the blank at the left, write the letter of the choice that best completes the statement or answers the question. *(3 points each)*

_____ **11.** Australia is a country, an island, and _____.

    A. a peninsula   **C.** a continent

    B. a tectonic plate   **D.** an archipelago

_____ **12.** The Great Barrier Reef is made of _____.

    A. skeletons of tiny sea animals   **C.** underwater plants

    B. volcanic rock   **D.** seaweed

_____ **13.** What kind of islands were formed by the rising and folding of rock from the ocean floor?

    A. atolls   **C.** high islands

    B. continental islands   **D.** low islands

_____ **14.** How were Tahiti and the Fiji Islands formed?

    A. by tectonic activity   **C.** from glacial deposits

    B. from coral reefs   **D.** by volcanic eruptions

_____ **15.** Because New Zealand lies on a fault line, it has ____.

    A. volcanoes and geysers   **C.** thousands of islands

    B. flat plains   **D.** glaciers and deep fjords

_____ **16.** Why are Antarctica's rich deposits of coal and iron ore not being mined?

    A. It would be too costly to mine there.

    B. Nations have agreed to protect the environment.

    C. Mining there would be very difficult.

    D. All of these are true.

_____ **17.** Which word best describes most of the interior of Australia?

    A. mountainous   **C.** dry

    B. hot   **D.** humid

_____ **18.** Which of these plants is native to Australia?

    A. bamboo   **C.** pineapple

    B. rubber trees   **D.** eucalyptus

_____ **19.** Rainfall in Oceania is affected by an island's ____.

    A. nearness to the Tropics

    B. nearness to major ocean currents

    C. elevation

    D. vegetation

_____ **20.** Temperatures in Antarctica reach ____ in the summer.

    A. −4° to −31°F   **C.** 15° to 38°F

    B. 4° to 31°F   **D.** 32° to 48°F

Applying Skills: Reading a Map Use the map below to answer the
questions that follow. *(5 points each)*

Australia and New Zealand: Climate Zones

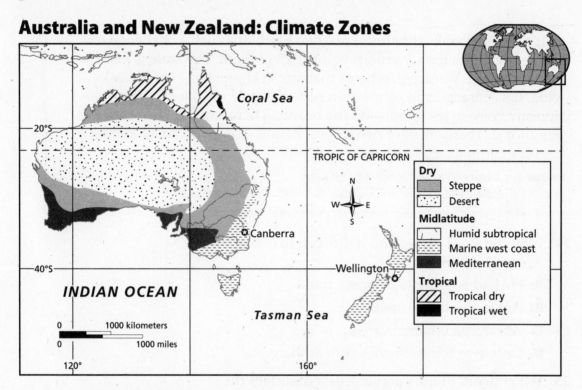

_____ 21. Why does the northern coast of Australia have
a tropical climate?

    A. It is surrounded by water.   **C.** It is a lowland plain.

    B. It is near the desert.   **D.** It is close to the Equator.

_____ 22. Which area of Australia has a Mediterranean climate?

    A. interior   **C.** west

    B. south   **D.** north

_____ 23. Which conclusion can be drawn from the map?

    A. Most coastal areas are warmer than interior areas.

    B. Most coastal areas receive more rainfall than interior areas.

    C. New Zealand lies mostly at a low elevation.

    D. Australia has warm temperatures throughout the year.

Directions: Document-Based Questions Use the document below to answer the questions that follow. *(5 points each)*

> It's indescribable. It's almost not like Earth. It's such a challenge to transmit via film the sensations you feel over there. The scale is just mindboggling. You have icebergs that are 30 kilometers (18.6 miles) wide. It's a strange and eerie environment, hence my use of an impressionistic voice to try to transmit the beauty. There's no human reference point for it. There are only two color schemes. You don't smell anything. It's very complicated to try to convey this.
>
> **Source:** Luc Jacquet, Director of *March of the Penguins.*
> news.nationalgeographic.com/news/2005/06/0624_050624_marchpenguin_2.html.

_____ **24.** Why did Luc Jacquet find it difficult to explain what Antarctica is like?

    A. He had nothing to compare it to.

    B. Antarctica lacks smells.

    C. Antarctica is complicated.

    D. Only two color schemes appear there.

_____ **25.** Which word in the interview best describes the environment of Antarctica?

    A. impressionistic   **C.** eerie

    B. scale   **D.** complicated

_____ **26.** The director was impressed by which of the following?

    A. the size of Antarctica's icebergs

    B. the power of the wind

    C. the harshness of the weather

    D. the abundant color

Directions: Essay On a separate sheet of paper, answer the question below. *(10 points)*

    27. Why do most people of Australia live along the northern, eastern, and southwestern coasts?

SCORE

Directions: Matching Match each item in Column A with its description in Column B. Write the correct letters in the blanks. *(3 points each)*

Column A

A. Murray

B. ice cap

C. Great Artesian Basin

D. Cook Strait

E. marsupials

F. icebergs

G. Marshall Islands

H. Uluru

I. eucalyptus

J. Canterbury Plains

Column B

_____ **1.** low-lying atoll

_____ **2.** New Zealand's best farming area

_____ **3.** a major river in Australia

_____ **4.** provides underground water

_____ **5.** tree with leathery leaves

_____ **6.** mammals that carry their young in a pouch

_____ **7.** covers much of Antarctica

_____ **8.** separates North Island and South Island

_____ **9.** float around Antarctica

_____ **10.** sacred to the Aborigines

Directions: Multiple Choice In the blank at the left, write the letter of the choice that best completes the statement or answers the question. *(3 points each)*

_____ **11.** The Great Dividing Range is really _____.
   A. a mountain chain   **C.** an escarpment
   B. a plateau   **D.** the outback

_____ **12.** Which island is part of Australia?
   A. Reef Island   **C.** Ayers Island
   B. South Island   **D.** Tasmania

_____ **13.** Because of the region's isolation, some native plants and animals are _____.
   A. flightless   **C.** extremely colorful
   B. marsupials   **D.** unique

_____ **14.** Mount Cook in New Zealand is part of which mountain range?
   A. Southern Alps
   B. Great Dividing Range
   C. Carpathians
   D. Canterbury Plains

_____ **15.** Oceania includes three kinds of islands: high islands, low islands, and _____ islands.
   A. volcanic
   B. continental
   C. coral
   D. barrier

_____ **16.** To protect Antarctica's environment, what have many nations agreed not to do?
   A. fish in the waters
   B. explore the ice cap
   C. mine the continent's resources
   D. hunt polar bears

_____ **17.** Which flightless bird is the national symbol of New Zealand?
   A. ostrich
   B. kiwi
   C. penguin
   D. emu

_____ **18.** Eucalyptus trees are plants that have adapted well to which condition?
   A. dry climate
   B. swampy soil
   C. high altitudes
   D. tropical storms

_____ **19.** Which type of climate covers New Zealand?
   A. steppe
   B. humid subtropical
   C. marine west coast
   D. Mediterranean

_____ **20.** What supplies New Zealand's geothermal energy?
   A. geysers
   B. rushing rivers
   C. coal deposits
   D. dams

Applying Skills: Reading a Map Use the map below to answer the questions that follow. *(5 points each)*

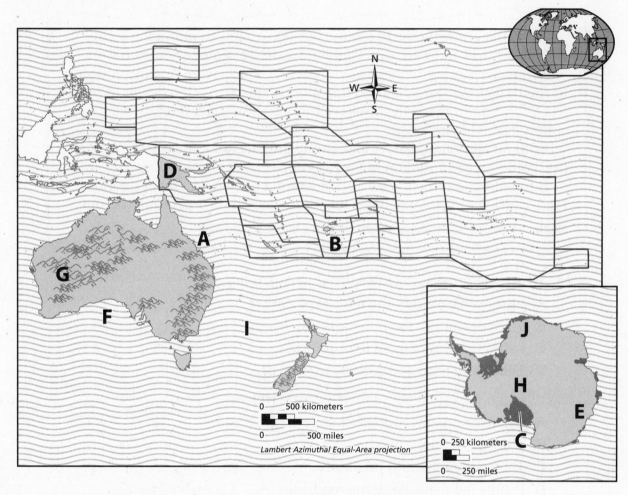

_____ **21.** Which physical feature is represented by the letter *A?*

    A. Great Australian Bight   **C.** Coral Sea

    B. Tasman Sea   **D.** Great Barrier Reef

_____ **22.** Which island country is represented by the letter *B?*

    A. Tonga   **C.** Marshall Islands

    B. Fiji Islands   **D.** Samoa

_____ **23.** Which landform is represented by the letter *C?*

    A. Wilkes Land   **C.** Ross Ice Shelf

    B. Gibson Ice Shelf   **D.** Queen Maud Land

Directions: Document-Based Questions Use the document below to answer the questions that follow. *(5 points each)*

> Australia is now home to around 500,000 camels roaming the country's vast tracts of desert, said Glenn Edwards, a senior scientist for the Northern Territory provincial government. Camels were first introduced to Australia in the mid-1800s to transport goods across the desert. When trucks and trains made the beasts of burden unneeded, their owners simply turned them loose.
>
> With no natural predators and ample grazing land, the camel population could exceed 1 million in the next decade. . . .
>
> Edwards said camels were also beginning to encroach on agricultural land, causing extensive damage to stock fences and rural infrastructure.
>
> **Source:** www.livescience.com/animalworld/australian_camels_041201.html.

_____ **24.** Why were camels first introduced to Australia?
   A. Europeans brought them for exploration.
   B. Traders brought them to cross the desert.
   C. Farmers brought them to pull plows.
   D. They were used as a substitute for beef.

_____ **25.** Why did the camel population increase so fast?
   A. No other grazing animals competed for pasture.
   B. They do not need much water.
   C. They had no natural predators.
   D. People fed them along the roadsides.

_____ **26.** Why are too many camels a problem?
   A. They encroach on agricultural land.
   B. They eat native plants.
   C. They use up the limited supply of water in the outback.
   D. They wander into residential neighborhoods and cause damage.

Directions: Essay On a separate sheet of paper, answer the question below. *(10 points)*

   27. What are the three ways that the islands of Oceania were formed?

History and Governments

Quiz 29-1

Directions: Matching Match each item in Column A with its description in Column B. Write the correct letters in the blanks. *(10 points each)*

Column A

A. New Guinea

B. Aborigines

C. New Zealand

D. Australia

E. Maori

Column B

_____ **1.** original settlers of New Zealand

_____ **2.** used as a colony for convicts

_____ **3.** believed that powerful spirits created the land and that their role is to care for it

_____ **4.** island settled about the same time as Australia

_____ **5.** first country in the world to give women the right to vote

Directions: Short Answer Answer each question or statement below on the line provided. *(10 points each)*

6. What is the main difference between the communities of early Aborigines and early Maori?

_____

7. Who claimed eastern Australia for Great Britain? What else did he accomplish?

_____

8. What is the Antarctic Treaty?

_____

9. From where did the first settlers of New Guinea originate, and how did they spread throughout Oceania?

_____

10. What is the main difference between the governments of Australia and New Zealand?

_____

SCORE

Directions: Matching Match each item in Column A with its description in Column B. Write the correct letters in the blanks. *(10 points each)*

Column A

A. stations

B. *fale*

C. taro

D. bush

E. pidgin

Column B

_____ **1.** rural areas where a small number of Australians live

_____ **2.** Samoan open-sided homes

_____ **3.** language formed by combining parts of several different languages

_____ **4.** plant used to make poi

_____ **5.** another name for Australian sheep ranches

Directions: Short Answer Answer each question or statement below on the line provided. *(10 points each)*

6. What is the background of the majority of Australians and New Zealanders? What is changing the diversity of these two countries?

_____

7. What is causing the migration of Pacific Islanders?

_____

8. In New Zealand, how do families of European descent differ from Maori families?

_____

9. What are Maori artisans skilled in?

_____

10. What is Dreamtime?

_____

SCORE

Directions: Matching Match each item in Column A with its description in Column B. Write the correct letters in the blanks. *(3 points each)*

Column A

A. Wellington

B. action songs

C. poi

D. boomerang

E. Maori

F. Port Moresby

G. bush

H. James Cook

I. *fale*

J. Antarctica

Column B

_____ **1.** flat hunting tool used by Aborigines

_____ **2.** explored the South Pacific

_____ **3.** half of these people died by 1840

_____ **4.** shared by many countries after 1959

_____ **5.** major city in New Zealand

_____ **6.** a paste made from taro

_____ **7.** capital of Papua New Guinea

_____ **8.** Maori art form that blends music with dance

_____ **9.** Samoan house with open sides

_____ **10.** rural areas of Australia

Directions: Multiple Choice In the blank at the left, write the letter of the choice that best completes the statement or answers the question. *(3 points each)*

_____ **11.** When did the Aborigines first travel to Australia?
A. before the Ice Age
B. during the Ice Age
C. after the Ice Age
D. during the early 1700s

_____ **12.** How do we know about the early history of the Aborigines?
A. from ancient rock paintings
B. from oral tradition
C. from writings preserved in clay jars
D. from ruins of ancient cities

_____ **13.** Which of these peoples began to explore Australia between 1500 and 1800?
A. Asians
B. Africans
C. Americans
D. Europeans

_____ 14. What was the main reason for the decline of native populations in this region during the period of colonization?
   A. A severe shortage of food occurred.
   B. The people had no resistance to European diseases.
   C. Civil wars broke out in all these regions.
   D. Weather conditions changed dramatically.

_____ 15. Australia and New Zealand have which kind of government?
   A. monarchy   **C.** parliamentary democracy
   B. military dictatorship   **D.** presidential

_____ 16. The population of which of these areas is growing fast?
   A. Australia   **C.** Oceania
   B. New Zealand   **D.** Antarctica

_____ 17. Today most immigrants to Australia come from ____.
   A. America   **C.** Europe
   B. Asia   **D.** Africa

_____ 18. Much of the art of ____ is based on Maori culture.
   A. New Zealand   **C.** Papua New Guinea
   B. Australia   **D.** Tahiti

_____ 19. The most widely practiced religion in Australia and Oceania is ____.
   A. Judaism   **C.** Christianity
   B. Islam   **D.** Dreamtime

_____ 20. The three largest ethnic groups in Oceania are ____.
   A. Maori, Europeans, and Aborigines
   B. Melanesians, Micronesians, and Maori
   C. Melanesians, Micronesians, and Polynesians
   D. Polynesians, Maori, and Aborigines

Applying Skills: Reading a Chart Use the chart below to answer the questions that follow. *(5 points each)*

New Zealand Population Projections				
Year	Ages 0–14	Ages 15–64	Ages 65+	Total
2006	873,200	2,726,100	510,500	4,109,800
2016	777,600	2,855,300	675,300	4,308,200
2026	683,300	2,843,700	900,400	4,427,400
2036	667,800	2,674,700	1,115,000	4,457,500

Source: Government of New Zealand, xtabs.stats.gov.nz/eng/TableViewer/wdsview/dispviewp.asp.

_____ **21.** How is the number of people ages 0–14 expected to change by 2036?

    A. It will increase slightly.

    B. It will increase to 667,800.

    C. It will decline by more than 200,000.

    D. It will remain stable.

_____ **22.** What is expected to happen to the number of people ages 65 and over by 2036?

    A. It will more than double.   **C.** It will decline by 500,000.

    B. It will increase slightly.   **D.** It will increase by 100,000.

_____ **23.** Given these population projections, what should New Zealand be concerned about?

    A. how to provide jobs for young people

    B. how to provide for an aging population

    C. how to provide housing for growing families

    D. the number of immigrants

Directions: Document-Based Questions Use the document below to answer the questions that follow. *(5 points each)*

> *Samoa* itself is said to mean "sacred center." . . . This is where the world began as the creator, Tagaloalagi, first called forth earth, sea, and sky from rock. . . . Language links and artifacts suggest that the first distinctly Polynesian culture may have developed here some 3,000 years ago. Over the centuries that followed, seafarers in double-hulled sailing vessels stocked with pigs, dogs, and fruits spread that culture across much of the Pacific.
>
> **Source:** *National Geographic.*

_____ **24.** According to the quote, what does *Samoa* mean?

    A. sacred center   **C.** Polynesian culture

    B. Pacific culture   **D.** seafarers

_____ **25.** When do scientists believe a distinctly Polynesian culture developed on Samoa?

    A. 3000 B.C.   **C.** 1000 B.C.

    B. 2000 B.C.   **D.** A.D. 1000

_____ **26.** According to the quote, Tagaloalagi brought forth all of the following EXCEPT ___ to create the world.

    A. sea   **C.** earth

    B. sky   **D.** rock

Directions: Essay On a separate sheet of paper, answer the question below. *(10 points)*

    27. Describe three stages in the settlement of Australia.

SCORE

Directions: Matching Match each item in Column A with its description in Column B. Write the correct letters in the blanks. *(3 points each)*

Column A

A. Australia

B. station

C. gold

D. 1,111

E. Papua New Guinea

F. Waitangi

G. 700

H. Melanesian

I. trust territory

J. Melbourne

Column B

_____ **1.** attracted settlers to Australia in 1851

_____ **2.** treaty that should have protected Maori lands

_____ **3.** area under temporary control of a country

_____ **4.** home to 20 million people

_____ **5.** number of languages in Papua New Guinea

_____ **6.** cattle or sheep ranch

_____ **7.** home to almost 6 million people

_____ **8.** large Australian city

_____ **9.** ethnic group of Oceania

_____ **10.** population density per square mile in Nauru

Directions: Multiple Choice In the blank at the left, write the letter of the choice that best completes the statement or answers the question. *(3 points each)*

_____ **11.** Aborigines of Australia developed the boomerang to ____.
   A. find water   **C.** hunt for small animals
   B. have a sporting event   **D.** imitate thunder

_____ **12.** The Maori people originated from which of these areas?
   A. Polynesia   **C.** Australia
   B. Japan   **D.** Hawaii

_____ **13.** Which British sailor is the most well-known explorer of the South Pacific islands?
   A. John Cabot   **C.** Sir Edwin Drake
   B. Sir Walter Raleigh   **D.** James Cook

_____ **14.** Why were Europeans and Americans interested in colonizing the Pacific Islands?

   A. They needed a place to send their convicts.

   B. They needed trading ports and refueling stations.

   C. They required a refuge for religious dissenters.

   D. The islands provided needed minerals and farmland.

_____ **15.** What was unique about the colonial governments of Australia?

   A. Women were elected officials.   **C.** All men were eligible to vote.

   B. Property owners could vote.   **D.** Each colony had its own legislature.

_____ **16.** In 1893 New Zealand became the first country in the world to _____.

   A. give women the right to vote

   B. become independent from Britain

   C. pass environmental laws

   D. return land to its indigenous peoples

_____ **17.** Which technologies did early Southeast Asians use to reach Fiji?

   A. sailboats and compasses   **C.** kayaks and star charts

   B. platform rafts with rudders   **D.** double canoes and star gazing

_____ **18.** In Australia, what is the bush?

   A. a small desert plant

   B. rural areas where few people live

   C. large cattle and sheep ranches

   D. a disease that affects cattle

_____ **19.** Who lives in a typical Maori household?

   A. a nuclear family of parents and children

   B. an extended family with many relatives

   C. the whole community

   D. a nuclear family and a village holy man

_____ **20.** What is poi?

   A. a snake that lives in Tahiti   **C.** a game played in New Zealand

   B. mashed taro   **D.** a type of canoe

Applying Skills: Reading a Map Use the map below to answer the questions that follow. *(5 points each)*

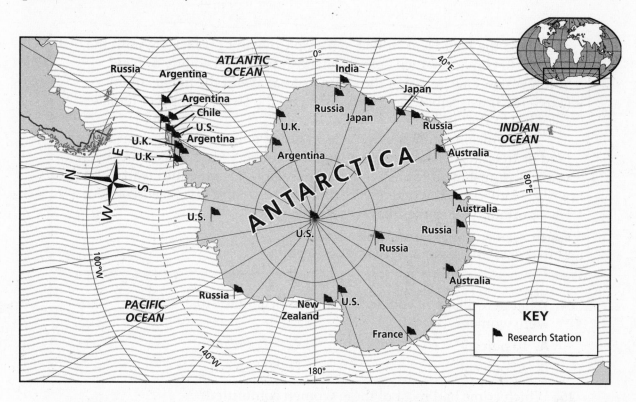

_____ **21.** Which country has a research station at the South Pole?

    A. United States   **C.** France

    B. Russia   **D.** Australia

_____ **22.** If you were taking a tour of research stations around the coast of Antarctica, which two languages would it be best to know or learn?

    A. Spanish and Russian   **C.** Russian and English

    B. Japanese and English   **D.** French and Japanese

_____ **23.** Which country has the most research stations in Antarctica?

    A. India   **C.** Australia

    B. United States   **D.** Russia

Directions: Document-Based Questions Use the document below to answer the questions that follow. *(5 points each)*

> In 1788 the First Fleet landed at Camp Cove in Port Jackson with the "cargo" of convicts which helped establish the penal colony of New South Wales. One in five of the convicts to arrive in the penal colony (1788–1823) was female, and they made up the largest group of female colonists in Port Jackson.
>
> The typical convict woman was in her twenties. She was from England or Ireland and had been convicted of robbery—sentenced for seven years as punishment for her crime. She was single and could read but not write. Many convict women were first offenders and given sentences of transportation for crimes that were quite minor.
>
> **Source:** Australian Government Culture and Recreation Portal, www.cultureandrecreation.gov.au/articles/portjacksonwomen.

_____ **24.** What percentage of convicts sent from Britain to Australia were women?

    A. 10 percent   **C.** 40 percent

    B. 20 percent   **D.** 50 percent

_____ **25.** Which crime had most of these women committed?

    A. murder   **C.** treason

    B. robbery   **D.** not paying taxes

_____ **26.** Which of the following can be inferred from the passage?

    A. Only uneducated women were shipped to the penal colonies.

    B. Camp Cove was the only penal colony in Australia that had women.

    C. Britain either had few prisons for women or the prisons were full of married women.

    D. Women convicts were treated less harshly than male convicts.

Directions: Essay On a separate sheet of paper, answer the question below. *(10 points)*

    27. Compare Australia's inland and coastal population density.

Directions: Matching Match each item in Column A with its description in Column B. Write the correct letters in the blanks. *(10 points each)*

Column A

A. United States

B. manufacturing

C. Sydney

D. geothermal energy

E. merinos

Column B

_____ **1.** industrial city in Australia

_____ **2.** a breed of sheep known for its fine wool

_____ **3.** trading partner of New Zealand

_____ **4.** became an important part of Australia's economy in the mid-1900s

_____ **5.** source of electricity in New Zealand

Directions: Short Answer Answer each question or statement below on the line provided. *(10 points each)*

6. Compare the 1840 Treaty of Waitangi and the 1992 Australian court ruling.

_____

7. What is Australia's main agricultural activity, and what effect has it had on the country's economy?

_____

8. What are three causes of Australia's environmental challenges?

_____

9. How are New Zealand's forests being used to help expand the country's economy?

_____

10. Why are China and Japan important to Australia's economy?

_____

SCORE

Directions: Matching Match each item in Column A with its description in Column B. Write the correct letters in the blanks. *(10 points each)*

Column A

A. Papua New Guinea

B. lingua franca

C. *fa'a Samoa*

D. copra

E. Vanuatu

Column B

_____ **1.** the meat from dried coconuts

_____ **2.** a common language used for communication and trade

_____ **3.** way of life that emphasizes living in harmony with the community and land

_____ **4.** people in this country honor volcanic spirits in their religious ceremonies

_____ **5.** largest and most populous country in Melanesia

Directions: Short Answer Answer each question or statement below on the line provided. *(10 points each)*

6. How are Kiribati and Nauru each dealing with the loss of their phosphate industries?

_____

7. How does the United States contribute to the economy of the islands in Micronesia?

_____

8. What two island groups in Micronesia are territories of the United States?

_____

9. How has the conflict between Melanesian and South Asian ethnic groups hurt Fiji's economy?

_____

10. Why do Samoa and Tonga rely less on foreign aid than other Polynesian countries?

_____

Antarctica

Quiz 30-3

Directions: Matching Match each item in Column A with its description in Column B. Write the correct letters in the blanks. *(10 points each)*

Column A

A. climate changes

B. scientific research stations

C. ozone

D. South Pole

E. krill

Column B

_____ **1.** the main food source for many animals in Antarctica

_____ **2.** protects Earth from the harmful rays of the sun

_____ **3.** many countries have these in Antarctica

_____ **4.** main environmental challenge of Antarctica

_____ **5.** located at 90°S

Directions: Short Answer Answer each question or statement below on the line provided. *(10 points each)*

6. How does the Antarctic Treaty benefit Antarctica's wildlife?

_____

7. How could global warming harm whales?

_____

8. How are chemicals from aerosol sprays harmful to the ozone?

_____

9. What did many countries hope to find by claiming territory in Antarctica? How did the Antarctic Treaty stop them?

_____

10. What do the remains of trees from millions of years ago tell geologists about Antarctica's past?

_____

Name_____ Date_____ Class_____

Directions: Matching Match each item in Column A with its description in Column B. Write the correct letters in the blanks. *(3 points each)*

Column A

A. Coral Sea

B. Guam

C. phosphate

D. Fiji

E. Vanuatu

F. ozone layer

G. Maori

H. lingua franca

I. nuclear weapons

J. Antarctica

Column B

_____ **1.** a conflict here has hurt tourism

_____ **2.** protects us from harmful rays of the sun

_____ **3.** area between Melanesia and Australia

_____ **4.** where climatologists study global warming

_____ **5.** common language of an area

_____ **6.** United States territory

_____ **7.** mineral salt to make fertilizer

_____ **8.** tested in the Pacific region by the United States

_____ **9.** people here believe that the volcanoes hold spirits

_____ **10.** have won lawsuits based on the Treaty of Waitangi

Directions: Multiple Choice In the blank at the left, write the letter of the choice that best completes the statement or answers the question. *(3 points each)*

_____ **11.** Which of the following describes Australia's current attitude toward immigration?

    A. Immigration from South Africa and Asia is discouraged.

    B. Only Europeans are encouraged to immigrate.

    C. Immigration from many countries is encouraged.

    D. Since the 1970s, the government has limited immigration.

_____ **12.** Australia is a world leader in the export of ____.

    A. wool and cattle hides   **C.** oil and natural gas

    B. vegetables and fruits   **D.** computers and electronic devices

_____ **13.** A major part of New Zealand's economy is the export of ____.

    A. coffee and coconut oil   **C.** wool and meat

    B. timber   **D.** iron ore, nickel, and zinc

_____ **14.** Which is a major export of Papua New Guinea?

    A. food products   **C.** copra

    B. phosphates   **D.** steel

_____ **15.** Which island country has traditional ethnic groups that use shells and feathers as money?

    A. Fiji   **C.** Solomon Islands

    B. New Caledonia   **D.** Guam

_____ **16.** Which of these island groups has historic ties to the United States?

    A. Fiji and Tasmania   **C.** Polynesia

    B. Melanesia   **D.** Micronesia

_____ **17.** This resource, once important to Kiribati and Nauru, is nearly used up.

    A. iron ore   **C.** oil

    B. phosphate   **D.** rich soil

_____ **18.** The Antarctic Treaty specifies that Antarctica cannot be used for ____.

    A. weapons testing or military use   **C.** environmental research

    B. scientific mining   **D.** tourism

_____ **19.** Which of these are serious environmental issues in Micronesia and Polynesia?

    A. nuclear radiation and phosphate mining

    B. oil spills and water pollution

    C. air pollution and tourism

    D. deforestation and chemical pollution

_____ **20.** Which of these words comes from the Samoan language?

    A. banana   **C.** hello

    B. tattoo   **D.** surf

Applying Skills: Reading a Map Use the map below to answer the questions that follow. *(5 points each)*

Maori Tribal Lands

_____ **21.** Which *iwi* is closest to New Zealand's capital?

    A. Ngai Tahu   **C.** Ngati Kahungunu

    B. Te Atiawa   **D.** Ngati Porou

_____ **22.** Which tribal lands are located in the interior?

    A. Ngati Tuwaharetoa   **C.** Waikato

    B. Ngati Porou   **D.** Ngati Awa

_____ **23.** The Ngai Tahu are concentrated on the ____ side of South Island.

    A. western   **C.** northern

    B. eastern   **D.** southern

Directions: Document-Based Questions Use the document below to answer the questions that follow. *(5 points each)*

Located in the middle of the driest state of the world's driest inhabited continent is a town where nearly 80 percent of the residents live underground. Coober Pedy, Aborigine for "white men down holes," was founded after William Hutchison discovered opals there in 1915. Returning World War I soldiers used their knowledge of constructing deep trenches to build underground homes. Nearly 70 percent of the world's precious opals come from the Coober Pedy Precious Stones Field. The lure of wealth from opals still draws miners to this desolate moonlike landscape. When not looking for gems, the locals retreat from the intense summer heat, biting winter cold, and spectacular dust storms into their underground homes. Neither furnaces nor air conditioners are needed underground, where the atmosphere stays a comfortable 77°F. In this town of 3,500 people from 45 different nations, tourism is a primary industry today. Underground museums, churches, and hotels cater to the 100,000 tourists who visit every year.

_____ **24.** How do you know that Coober Pedy is located in Australia?

    A. Australia has the world's largest desert.

    B. Aborigines live in Australia.

    C. World War I soldiers came from Australia.

    D. Australia has bitterly cold winters.

_____ **25.** Why was Coober Pedy originally founded?

    A. as a tourist attraction   **C.** as a summer retreat for soldiers

    B. as a gold-mining settlement   **D.** as an opal-mining settlement

_____ **26.** Which of these statements about Coober Pedy is false?

    A. Its landscape looks like the moon's surface.

    B. It has a diversity of people.

    C. Its opal deposits have been depleted.

    D. Its primary industry is tourism.

Directions: Essay On a separate sheet of paper, answer the question below. *(10 points)*

    27. How have some island nations of Oceania tried to overcome their relative lack of resources?

SCORE

Directions: Matching Match each item in Column A with its description in Column B. Write the correct letters in the blanks. *(3 points each)*

Column A

A. kiwifruit

B. copra

C. merinos

D. Nauru

E. whales

F. New Zealand

G. South Pole

H. shells

I. New Caledonia

J. krill

Column B

_____ **1.** reached in 1911

_____ **2.** agricultural product of New Zealand

_____ **3.** meat of a dried coconut

_____ **4.** a form of money in the Solomon Islands

_____ **5.** island where one-third of the people are French

_____ **6.** breed of sheep known for its fine wool

_____ **7.** a tiny shrimplike creature

_____ **8.** island where 80 percent of the land cannot support human life

_____ **9.** hunted nearly to extinction

_____ **10.** home to more sheep than people

Directions: Multiple Choice In the blank at the left, write the letter of the choice that best completes the statement or answers the question. *(3 points each)*

_____ **11.** The largest ethnic group of New Zealand is which of these?

    A. Pacific Islander

    B. British and Irish

    C. Maori

    D. Asian

_____ **12.** What was the result of Aboriginal lawsuits in recent years?

    A. Aborigines have gained control over land.

    B. Aborigines have achieved equal education.

    C. Aborigines gained high-paying jobs.

    D. Aborigines have been lifted out of poverty.

_____ **13.** What problem was caused by Hawaiian cane toads introduced into Australia?

    A. They ate the sugarcane crop.

    B. They are poisonous to other animals.

    C. They have almost died out.

    D. They are polluting the water.

_____ **14.** Australia's farming is limited by a lack of rainfall and ____.
- **A.** poor soils
- **B.** cold temperatures
- **C.** hot temperatures
- **D.** strong winds

_____ **15.** Why is New Zealand's ethnic balance changing?
- **A.** Pacific Islanders are emigrating.
- **B.** Asians have a high death rate.
- **C.** European birthrates are low.
- **D.** The Maori are emigrating.

_____ **16.** Which is the lingua franca of Vanuatu?
- **A.** French
- **B.** Papuan
- **C.** English
- **D.** Bislama

_____ **17.** Why have many nations reduced the use of aerosol sprays?
- **A.** Chemicals from the sprays destroy the ozone layer.
- **B.** The cans end up in the oceans and pollute the water.
- **C.** Chemicals from the sprays are killing penguins in Antarctica.
- **D.** Spray cans take up too much room in landfills.

_____ **18.** Which two nations battled in Micronesia?
- **A.** Germany and England
- **B.** Japan and the United States
- **C.** Australia and New Zealand
- **D.** France and Spain

_____ **19.** Which of the following limits farm production in Micronesia?
- **A.** dry summers
- **B.** hurricanes
- **C.** poor soil
- **D.** cold weather

_____ **20.** *Fa'a Samoa* emphasizes which of these?
- **A.** magic realism
- **B.** fishing as both a sport and a way to make a living
- **C.** traditional volcanic spirits
- **D.** living in harmony with the community and the land

Applying Skills: Reading a Map Use the map below to answer the
questions that follow. *(5 points each)*

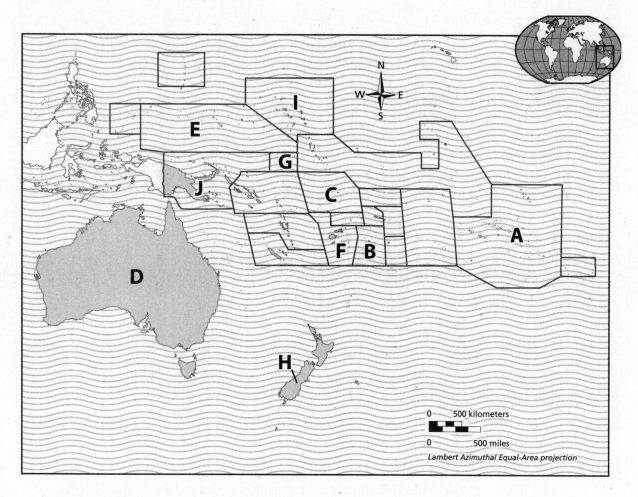

_____ **21.** Which is represented by the letter *B?*

    A. Tonga   **C.** Marshall Islands

    B. Fiji   **D.** Nauru

_____ **22.** Which country is represented by the letter *J?*

    A. Fiji   **C.** New Zealand

    B. Federated States of Micronesia   **D.** Papua New Guinea

_____ **23.** Which country is represented by the letter *I?*

    A. French Polynesia   **C.** Marshall Islands

    B. Federated States of Micronesia   **D.** Tuvalu

Australia, Oceania, and Antarctica Today

Chapter 30 Test Form B (continued)

Directions: Document-Based Questions Use the document below to answer the questions that follow. *(5 points each)*

> Authorities in Tonga have confirmed at least five people were killed during riots in the capital Nuku'alofa yesterday. It is believed the victims may have been trapped in one of the buildings set alight by pro-democracy demonstrators.
>
> . . . Armed soldiers are patrolling Nuku'alofa and a curfew is in force as police reportedly begin rounding up the riots' ringleaders.
>
> As a response to the riots, the Tongan government has agreed to step up the pace of political reform. The emergency meeting of the Cabinet, nobles, and elected commoners resolved to give MPs elected by popular vote the majority voice in the next elections in 2008.
>
> **Source:** ABC News Online, November 17, 2006.
> www.abc.net.au/news/newsitems/200611/s1790952.htm.

_____ 24. What caused the deaths of people in Nuku'alofa?

   A. armed soldiers firing into crowds

   B. fires set by pro-democracy demonstrators

   C. police shooting at protesters

   D. gangs of ringleaders

_____ 25. Why were people rioting in Tonga in 2006?

   A. They wanted more government aid.

   B. They wanted a more democratic government.

   C. They opposed the pro-democracy demonstrations.

   D. They were responding to a curfew that the government had imposed.

_____ 26. The government of Tonga responded to the riots by doing all of the following EXCEPT ____.

   A. imposing a curfew

   B. calling an emergency meeting of the Cabinet

   C. resolving to make Tonga more democratic

   D. allowing commoners to be freely elected

Directions: Essay On a separate sheet of paper, answer the question below. *(10 points)*

   27. Identify evidence of international cooperation in the exploration and use of Antarctica.

Australia, Oceania, and Antarctica

Unit 10 Posttest

Directions: Matching Match each item in Column A with its description in Column B. Write the correct letters in the blanks. *(5 points each)*

Column A

A. phosphates

B. New Zealand

C. Samoa

D. gold

E. Port Moresby

F. continental islands

G. kiwi

H. ice shelf

I. Canterbury Plains

J. ice cap

Column B

_____ **1.** capital of Papua New Guinea

_____ **2.** New Zealand's best farming land

_____ **3.** national symbol of New Zealand

_____ **4.** layer of ice above water in Antarctica

_____ **5.** first country to give women the right to vote

_____ **6.** drew settlers to Australia in the 1850s

_____ **7.** has been depleted from Kiribati

_____ **8.** layer of ice covering much of Antarctica

_____ **9.** formed by the rising and folding of rock from the ocean floor

_____ **10.** the "Cradle of Polynesia"

Directions: Multiple Choice Write the letter of the choice that best completes the statement or answers the question. *(5 points each)*

_____ **11.** Almost all of Oceania's smaller islands are in which climate zone?
  A. humid subtropical
  B. tropical wet
  C. tropical dry
  D. Mediterranean

_____ **12.** Which part of Australia has a tropical dry climate?
  A. the northern coast
  B. the interior
  C. the western coast
  D. almost all of Australia

_____ **13.** Why is Antarctica extremely cold?
  A. It never receives direct sun rays.
  B. The ocean around it is very cold.
  C. Polar winds chill the interior.
  D. All of these are true.

_____ **14.** Which major change occurred in the South Pacific region by 1500 B.C.?
  A. People moved to smaller islands.
  B. Volcanoes began erupting.
  C. Europeans migrated there.
  D. The Ice Age ended.

_____ **15.** When did most of Micronesia become U.S. trust territories?
  A. after World War I
  B. during Roosevelt's presidency
  C. following World War II
  D. after the Korean War

Applying Skills: Reading a Chart Use the chart below to answer the questions that follow. *(5 points each)*

Adelie and Emperor Penguins of Antarctica		
	Adelie Penguins	**Emperor Penguins**
Size	29.5 inches	47 inches
Maximum weight	14 pounds	99 pounds
Egg laying	November	May
Hatching	December	July
Chicks depart	February	December/January
Main food	Krill	Squid and fish

_____ **16.** During which season do Emperor penguin chicks depart?

    A. winter   **C.** summer

    B. spring   **D.** fall

_____ **17.** For how much longer do Emperor penguin chicks stay with their parents than Adelie penguin chicks?

    A. 2 months longer   **C.** 4 months longer

    B. 3 months longer   **D.** 5 months longer

_____ **18.** After laying the eggs, the female Emperor penguin leaves to find food. For how long must the male Emperor penguin keep the eggs warm until they hatch?

    A. one month   **C.** three months

    B. two months   **D.** four months

Directions: Essay On a separate sheet of paper, answer the question below. *(10 points)*

    19. Compare the Maori of New Zealand to the Aborigines of Australia in their historic origins, their treatment by Europeans, and their place in these countries today.

Unit 1 Pretest
THE WORLD

Matching

1. H
2. D
3. F
4. C
5. A
6. J
7. I
8. E
9. B
10. G

Multiple Choice

11. A
12. C
13. B
14. C
15. A
16. D
17. C
18. C

Section Quiz 1-1
THINKING LIKE A GEOGRAPHER

Matching

1. E
2. A
3. D
4. C
5. B

Short Answer

6. The five themes of geography are location, place, human-environment interaction, movement, and regions.

7. A physical geographer examines the physical features of a place, such as landforms, plants, animals, and weather.

8. Western societies divide history into Prehistory, Ancient History, Middle Ages, and Modern History.

9. Satellites can provide detailed images and photographs, measure temperatures and pollution, and record exact locations on Earth.

10. Geographers in government often help decide how land and resources might be used. Geographers in the business world often work as researchers and analysts.

Section Quiz 1-2
THE EARTH IN SPACE

Matching

1. E
2. B
3. D
4. A
5. C

Short Answer

6. Mars is an inner planet, and Jupiter is an outer planet. Mars is relatively small and solid, while Jupiter is large and composed mostly of gases.

7. Our solar system is made up of Earth, seven other major planets, and thousands of smaller bodies revolving around the sun.

8. In low-latitude areas near the Equator, the sun's rays hit directly, resulting in warm temperatures. In high-latitude areas near the North and South Poles, the sun's rays hit indirectly, resulting in cool or cold temperatures.

9. Earth is tilted 23½ degrees on its axis.

10. The midlatitudes are affected by warm air masses from the Tropics and cold air masses from the North and South Poles. Because of these air masses, the midlatitudes have dramatic seasonal differences.

Answer Key

Chapter 1 Test, Form A
USING GEOGRAPHY SKILLS

Matching

1. I
2. E
3. F
4. A
5. D
6. H
7. B
8. J
9. C
10. G

Multiple Choice

11. D
12. A
13. A
14. B
15. A
16. B
17. B
18. C
19. A
20. B
21. A
22. D
23. A
24. B
25. D
26. B

Essay

27. The study of history helps geographers understand how places appeared in the past. This knowledge allows them to examine changes in a place over a period of time.

Chapter 1 Test, Form B
USING GEOGRAPHY SKILLS

Matching

1. D
2. I
3. C
4. H
5. G
6. F
7. B
8. A
9. E
10. J

Multiple Choice

11. B
12. C
13. A
14. D
15. C
16. B
17. D
18. A
19. D
20. B
21. B
22. B
23. D
24. A
25. D
26. B

Essay

27. When the Earth rotates, it spins on its axis. We cannot feel the Earth moving because the atmosphere around the Earth—the layer of oxygen and gases that surrounds the Earth—moves with it.

Quiz 2-1
FORCES SHAPING THE EARTH

Matching

1. C
2. D
3. A
4. B
5. E

Short Answer

6. Earth's layers are the core, the mantle, and the crust.

7. The theory of plate tectonics explains how the continents were formed and why they move.

8. The seven continents are North America, South America, Europe, Asia, Africa, Australia, and Antarctica.

9. Earthquakes are sudden and violent movements of the Earth's crust. They are caused by the collision of ocean and continental plates, which makes the crust unstable.

10. Chemicals cause weathering when acids in air pollution mix with rain and fall back to Earth. Chemicals eat away rock and stone surfaces.

Quiz 2-2
LANDFORMS AND WATER RESOURCES
Matching

1. C
2. E
3. A
4. B
5. D

Short Answer

6. A plain is a flat lowland, typically found along coasts and lowland river valleys. A plateau is a flatland at higher elevation.

7. The Mariana Trench is located in the western Pacific Ocean.

8. Salt water is found in these bodies of water.

9. People can pump freshwater from aquifers, which are underground layers of rock through which water flows.

10. The water cycle is an ongoing process in which the water goes from the oceans, to the air, to the ground, and finally back to the oceans.

Quiz 2-3
CLIMATE REGIONS
Matching

1. B
2. E
3. C
4. A
5. D

Short Answer

6. Trade winds are winds that blow from east to west between the Tropics and the Equator. Westerlies are winds that blow over North America and move from west to east in the area between the Tropics and 60°N latitude.

7. In the eastern Pacific, places like Ecuador, Peru, and Chile receive unusually heavy rain, which often causes flooding. In the western Pacific, places like Australia, India, and Africa experience drought, and North America may experience severe storms.

8. Sun, wind, water, and the shape of the land affect climate.

9. A mountain causes a rain shadow because it blocks rain from reaching the leeward side of the mountain. The interior region is dry.

10. Urban climates are hotter than rural climates because paved streets and stone buildings soak up the sun's heat energy.

Quiz 2-4
HUMAN-ENVIRONMENT INTERACTION
Matching

1. E
2. C
3. A
4. B
5. D

Short Answer

6. The lithosphere is another name for the Earth's crust. It includes all the land above and below the oceans.

7. *Global warming* is the term used to describe greenhouse gases that have trapped more of the sun's heat near the Earth's surface, raising the temperature around the planet.

8. Wasteful irrigation methods, chemicals from industrial processes, and pesticides harm the water supply.

9. Rain forests support the water cycle, help replenish oxygen in the atmosphere, and are home to unique kinds of plants and animals.

10. Contour plowing is a technique farmers use to limit the loss of topsoil. They plow along the curves of the land rather than in straight lines, which prevents the soil from washing away.

Chapter 2 Test, Form A
EARTH'S PHYSICAL GEOGRAPHY

Matching

1. B
2. G
3. F
4. J
5. C
6. I
7. A
8. E
9. H
10. D

Multiple Choice

11. B
12. A
13. C
14. D
15. D
16. C
17. C
18. B
19. B
20. B
21. B
22. D
23. B
24. C
25. A
26. C

Essay

27. *El Niño* is Spanish for "the boy." During an El Niño event, unusually heavy rains fall in Ecuador, Peru, and Chile. At the same time, droughts can strike Indonesia, Australia, India, and Africa. El Niño also causes severe storms in North America.

Chapter 2 Test, Form B
EARTH'S PHYSICAL GEOGRAPHY

Matching

1. I
2. D
3. E
4. F
5. A
6. C
7. J
8. G
9. H
10. B

Multiple Choice

11. C
12. D
13. A
14. A
15. D
16. C
17. D
18. C
19. A
20. C
21. A
22. D
23. B
24. A
25. C
26. C

Essay

27. The Himalaya were formed by the movement of tectonic plates. Two continental plates collided and pushed against each other with tremendous force. This caused the land along the line where the plates met to rise and form the Himalaya.

Section Quiz 3-1
WORLD POPULATION

Matching

1. D
2. C
3. B
4. E
5. A

Short Answer

6. The five regions are East Asia, South Asia, Southeast Asia, Europe, and eastern North America. They are

Answer Key

attracted by fertile soil, mild climates, natural resources, and water resources.

7. High numbers of healthy births combined with lower death rates lead to population growth.

8. A refugee is a person who is forced to flee his or her country. Warfare, persecution, famine, and other natural disasters create refugee populations.

9. International migration is the migration of people from one country to another.

10. Migration decreases the population or slows population growth and can ease overcrowding. The country's economy can be weakened if skilled and educated workers emigrate.

Section Quiz 3-2
GLOBAL CULTURES
Matching

1. E
2. C
3. D
4. B
5. A

Short Answer

6. Anthropologists analyze cultures today to learn how elements of culture are related. Archaeologists study physical and historical objects to understand how people lived in the past.

7. A dictatorship is an unlimited form of government in which the leader is all-powerful. A democracy is a limited form of government in which the people hold the power.

8. Geographers look at the quality of life—how well people eat, how comfortably they live, and what kind of health care they receive.

9. The first highly developed cultures, or civilizations, were located in river valleys in present-day Iraq, Egypt, India, and China.

10. In the past, culture spread through migration, trade, and conquest. Today, the Internet has increased the spread of cultures around the world.

Section Quiz 3-3
RESOURCES, TECHNOLOGY, AND WORLD TRADE
Matching

1. C
2. E
3. D
4. B
5. A

Short Answer

6. The four types of economic systems are traditional, command, market, and mixed.

7. Developed economies have a mix of agriculture, a great deal of manufacturing, and service industries. They also tend to rely on new technologies, and workers have relatively high incomes.

8. Trade allows nations to export their extra products and resources to nations that need them, and to import needed resources or the products they cannot make themselves.

9. A tariff is a tax that increases the price of an imported good. A country might use it to make imported goods more expensive and to encourage its people to buy less expensive goods manufactured in their own country.

10. Stopping oil production in one country could cause oil shortages and high oil prices in interdependent countries.

363

Copyright © by The McGraw-Hill Companies, Inc.

Chapter 3 Test, Form A
EARTH'S HUMAN AND CULTURAL GEOGRAPHY

Matching

1. C	6. B
2. E	7. F
3. H	8. D
4. A	9. G
5. I	10. J

Multiple Choice

11. C	19. C
12. C	20. D
13. A	21. C
14. D	22. B
15. C	23. D
16. B	24. C
17. A	25. A
18. A	26. C

Essay

27. Emigration can ease overcrowding in a country, but if skilled workers leave, emigration may hurt the country's economy. Immigrants bring new forms of music, art, foods, and language. Sometimes native-born citizens fear or resent immigrants and the changes they bring, and violence is directed toward the immigrants.

Chapter 3 Test, Form B
EARTH'S HUMAN AND CULTURAL GEOGRAPHY

Matching

1. H	6. F
2. A	7. C
3. D	8. I
4. E	9. J
5. G	10. B

Multiple Choice

11. A	19. A
12. B	20. B
13. A	21. A
14. A	22. C
15. B	23. B
16. D	24. C
17. C	25. C
18. D	26. B

Essay

27. Many people have seen their jobs destroyed through globalization. Because of this, their lives have become more insecure. As their lives become more insecure, they feel more and more powerless against forces beyond their control. In this way, globalization continues to create poverty and instability.

Unit 1 Posttest
THE WORLD

Matching

1. I	6. G
2. H	7. J
3. A	8. E
4. C	9. F
5. B	10. D

Multiple Choice

11. D	15. B
12. C	16. C
13. B	17. B
14. A	18. B

Essay

19. The slopes of a mountain facing the sun can heat more quickly than nearby land. Higher up in the mountains, however, air becomes very thin and cannot hold heat very well. The temperature drops as elevations become higher.

Unit 2 Pretest
THE UNITED STATES AND CANADA
Matching

1. I
2. E
3. D
4. C
5. B
6. J
7. G
8. H
9. F
10. A

Multiple Choice

11. C
12. B
13. A
14. D
15. B
16. A
17. C
18. D

Section Quiz 4-1
PHYSICAL FEATURES
Matching

1. D
2. E
3. C
4. A
5. B

Short Answer

6. Except for a fertile, hilly area called the Piedmont, the soil of the Atlantic coastal plain is thin and rocky. Soils along the Gulf of Mexico are better than those along the Atlantic coast.

7. The Appalachian Mountains are older than the Rocky Mountains. The Appalachian Mountains are short and have rounded peaks from erosion over time, while the Rocky Mountains are much higher.

8. The Great Plains once provided food for millions of buffalo. Today farmers grow grains there, and ranchers raise cattle on the land.

9. The St. Lawrence River and the Mississippi River serve as important transportation links. Ships on these rivers carry goods from inland ports to the rest of the world.

10. The oil reserves in Alberta are mixed with sand, making them more costly to obtain than liquid crude oil.

Section Quiz 4-2
CLIMATE REGIONS
Matching

1. E
2. D
3. B
4. A
5. C

Short Answer

6. Tornadoes form over land, while hurricanes form over the ocean. Both are severe storms that produce high winds that can do serious damage.

7. Evergreens have a waxy coating on their needles that helps the trees keep in moisture.

8. It is common to see evergreen forests, ferns, and mosses in a marine west coast climate.

9. The Great Plains receive more rain than the inland West region. The Pacific coastal mountains block humid ocean winds from reaching the inland West, which has a desert climate. The Great Plains benefit from moisture-bearing winds from the Gulf of Mexico and from the Arctic.

10. Areas of northeastern and southeastern North America have similar climates in the summer because warm air from the south blocks cold Arctic air from reaching the eastern areas.

Chapter 4 Test, Form A
PHYSICAL GEOGRAPHY OF THE UNITED STATES AND CANADA

Matching

1. B
2. J
3. C
4. G
5. D
6. F
7. H
8. A
9. I
10. E

Multiple Choice

11. D
12. A
13. B
14. D
15. A
16. C
17. D
18. A
19. D
20. C
21. B
22. D
23. A
24. A
25. C
26. D

Essay

27. The two states that lie apart from the contiguous 48 states are Alaska and Hawaii. Alaska is located in the northwestern part of North America, adjacent to Canada. Hawaii is an island group in the Pacific Ocean, about 2,400 miles southwest of California.

Chapter 4 Test, Form B
PHYSICAL GEOGRAPHY OF THE UNITED STATES AND CANADA

Matching

1. E
2. H
3. G
4. I
5. J
6. F
7. C
8. D
9. B
10. A

Multiple Choice

11. A
12. B
13. A
14. C
15. B
16. D
17. B
18. C
19. B
20. A
21. C
22. B
23. B
24. B
25. D
26. A

Essay

27. The two areas of the United States with tropical climates are southern Florida and Hawaii. In southern Florida, temperatures are hot in summer and warm in winter; rainfall occurs mainly during the summer. In Hawaii, year-round temperatures average above 70°F, and enough rain falls to support the growth of tropical rain forests.

Section Quiz 5-1
HISTORY AND GOVERNMENTS

Matching

1. B
2. E
3. D
4. C
5. A

Short Answer

6. New machines made planting and harvesting crops faster and easier. Manufacturers developed the factory system to produce many goods. Roads, canals, steamboats, and railroads allowed manufacturers to move their goods to markets more quickly.

7. France, Great Britain, and Spain all had colonies in what is now the United States. France and Great Britain had colonies in what is now Canada.

8. The United States gained independence when 13 colonies declared and then fought for their independence from Great Britain. Canadians fought alongside the British and Americans in two World Wars, which led to Canada's full independence from Great Britain.

9. The three branches of the United States government are the executive, the legislative, and the judicial branches.

10. They used peaceful methods that led to social changes for African Americans, Native Americans, Latino Americans, and women in the United States.

Section Quiz 5-2
CULTURES AND LIFESTYLES

Matching

1. E
2. D
3. A
4. C
5. B

Short Answer

6. The United States has become a nation of diverse peoples with a strong national identity. Canada also has been shaped by its immigrant population, yet some Canadians are more connected to their region than to Canada as a country.

7. Canadians refer to their indigenous people as the "First Nations."

8. The rich diversity of the people in the United States and a focus on the landscape and history of particular regions are two common themes of American literature.

9. Both are writers. Amy Tan examines the lives of Chinese Americans, and Oscar Hijuelos writes about the country's Latinos.

10. The film industry generates enormous profits for both countries. Films entertain Americans and Canadians, as well as people around the world.

Chapter 5 Test, Form A
HISTORY AND CULTURES OF THE UNITED STATES AND CANADA

Matching

1. D	6. I
2. B	7. C
3. J	8. G
4. E	9. A
5. F	10. H

Multiple Choice

11. B	19. C
12. D	20. C
13. C	21. D
14. A	22. D
15. A	23. B
16. B	24. B
17. D	25. C
18. B	26. A

Essay

27. The country most affected by the 1882 ban was China, from which nearly all immigration was blocked. The United States limited immigration because some U.S. citizens had become concerned about cultural change.

Chapter 5 Test, Form B
HISTORY AND CULTURES OF THE UNITED STATES AND CANADA

Matching

1. C	6. H
2. D	7. E
3. I	8. B
4. A	9. J
5. F	10. G

Answer Key

Multiple Choice

11. C	19. B
12. D	20. C
13. D	21. D
14. C	22. B
15. D	23. C
16. C	24. A
17. A	25. D
18. C	26. C

Essay

27. American colonists became resentful of British taxes and trade policies. Fighting broke out between the colonists and British forces, and the colonists declared their independence in 1776.

Section Quiz 6-1
LIVING IN THE UNITED STATES AND CANADA TODAY

Matching

1. D
2. A
3. C
4. E
5. B

Short Answer

6. Both the United States and Canada have free market economies, in which people can buy and sell what they want with limited government involvement. Canada's government, however, provides a more direct role in providing services to the public, such as health care.

7. In a free market economy, business owners produce the products that they think will be the most profitable. Consumers shop for the best products at the lowest prices.

8. Farming has been an economic focus of the Midwest because the region's rich soils allow farmers to grow crops such as corn, wheat, and soybeans. The Northwest has poor soil for farming.

9. Both regions are rich in agriculture and oil.

10. Quebec's independence movement makes many outside businesses reluctant to invest in Quebec's economy.

Section Quiz 6-2
ISSUES AND CHALLENGES

Matching

1. B
2. E
3. D
4. A
5. C

Short Answer

6. The United States has a trade deficit because it spends more on imports than it earns from exports. Canada has a trade surplus and earns more from exports than it spends on imports.

7. Lower water levels on the Great Lakes can harm fish populations, and they also prevent the passage of heavy ships, decreasing the amount of goods that can be shipped.

8. NAFTA has affected trade between Canada and the United States by lifting trade barriers and allowing goods to flow freely between the two countries.

9. Canada opposed the U.S. decision to invade Iraq. Instead, it wanted the American government to continue seeking a peaceful solution through the United Nations.

10. Canada has passed laws to reduce the amount of fossil fuels that are burned, while the United States has funded research to find new energy sources that are less harmful to the environment.

Chapter 6 Test, Form A
THE UNITED STATES AND CANADA TODAY

Matching

1. H   6. G
2. A   7. B
3. C   8. E
4. J   9. F
5. D   10. I

Multiple Choice

11. B   19. D
12. A   20. B
13. B   21. A
14. D   22. C
15. A   23. A
16. B   24. D
17. C   25. D
18. A   26. C

Essay

27. Although stocks provide a greater chance for a higher financial payoff, they also involve risk. If a business fails, its stocks become worthless. Saving money in a bank is less risky than buying stock because the government guarantees that savers will get some of their money back if the bank fails or goes out of business. Savings accounts are better protected than stocks, but they usually provide less financial payoff.

Chapter 6 Test, Form B
THE UNITED STATES AND CANADA TODAY

Matching

1. J   6. G
2. E   7. A
3. F   8. C
4. I   9. H
5. D   10. B

Multiple Choice

11. C   19. D
12. B   20. C
13. B   21. B
14. D   22. C
15. B   23. A
16. A   24. B
17. C   25. C
18. A   26. B

Essay

27. Lower lake levels decrease the amount of goods that can be shipped. The ships cannot carry extremely heavy loads because they might run aground. Lower lake levels also harm the fish population. In addition, tourism is affected when water pulls back from the area's beaches.

Unit 2 Posttest
THE UNITED STATES AND CANADA

Matching

1. C   6. G
2. A   7. I
3. H   8. J
4. F   9. E
5. B   10. D

Multiple Choice

11. C   15. A
12. B   16. C
13. A   17. B
14. D   18. C

Essay

19. In 1860 Abraham Lincoln, an opponent of slavery, was elected president. By early 1861, several southern states had withdrawn from the United States to set up a new country. This action led

to a civil war. After four years of fighting, northern forces won. The country was reunited, and slavery ended.

Unit 3 Pretest
LATIN AMERICA

Matching

1. C
2. J
3. B
4. E
5. H

6. D
7. G
8. A
9. I
10. F

Multiple Choice

11. C
12. A
13. B
14. D

15. A
16. B
17. C
18. D

Quiz 7-1
PHYSICAL FEATURES

Matching

1. C
2. E
3. A
4. D
5. B

Short Answer

6. Jamaica's large deposits of bauxite are unique to the Caribbean islands because most of the islands have relatively few mineral resources.

7. Lake Titicaca is the world's highest lake that can be used by large ships.

8. Central America's thick forests, rugged mountains, and coastal marshes make it difficult to transport goods.

9. The rain forests provide a range of products, such as timber, rubber, palm oil, and Brazil nuts.

10. The Pampas are plains that cover much of Argentina and Uruguay. They provide grazing land for beef cattle and fertile soil for growing grains.

Quiz 7-2
CLIMATE REGIONS

Matching

1. D
2. A
3. B
4. E
5. C

Short Answer

6. El Niño brings winds carrying heavy rains that cause flooding along Peru's coast, while in northeastern Brazil, El Niño can bring a long dry season, causing crop failures.

7. The Atacama Desert is along the Pacific coast of northern Chile. The Andes make this one of the driest places on Earth by creating a rain shadow, or by blocking winds that carry moisture from the Atlantic Ocean. In addition, the cold Peru Current does not evaporate much, leaving only dry air to hit the coast.

8. The four altitude zones from lowest to highest elevation are the *tierra caliente*, *tierra templada*, *tierra fría*, and *tierra helada*.

9. Rain forest trees grow so close together that their tops form a dense canopy, or an umbrella-like covering of leaves, that keeps sunlight from reaching the forest floor.

10. The climates south of the Tropic of Capricorn are temperate rather than tropical because they do not receive the direct rays of the sun for much of the year.

Chapter 7 Test, Form A
PHYSICAL GEOGRAPHY OF LATIN AMERICA

Matching

1. I
2. E
3. J
4. F
5. B
6. H
7. D
8. G
9. C
10. A

Multiple Choice

11. C
12. B
13. D
14. A
15. B
16. B
17. D
18. A
19. C
20. D
21. C
22. A
23. D
24. A
25. D
26. B

Essay

27. Islands in the Caribbean can be divided into three groups: the Greater Antilles, the Lesser Antilles, and the Bahamas. The Greater Antilles include the largest islands—Cuba, Hispaniola, Puerto Rico, and Jamaica. The Lesser Antilles is an archipelago, or a chain of islands that stretch from the Virgin Islands to Trinidad. The third group is the Bahamas, another archipelago.

Chapter 7 Test, Form B
PHYSICAL GEOGRAPHY OF LATIN AMERICA

Matching

1. J
2. D
3. I
4. B
5. C
6. G
7. A
8. E
9. F
10. H

Multiple Choice

11. A
12. C
13. A
14. C
15. C
16. B
17. B
18. C
19. D
20. D
21. C
22. A
23. D
24. A
25. C
26. A

Essay

27. The *tierra templada* is one of four altitude zones located in the Andes. This zone, with an altitude of 3,000 to 6,000 feet, has a moist, pleasant climate. Temperatures usually fall between 65°F and 75°F. Abundant rainfall encourages the growth of forests. The climate is also ideal for growing crops such as corn, wheat, and coffee.

Quiz 8-1
HISTORY AND GOVERNMENTS

Matching

1. B
2. C
3. E
4. A
5. D

Short Answer

6. Hernán Cortés conquered the Aztec. Francisco Pizarro conquered the Incas.

7. The Maya built huge stone temples, were skilled at astronomy, developed a calendar, had a number system based on 20, and used hieroglyphics to record their history.

8. Brazil was colonized by Portugal, while Bolivia was a colony of Spain. Brazil gained its independence from Portugal without bloodshed. Military

forces led by Simón Bolívar helped Bolivia gain its independence from Spain.

9. François-Dominique Toussaint-Louverture led the first successful revolt against European rule in Haiti.

10. Cuba is a communist state, in which the government controls the economy and society.

Quiz 8-2
CULTURES AND LIFESTYLES

Matching

1. D
2. C
3. A
4. B
5. E

Short Answer

6. They are descended from enslaved Africans whom Europeans brought as laborers during colonial days.

7. Asian immigrants have brought Islam, Hinduism, and Buddhism to Latin America.

8. Rural Latin Americans expect to find better jobs, schools, housing, and health care when they move to cities. They often do not find these things and are forced to live in crowded neighborhoods with poor housing, a lack of sanitation, and rising crime.

9. In some parts of the Caribbean, the mother is the leader of the family. In most of Latin America, the father is the family leader.

10. Magic realism is a style of writing invented in Latin America. It combines fantastic events with the ordinary. Many European and Asian writers have adopted this style.

Chapter 8 Test, Form A
HISTORY AND CULTURES OF LATIN AMERICA

Matching

1. E
2. D
3. I
4. F
5. C
6. G
7. A
8. B
9. J
10. H

Multiple Choice

11. A
12. D
13. B
14. C
15. C
16. C
17. B
18. A
19. B
20. C
21. B
22. A
23. D
24. A
25. B
26. C

Essay

27. Latin America's population is growing, but resources are limited. Crime and corruption have increased, caused in great part by the growing trade in illegal drugs. The gap between the wealthy and the poor creates social tensions.

Chapter 8 Test, Form B
HISTORY AND CULTURES OF LATIN AMERICA

Matching

1. C
2. J
3. D
4. G
5. A
6. F
7. H
8. B
9. I
10. E

Answer Key

Multiple Choice

11. B	**19.** C
12. A	**20.** D
13. D	**21.** C
14. D	**22.** D
15. C	**23.** A
16. D	**24.** B
17. D	**25.** D
18. C	**26.** C

Essay

27. Family life is very important in Latin America. Traditionally, the father is the family leader and chief decision maker, except in some parts of the Caribbean where the mother is likely to be leader of the family. Often several generations live together, and adults are expected to care for their aged parents. Adult brothers and sisters often live near each other, and their children—who are cousins—can form close relationships.

Quiz 9-1
MEXICO
Matching

1. E
2. A
3. D
4. C
5. B

Short Answer

6. Many Mexican cities have their main government buildings and the largest church organized around large public squares known as plazas.

7. In the 2000 Mexican presidential election, voters elected a president from a different political party for the first time in 70 years. This happened

because of economic troubles and the people's lack of political power.

8. The energy industry is located in the coastal area along the Gulf of Mexico, because major oil and gas deposits are located offshore.

9. Farming, ranching, mining, and manufacturing take place in Mexico's North.

10. Central Mexico has a mild climate due to its high elevation, making it comfortable for people to live there.

Quiz 9-2
CENTRAL AMERICA AND THE CARIBBEAN
Matching

1. D
2. E
3. A
4. C
5. B

Short Answer

6. Guatemala has a history of unrest, with the most recent war occurring in the late 1990s. Costa Rica is a stable democracy that has had no wars since the 1800s.

7. Crop production has shifted from only bananas and coffee to other crops with higher values, like fruits, flowers, and spices.

8. Cuba has a communist government, which decides how resources are used and what goods and services are produced. This has not brought success to Cuba's economy, and many Cubans live in poverty.

9. Cuba's government is just starting to develop its tourism industry to end its dependence on the sale of sugar. Puerto Rico, however, makes more money from tourism than any other country in the Caribbean.

10. Panama profits from fees that it charges ships for using the Panama Canal.

Quiz 9-3
SOUTH AMERICA

Matching

1. D
2. E
3. A
4. B
5. C

Short Answer

6. People of European, Asian, African, and Native American ancestry make up Brazil's population. Argentina's population is mainly of European ancestry, especially Spanish and Italian.

7. Argentina hoped to help its economy grow by borrowing money from foreign banks. Because of the high debt, however, Argentina defaulted on its loans. People from other countries stopped investing in Argentina, causing a severe economic slowdown in the country.

8. Hugo Chávez planned to use oil money to better the lives of the poor. However, his strong rule has split the country into opposing groups.

9. Today, the governments of Chile and Argentina are democratically elected. In the past, these two countries were ruled by military governments that often harshly treated those who opposed their policies.

10. Agriculture provides energy for Brazil in the form of sugarcane, which is used to produce a substitute for gasoline.

Chapter 9 Test, Form A
LATIN AMERICA TODAY

Matching

1.	D	6.	H
2.	A	7.	I
3.	F	8.	B
4.	C	9.	G
5.	J	10.	E

Multiple Choice

11.	B	19.	D
12.	C	20.	C
13.	D	21.	A
14.	A	22.	C
15.	C	23.	A
16.	C	24.	A
17.	B	25.	C
18.	A	26.	B

Essay

27. Unlike most of its neighbors, Costa Rica has a stable democracy. No wars have been fought within or outside the country since the 1800s. Costa Rica has no army; it does have a police force to keep law and order. Costa Rica also has fewer poor people and a higher literacy rate than any other Central American country.

Chapter 9 Test, Form B
LATIN AMERICA TODAY

Matching

1.	D	6.	B
2.	H	7.	G
3.	J	8.	C
4.	I	9.	F
5.	A	10.	E

Answer Key

Multiple Choice

11. D	19. A
12. B	20. D
13. C	21. D
14. A	22. A
15. B	23. C
16. D	24. A
17. A	25. C
18. C	26. B

Essay

27. Colombia has many natural resources, including coal, oil, and copper. Colombia is the world's leading supplier of emeralds. Colombia also exports coffee, which is famous for its flavor, and bananas, sugarcane, rice, and cotton.

Unit 3 Posttest
LATIN AMERICA

Matching

1. E	6. D
2. A	7. G
3. I	8. H
4. J	9. C
5. B	10. F

Multiple Choice

11. A	15. B
12. A	16. D
13. D	17. B
14. D	18. A

Essay

19. Latin Americans distrusted the United States because of the great wealth of the United States. They thought the United States might try to control them like their former rulers had done. To improve relations, the United States announced the Good Neighbor Policy toward Latin America in the 1930s. The United States promised not to send military forces to Latin America and to show greater respect for the rights of Latin American countries.

Unit 4 Pretest
EUROPE

Matching

1. C	6. I
2. A	7. H
3. G	8. J
4. B	9. F
5. E	10. D

Multiple Choice

11. C	15. D
12. A	16. B
13. D	17. D
14. B	18. D

Quiz 10-1
PHYSICAL FEATURES

Matching

1. D
2. C
3. A
4. B
5. E

Short Answer

6. Coal mining provides jobs in Poland, but coal pollution causes breathing problems, eye irritation, and lung disease.

7. Acid rain forms when harmful particles from air pollution mix with precipitation and fall to Earth.

8. Hydroelectric power and wind power are called "clean" energy because they produce little pollution. Germany, Denmark, and Spain are the world's leaders in building wind farms.

Answer Key

9. Fertilizer from these farms runs off into the Danube and causes algae growth. Algae robs the river of so much oxygen that the fish cannot survive.

10. The Mediterranean Sea provides several varieties of fish and is used for transportation and recreation.

Quiz 10-2
CLIMATE REGIONS

Matching

1. C
2. A
3. B
4. D
5. E

Short Answer

6. Deciduous trees are able to grow well because of the mild temperatures and abundant precipitation.

7. The current carries warmth that gives the region milder temperatures and longer growing seasons. Land closest to the water experiences a narrower range of temperatures than land farther inland.

8. The three main climate zones are marine west coast, humid continental, and Mediterranean.

9. Mountains create a rain shadow effect where rain falls on one side of the mountain, but the other side stays drier. Norway and Spain are affected by a rain shadow effect.

10. Global warming is raising average temperatures. Coastal areas are especially concerned that melting glaciers will produce higher ocean levels and flood low-lying areas, such as the Netherlands and Venice, Italy.

Chapter 10 Test, Form A
PHYSICAL GEOGRAPHY OF EUROPE

Matching

1. G	6. H
2. F	7. J
3. D	8. I
4. C	9. E
5. A	10. B

Multiple Choice

11. C	19. D
12. B	20. A
13. A	21. B
14. D	22. C
15. C	23. C
16. C	24. B
17. A	25. D
18. B	26. C

Essay

27. Europeans developed skills in sailing and fishing, which encouraged trade and helped the economy grow. The closeness to the sea meant people could move easily between Europe and other continents. This allowed Europe to influence and be influenced by Asia, Africa, and the Americas.

Chapter 10 Test, Form B
PHYSICAL GEOGRAPHY OF EUROPE

Matching

1. F	6. I
2. B	7. J
3. C	8. G
4. E	9. H
5. A	10. D

Answer Key

Multiple Choice

11. C	**19.** B
12. A	**20.** A
13. C	**21.** B
14. A	**22.** C
15. D	**23.** A
16. D	**24.** C
17. B	**25.** B
18. A	**26.** D

Essay

27. Norway has a much colder climate and more rainfall. Cold, wet winters and cool, wet summers help produce abundant forests. Forestry is a major occupation, along with fishing. Farming is not as important. Norwegians like winter sports. In Italy, Mediterranean breezes moderate the temperature, and warm weather crops grow well. Italy produces grapes and olive trees, but forests are rare. It gets very hot and dry in the summers, causing people to reduce their activities then.

Quiz 11-1
HISTORY AND GOVERNMENTS

Matching

1. C
2. A
3. E
4. B
5. D

Short Answer

6. In a democracy, all citizens share in running the government. In a republic, people choose leaders to run the government.

7. Charlemagne's empire, like the European Union today, united much of western Europe.

8. The Black Death led to the decline of feudalism because so many people were killed that a shortage of labor occurred. This helped the remaining workers earn high wages and gain more freedom.

9. The Reformation divided Christians into Protestants and Roman Catholics, shattering religious unity and reducing the authority of the Catholic Church. As the power of church leaders was challenged, kings and queens claimed more authority for themselves.

10. Thinkers of the Renaissance believed that both faith and reason were paths to knowledge. Thinkers of the Enlightenment believed that reason, rather than faith or tradition, could bring truth and error to light.

Quiz 11-2
CULTURES AND LIFESTYLES

Matching

1. D
2. E
3. C
4. B
5. A

Short Answer

6. Although the number of immigrants is increasing, the overall population of Europe is decreasing because Europe has a low fertility rate.

7. Disputes among ethnic groups split Yugoslavia into five separate countries.

8. Answers may include any four of the following: ice hockey, skiing, hiking, biking, rugby, and soccer.

9. The Chunnel connects England and France. It is a unique tunnel because the trains travel underwater.

10. Abstract is not realistic and does not portray the world as the human eye sees it. Romanticism is inspired by nature and historic events and aims to stir strong emotions. Impressionism uses bold colors and brushstrokes to create "impressions" of the natural world.

Chapter 11 Test, Form A
HISTORY AND CULTURES OF EUROPE

Matching

1.	F	6.	B
2.	G	7.	A
3.	H	8.	D
4.	I	9.	E
5.	C	10.	J

Multiple Choice

11.	B	19.	D
12.	B	20.	C
13.	B	21.	A
14.	A	22.	D
15.	D	23.	B
16.	B	24.	A
17.	B	25.	D
18.	A	26.	B

Essay

27. The Enlightenment led people to think about their natural rights and to overthrow governments that did not protect these rights. As a result, political revolutions erupted in Europe in the 1800s. Industrial advances made during the Industrial Revolution helped European countries grow more powerful, develop new weapons, and compete for colonies. Tensions soon led to World War I and World War II.

Chapter 11 Test, Form B
HISTORY AND CULTURES OF EUROPE

Matching

1.	J	6.	B
2.	I	7.	A
3.	D	8.	H
4.	E	9.	F
5.	C	10.	G

Multiple Choice

11.	D	19.	D
12.	B	20.	A
13.	A	21.	D
14.	B	22.	B
15.	A	23.	D
16.	D	24.	A
17.	B	25.	B
18.	C	26.	C

Essay

27. Since World War II, many immigrants have come from Asia, Africa, and Latin America. Some countries require immigrants to learn their language. Some try to keep immigrants out. Others offer educational and job opportunities for immigrants because they need them to prevent population decline.

Quiz 12-1
NORTHERN EUROPE

Matching

1. E
2. D
3. B
4. C
5. A

Answer Key

Short Answer

6. Iceland uses geothermal energy produced by natural underground sources of steam.

7. Copenhagen is located at the entrance to the Baltic Sea. Many large ships unload their cargoes here because the Baltic Sea is not deep enough for them.

8. The United Kingdom, Denmark, Norway, and Sweden have constitutional monarchies.

9. Finland's people differ from other Scandinavians in language and culture. The ancestors of Finland's people probably came from Siberia in Russia, while the other Scandinavians are descended mostly from Germanic peoples.

10. The Celts are the ancestors of the Irish, many of whom still speak Irish Gaelic, a Celtic language.

Quiz 12-2
EUROPE'S HEARTLAND

Matching
1. E
2. A
3. D
4. C
5. B

Short Answer

6. They face unemployment, poor schools, and poverty in these countries. They have little contact with the majority culture.

7. Specialization in grapes and cheeses allows France to make the best use of its farmland.

8. Polders are drained wetlands created by building dikes. The Dutch use polders as rich farmland.

9. Industry has been most responsible for making Germany a global economic power and a leader in the European Union.

10. Flanders is one region, and its people are known as Flemings. Wallonia is another region whose people are known as Walloons. Brussels is the region with people from both Flanders and Wallonia.

Quiz 12-3
SOUTHERN EUROPE

Matching
1. E
2. B
3. C
4. D
5. A

Short Answer

6. Both areas have poor farmland.

7. Agriculture has declined in importance in all the major countries of southern Europe.

8. Spain's regions had little autonomy before the 1970s because the country was ruled by a dictator. In the 1970s, Spain became a democracy.

9. The capital of Spain is Madrid; the capital of Italy is Rome.

10. Cultural traditions are important to Spain's economy because they attract tourists. Two popular examples are bullfighting and flamenco dancing.

Answer Key

Quiz 12-4
EASTERN EUROPE

Matching

1. B
2. A
3. C
4. E
5. D

Short Answer

6. The economies of many eastern European nations changed from a command economy to a market economy.

7. After the collapse of communism, Yugoslavia broke up into six countries due to the struggle for power by many different ethnic groups. The six countries are Slovenia, Croatia, Bosnia and Herzegovina, Macedonia, Serbia, and Montenegro.

8. Rapid industrialization has helped Czechs enjoy a high standard of living compared to other eastern Europeans. However, it has caused environmental problems, such as acid rain.

9. Most eastern Europeans are related to Slavic and Germanic peoples. The Hungarians are related to the Magyars, who moved from Central Asia into eastern Europe about 1,000 years ago.

10. The Baltic Republics are Lithuania, Latvia, and Estonia.

Chapter 12 Test, Form A
EUROPE TODAY

Matching

1. G
2. I
3. D
4. J
5. A
6. B
7. E
8. H
9. C
10. F

Multiple Choice

11. C
12. D
13. B
14. B
15. C
16. B
17. A
18. D
19. B
20. C
21. A
22. D
23. C
24. B
25. D
26. B

Essay

27. Northern Italy is prosperous, and the people have a relatively high standard of living. A rich farming region lies in the Po River Valley. Farmers there raise livestock and grow grapes, olives, and other crops. Northern Italy also has manufacturing cities, such as Milan, Turin, and Genoa, which produce cars, technical instruments, appliances, clothing, and high-quality goods. Southern Italy is poorer and less industrialized than northern Italy. Much of the terrain is mountainous, with limited mineral deposits, poor land for farming and grazing, and few navigable rivers. Unemployment is high.

Chapter 12 Test, Form B
EUROPE TODAY

Matching

1. D
2. G
3. A
4. E
5. C
6. F
7. B
8. H
9. J
10. I

Answer Key

Multiple Choice

11. B	19. B
12. A	20. A
13. C	21. D
14. C	22. A
15. C	23. C
16. C	24. A
17. A	25. C
18. B	26. D

Essay

27. The Irish people are strong Catholics, and many of their Catholic neighbors in Northern Ireland would like to unite with them. However, most Protestants in Northern Ireland—the dominant group—wish to remain part of the United Kingdom. This dispute has led to violence.

Unit 4 Posttest
EUROPE

Matching

1. E	6. J
2. G	7. D
3. A	8. B
4. I	9. F
5. C	10. H

Multiple Choice

11. D	15. B
12. A	16. C
13. B	17. B
14. A	18. D

Essay

19. Rome spread classical culture and Christianity. Roman law shaped the legal systems in many countries. The Roman idea of a republic later influenced the founders of the United States. The Latin language of Rome became the basis for many modern European languages. Roman architectural styles, such as domes and arches, are seen in Western architecture today.

Unit 5 Pretest
RUSSIA

Matching

1. H	6. D
2. J	7. E
3. I	8. C
4. G	9. B
5. F	10. A

Multiple Choice

11. C	15. C
12. A	16. D
13. B	17. A
14. C	18. B

Section Quiz 13-1
PHYSICAL FEATURES

Matching

1. C
2. D
3. E
4. B
5. A

Short Answer

6. Most Russians (75 percent) live in European Russia with its mild climate. Asian Russia includes Siberia, one of the coldest climates in the world. Few people live in Asian Russia.

7. The port of St. Petersburg is one of the busiest in Russia, but it is frozen three to four months every year.

8. Asian Russia, or Siberia, has large reserves of fossil fuels: coal, oil, and natural gas. Siberia's large size and cold climate make it difficult to reach these resources, however.

9. Lake Baikal is in southern Siberia. It is important because it contains one-fifth of the world's supply of unfrozen freshwater.

10. Kamchatka is located in far eastern Russia along the rim of the Pacific Ocean, known as the Ring of Fire. Tectonic plates meet in this region, and the Earth's crust is unstable.

Section Quiz 13-2
CLIMATE AND THE ENVIRONMENT

Matching

1. A
2. B
3. D
4. C
5. E

Short Answer

6. The land in the north lies at a low elevation, which allows the southerly flow of cold Arctic air. In southern Russia, tall mountains stop the warm winds coming from the lower latitudes.

7. Only mosses, lichens, and small shrubs can survive in the tundra.

8. Russia has high levels of pollution because, in the 1900s, its leaders stressed economic growth and ignored the damage this growth caused to the environment.

9. Smog is causing a decline in health, and many Russians suffer from lung diseases and cancer. Chemical pollution in Lake Baikal may be causing a decline in the population of some animal species.

10. Countries are giving Russia aid to improve sewer systems and to clean up heavily polluted sites.

Chapter 13 Test, Form A
PHYSICAL GEOGRAPHY OF RUSSIA

Matching

1. I	6. C
2. D	7. E
3. G	8. H
4. A	9. B
5. J	10. F

Multiple Choice

11. A	19. D
12. D	20. C
13. B	21. B
14. D	22. C
15. C	23. A
16. B	24. A
17. D	25. B
18. D	26. D

Essay

27. The Ring of Fire is a region along the rim of the Pacific Ocean where tectonic plates meet and cause the Earth's crust to become unstable. As a result, the far eastern Kamchatka Peninsula has many volcanoes.

Chapter 13 Test, Form B
PHYSICAL GEOGRAPHY OF RUSSIA

Matching

1. G	6. A
2. E	7. J
3. I	8. D
4. B	9. C
5. F	10. H

Multiple Choice

11.	C	**19.**	B
12.	D	**20.**	B
13.	A	**21.**	D
14.	A	**22.**	A
15.	D	**23.**	C
16.	C	**24.**	B
17.	B	**25.**	D
18.	A	**26.**	C

Essay

27. During the 1900s, Russian leaders stressed economic growth. Economic growth caused damage to the environment. Russia has a huge problem with smog and with factories pouring pollutants into the air. These pollutants cause lung diseases and cancer.

Section Quiz 14-1
HISTORY AND GOVERNMENTS

Matching

1. B
2. D
3. A
4. E
5. C

Short Answer

6. The serfs had little freedom because they were farm laborers who could be bought or sold with the land.

7. Vladimir Lenin turned the Russian Empire into the Union of Soviet Socialist Republics. Lenin tried to make everyone in society more equal by doing away with the private ownership of business.

8. Perestroika, or "rebuilding," gave more freedom to factory managers and called for the creation of small, privately owned businesses. This led the people to doubt communism even more.

9. Glasnost means "openness" in English. Under glasnost, Soviet citizens could say and write what they thought without fear of being punished.

10. He increased government control to deal with crime and violence and the challenges from ethnic minorities.

Section Quiz 14-2
CULTURES AND LIFESTYLES

Matching

1. C
2. E
3. B
4. A
5. D

Short Answer

6. Leo Tolstoy wrote *War and Peace.* The novel reflected a strong sense of nationalism by describing the Russians' defense against the French invasion in 1812.

7. *Maslenitsa* celebrates the end of winter. Russians celebrate by organizing snowball fights, sleigh rides, and parties. They also burn straw dolls to signify the beginning of spring.

8. Most people have traveled by railroad in Russia. Today, however, people are buying more cars, and the government is building new roads such as a new cross-country highway.

9. The Russian lifestyle is influenced by the region's cold climate and vast size, as well as the country's changing economic system.

10. Russians have excelled in emphasizing education in the sciences and space exploration. Russia also has produced world-class hockey players, figure skaters, and gymnasts.

Answer Key

Chapter 14 Test, Form A
HISTORY AND CULTURES OF RUSSIA

Matching

1. H
2. F
3. G
4. J
5. B
6. I
7. E
8. A
9. D
10. C

Multiple Choice

11. B
12. D
13. C
14. A
15. A
16. B
17. D
18. A
19. D
20. C
21. C
22. D
23. D
24. A
25. B
26. D

Essay

27. In order to succeed with their invasion, the French had to march hundreds of miles and capture Moscow. Although the French eventually took Moscow, they were left with few supplies and could not withstand the brutal Russian winter. The French were forced to retreat because of the Russian attacks, cruel weather, and the lack of supplies. Thousands died from the harsh conditions during the retreat.

Chapter 14 Test, Form B
HISTORY AND CULTURES OF RUSSIA

Matching

1. H
2. J
3. E
4. B
5. I
6. C
7. D
8. F
9. A
10. G

Multiple Choice

11. C
12. A
13. B
14. B
15. B
16. C
17. C
18. C
19. C
20. D
21. D
22. A
23. C
24. C
25. D
26. B

Essay

27. Russia does not have an effective highway system. Major cities are not linked by multilane highways, and existing roads are in poor condition. Few gas stations and restaurants are located along the roads.

Section Quiz 15-1
A CHANGING RUSSIA

Matching

1. C
2. B
3. A
4. E
5. D

Short Answer

6. The Moscow region, the St. Petersburg and the Baltic region, and the Volga and Urals region are involved in manufacturing.

7. Russian is a federation because it is made up of different regions and territories. It is a federal republic because power is divided between the national and regional governments.

8. Privatization is the transfer of ownership of business from the government to individuals. Russian consumers have benefited because businesses

compete for their money and provide what consumers need, want, and are willing to pay.

9. The Russian middle class has embraced the ideas, music, and fashion they have seen in American and European books, television shows, and CDs.

10. A decline in Russian life expectancy is a result of poor nutrition, alcoholism, drug abuse, pollution, and lack of government support of health care.

Section Quiz 15-2
ISSUES AND CHALLENGES

Matching

1. E
2. A
3. D
4. B
5. C

Short Answer

6. Boris Yeltsin stopped the region of Chechnya from separating from Russia because he believed other regions would also demand independence.

7. Putin organized the country into seven large districts and appointed governors who would carry out his policies.

8. Many Russians still understand little about their government. This confusion is one of Russia's roadblocks as it tries to move toward democracy.

9. It might be difficult for the Russian courts to control oligarchs because the legal system often favors rich, powerful citizens.

10. Banks contribute to job growth by collecting people's deposits and lending some of that money to people to buy houses and cars and start new businesses. To encourage bank deposits,

the government has created a deposit insurance system.

Chapter 15 Test, Form A
RUSSIA TODAY

Matching

1. I
2. G
3. A
4. F
5. E
6. C
7. D
8. B
9. H
10. J

Multiple Choice

11. D
12. B
13. A
14. C
15. D
16. A
17. C
18. B
19. D
20. A
21. A
22. C
23. D
24. A
25. C
26. D

Essay

27. The United States and other countries were concerned about Vladimir Putin's growing power and his declining support for democracy. Russia's relations with countries that were once a part of the Soviet Union grew uneasy. Some Russian leaders wanted to see Russia's influence increase, which worried people in the former Soviet countries.

Chapter 15 Test, Form B
RUSSIA TODAY

Matching

1. D
2. I
3. J
4. F
5. G
6. H
7. B
8. E
9. A
10. C

Answer Key

Multiple Choice

11. C	**19.** A
12. B	**20.** D
13. C	**21.** B
14. B	**22.** C
15. A	**23.** A
16. D	**24.** A
17. B	**25.** D
18. C	**26.** C

Essay

27. Siberia holds valuable deposits of iron ore, uranium, gold, and coal. Vast amounts of timber also are located there. The cold climate, rugged landscape, and frozen ground make these resources difficult to obtain.

Unit 5 Posttest
RUSSIA

Matching

1. G	**6.** J
2. A	**7.** I
3. E	**8.** F
4. H	**9.** B
5. D	**10.** C

Multiple Choice

11. B	**15.** C
12. A	**16.** C
13. D	**17.** B
14. A	**18.** A

Essay

19. Other countries are providing Russia with aid to improve sewage systems and clean up heavily polluted sites. Cities are building more efficient power plants that use less energy and burn fuel more cleanly. However, Russia will not have a healthy environment for a very long time.

Unit 6 Pretest
NORTH AFRICA, SOUTHWEST ASIA, AND CENTRAL ASIA

Matching

1. D	**6.** F
2. I	**7.** B
3. G	**8.** J
4. A	**9.** C
5. E	**10.** H

Multiple Choice

11. C	**15.** C
12. C	**16.** A
13. A	**17.** C
14. B	**18.** B

Quiz 16-1
PHYSICAL FEATURES

Matching

1. C
2. B
3. A
4. E
5. D

Short Answer

6. Farmers along the Nile must add fertilizers to the soil because the Aswān High Dam controls flooding of farmland, which once added nutrient-rich silt to the land.

7. Oil revenues have caused divisions by making some countries in the region very wealthy, while countries that do not have much oil remain poor.

8. Lebanon is the only country in the region that has enough timber to support a lumber industry.

9. Fishing industries of the Caspian Sea have been hurt by poaching, or illegal fishing, which has decreased the number of sturgeon. Fishing industries of the Aral Sea have been hurt by irrigation projects, which have drained the two main rivers feeding the sea and made the seawater too salty for fish.

10. Both have served as trade routes. The Strait of Gibraltar allows people to pass between the Mediterranean Sea and Atlantic Ocean, while the Khyber Pass allows people to pass from Southwest Asia to other parts of Asia.

Quiz 16-2
CLIMATE REGIONS
Matching
1. D
2. A
3. B
4. C
5. E

Short Answer

6. Dry continental air masses warmed by the sun blow over North Africa, Southwest Asia, and Central Asia. As a result, much of the land is desert with a dry, hot climate.

7. Libya draws water from aquifers. Syria rations its water, or limits the amount available to each person.

8. Turkey's coastal areas have a Mediterranean climate. These areas are warm and receive enough rain to support agriculture. The steppes are drier and receive only enough rain to support grasses for herding or crops for dry farming.

9. The land around Saharan oases is fertile as a result of water from springs or wells.

10. Rain shadows caused by high peaks, along with dry continental winds, have formed the Kara-Kum and Kyzyl Kum deserts in Central Asia.

Chapter 16 Test, Form A
PHYSICAL GEOGRAPHY OF NORTH AFRICA, SOUTHWEST ASIA, AND CENTRAL ASIA

Matching

1. C	6. H
2. I	7. E
3. A	8. F
4. G	9. J
5. B	10. D

Multiple Choice

11. C	19. D
12. A	20. B
13. D	21. C
14. A	22. B
15. B	23. A
16. A	24. D
17. D	25. C
18. A	26. A

Essay

27. Some nations have rationed water. Others are using underground water from aquifers, or building dams to control water flow and use. A few countries can afford to use desalinization, which removes salt from seawater to make it drinkable.

Chapter 16 Test, Form B
PHYSICAL GEOGRAPHY OF NORTH AFRICA, SOUTHWEST ASIA, AND CENTRAL ASIA

Matching

1. E	6. D
2. J	7. C
3. G	8. B
4. A	9. F
5. I	10. H

Answer Key

Multiple Choice

11.	C	**19.**	C
12.	D	**20.**	B
13.	B	**21.**	C
14.	B	**22.**	A
15.	D	**23.**	B
16.	C	**24.**	C
17.	C	**25.**	D
18.	A	**26.**	B

Essay

27. The Sahara is very dry and has extremely hot temperatures in the summer. Steppes are treeless grassy plains that receive a little more rainfall than deserts. Temperatures are much cooler there. Coastal areas of North Africa and the eastern Mediterranean have mild climates with plenty of rain.

Quiz 17-1
HISTORY AND RELIGION

Matching

1. C
2. E
3. B
4. A
5. D

Short Answer

6. The Sumerians invented cuneiform. Cuneiform used wedge-shaped marks, and hieroglyphics used pictures.

7. Judaism, Christianity, and Islam are examples of monotheism, or the belief in one God. The religions of the Sumerians and Egyptians were based on polytheism, or the worship of many gods and goddesses.

8. Muslims were the leading merchants in many parts of Asia and Africa. They used coins, which made trade easier, and kept records of their business deals, which developed into banking. The trade of these merchants helped Muslim cities grow and made them centers of government and learning.

9. Iraq

10. Terrorism is the use of violence against civilians to achieve a political goal. The goal of al-Qaeda is to remove all American and European influences from the Muslim world.

Quiz 17-2
CULTURES AND LIFESTYLES

Matching

1. E
2. B
3. D
4. C
5. A

Short Answer

6. Qatar's economy is based on oil production and has resulted in a high standard of living for the country's citizens. Afghanistan is a developing country in which farming and herding are major economic activities, and life has changed little for hundreds of years.

7. Residents of these cities face overcrowding, a lack of jobs, inadequate transportation, and poor housing.

8. In many countries of this region, women are expected to obey their husbands, stay home, raise children, agree to an arranged marriage, and dress modestly.

9. Oil revenues have enabled Saudi Arabia to raise the standard of living of its people. Education and health care are free to Saudis.

10. Islam is divided into Sunni and Shia. Both groups follow the Quran and share many beliefs. They disagree on how the Muslim faith should be governed.

Chapter 17 Test, Form A
HISTORY AND CULTURES OF NORTH AFRICA, SOUTHWEST ASIA, AND CENTRAL ASIA

Matching

1. E
2. B
3. C
4. A
5. D
6. H
7. J
8. F
9. I
10. G

Multiple Choice

11. C
12. A
13. D
14. A
15. C
16. B
17. D
18. A
19. B
20. A
21. A
22. C
23. B
24. C
25. D
26. B

Essay

27. They all believe in one God who holds all power and who created the universe. They believe God determines right and wrong. People are expected to love God, obey God's will, and show kindness to others.

Chapter 17 Test, Form B
HISTORY AND CULTURES OF NORTH AFRICA, SOUTHWEST ASIA, AND CENTRAL ASIA

Matching

1. E
2. I
3. B
4. J
5. A
6. H
7. G
8. C
9. F
10. D

Multiple Choice

11. C
12. A
13. B
14. C
15. C
16. A
17. D
18. C
19. D
20. C
21. A
22. D
23. B
24. C
25. B
26. C

Essay

27. Answers will vary. In the cities, many women used to stay home to manage households, but today many of them have jobs in business, education, and government. In some countries, such as Saudi Arabia, women must go to classes separate from men, and they are allowed to enter only certain professions, such as teaching and medicine. Other countries, such as Turkey, allow women to vote and hold public office.

Quiz 18-1
NORTH AFRICA

Matching

1. B
2. D
3. C
4. E
5. A

Short Answer

6. They are able to grow more than one crop per year because the Aswān High Dam controls the Nile River's floodwaters. The dam releases water several times during the year.

7. Casablanca and Marrakesh benefit Morocco's economy by attracting tourists to their historic sites.

8. All North African countries have economies based in part on oil.

9. Algerian Arabs rose up against the French in 1954. After a bloody civil war ended in 1962, Algeria won independence.

10. Muammar al-Qaddafi is the dictator of Libya and controls the government. The king of Morocco is head of state, but elected officials in Morocco run the government.

Quiz 18-2
SOUTHWEST ASIA
Matching
1. D
2. E
3. C
4. B
5. A

Short Answer

6. Saudi Arabia's government is building new industries and improving its agriculture.

7. The Turkish republic is secular, or non-religious. It has done away with many Muslim traditions and made the country more European. The Iranian republic is an Islamic republic, a government run by Muslim religious leaders and with laws based on Islamic teachings.

8. The Iraqi government faces disputes among the country's Sunnis, Shias, and Kurds. In Afghanistan, the government has not been able to gain control of the entire country because of powerful local leaders and Taliban fighters.

9. Bedouins are nomads who live in tents and herd livestock. Many of the people in Jordan's capital, Amman, work in service and manufacturing industries.

10. Syria, Jordan, and Israel use irrigation to grow crops.

Quiz 18-3
CENTRAL ASIA
Matching
1. C
2. A
3. E
4. B
5. D

Short Answer

6. The two regions of Central Asia are the Central Asian Republics and the Caucasus Republics. The Central Asian Republics include Kazakhstan, Uzbekistan, Turkmenistan, Kyrgyzstan, and Tajikistan. The Caucasus Republics include Georgia, Armenia, and Azerbaijan.

7. Most people in Azerbaijan are Shia Muslims, whereas Armenians and Georgians are of Christian heritage.

8. The collision of tectonic plates in Georgia causes warm mineral springs around Georgia's capital of Tbilisi. In Armenia, the collision of tectonic plates has created many faults where frequent earthquakes occur.

9. Both are seeking foreign investments to help improve their economies.

10. During World War I, the Ottoman Turks killed hundreds of thousands of Armenians in a genocide. Today Armenia and Azerbaijan are fighting over an Armenian enclave in Azerbaijan.

Answer Key

Chapter 18 Test, Form A
NORTH AFRICA, SOUTHWEST ASIA, AND CENTRAL ASIA TODAY

Matching

1. C
2. I
3. A
4. H
5. F
6. B
7. G
8. J
9. E
10. D

Multiple Choice

11. A
12. D
13. C
14. A
15. A
16. D
17. D
18. B
19. C
20. B
21. D
22. B
23. C
24. A
25. C
26. A

Essay

27. Large cotton farms used so much water for irrigation that they drained the rivers flowing into the Aral Sea. In turn, this reduced the size of the sea and crippled the fishing industry.

Chapter 18 Test, Form B
NORTH AFRICA, SOUTHWEST ASIA, AND CENTRAL ASIA TODAY

Matching

1. H
2. A
3. B
4. J
5. E
6. D
7. G
8. I
9. C
10. F

Multiple Choice

11. B
12. D
13. D
14. B
15. C
16. B
17. C
18. D
19. A
20. D
21. C
22. D
23. D
24. A
25. B
26. D

Essay

27. Answers will vary. The countries of North Africa were at one time all controlled by European powers. They each have won their freedom. North Africa's people have mixed Berber and Arab heritage. Most of these countries depend on oil for part of their economy. The warm breezes of the Mediterranean provide rainfall for the coastal regions, but the interior is the dry Sahara.

Unit 6 Posttest
NORTH AFRICA, SOUTHWEST ASIA, AND CENTRAL ASIA

Matching

1. H
2. I
3. E
4. A
5. J
6. D
7. C
8. G
9. F
10. B

Multiple Choice

11. D
12. C
13. D
14. B
15. B
16. A
17. C
18. B

Essay

19. The Five Pillars of Islam are acts of worship that are required from faithful Muslims. The first duty is to make

the statement of faith: "There is no God but Allah, and Muhammad is His messenger." Second, Muslims must pray five times a day while facing Makkah. The third duty is to give money to help people in need. The fourth duty is to fast, or not eat or drink, during daylight hours of the holy month of Ramadan. The last pillar of faith is to undertake a holy journey, or hajj, to Makkah to pray.

Unit 7 Pretest
AFRICA SOUTH OF THE SAHARA

Matching

1. G
2. E
3. C
4. F
5. A
6. J
7. I
8. H
9. B
10. D

Multiple Choice

11. C
12. A
13. D
14. B
15. C
16. C
17. A
18. A

Section Quiz 19-1
PHYSICAL FEATURES

Matching

1. D
2. C
3. E
4. A
5. B

Short Answer

6. Lake Victoria provides freshwater and fish. Lake Volta provides hydroelectric power.

7. A series of 30 waterfalls hinders transportation on the Congo River.

8. In Nigeria, oil has replaced agriculture as the principal export.

9. As industrial diamonds, they are used to make drills, saws, and grinding tools.

10. The Congo Basin formed when tectonic activity lifted up the land surrounding it. The Great Rift Valley formed when shifting tectonic plates created a large break in the Earth's surface.

Section Quiz 19-2
CLIMATE REGIONS

Matching

1. D
2. C
3. E
4. A
5. B

Short Answer

6. Rain forests receive more rain than savannas. Rain forests support a variety of plants from shrubs, ferns, and mosses to palms and large trees. The savanna supports grasses and scattered woods.

7. The Kalahari is a desert. One type of tree survives in the Kalahari by using its long roots to reach moisture deep in the sand.

8. Climate change brings long periods of extreme dryness and water shortages, which leads to desertification on the steppes.

9. Moderate climates are found along coastal Southern Africa and in the highlands of East Africa.

10. Farmers in the rain forest often clear more land because the soil quickly become less fertile.

Answer Key

Chapter 19 Test, Form A
PHYSICAL GEOGRAPHY OF AFRICA SOUTH OF THE SAHARA

Matching

1. J
2. F
3. G
4. A
5. C
6. I
7. D
8. B
9. H
10. E

Multiple Choice

11. B
12. A
13. A
14. C
15. C
16. A
17. D
18. B
19. B
20. D
21. D
22. C
23. A
24. A
25. C
26. D

Essay

27. Today the rain forests are threatened by deforestation. Farmers clear the land for new farmland and also depend on cut wood for fuel. Many countries rely on the sale of products from the rain forest for income.

Chapter 19 Test, Form B
PHYSICAL GEOGRAPHY OF AFRICA SOUTH OF THE SAHARA

Matching

1. F
2. G
3. E
4. B
5. D
6. A
7. J
8. H
9. C
10. I

Multiple Choice

11. B
12. D
13. B
14. B
15. C
16. C
17. D
18. B
19. C
20. A
21. D
22. C
23. B
24. B
25. C
26. A

Essay

27. The savanna, mostly grassland with some trees, receives heavy rain in the summer and light rain in the winter. Temperatures are hot all year. The steppe is farther from the Equator, so temperatures are not as high. Trees, shrubs, and grasses grow there, but less rainfall and extreme dryness sometimes lead to desertification. The desert regions receive very little rain. Temperatures are high, and there is very little vegetation.

Section Quiz 20-1
HISTORY AND GOVERNMENTS

Matching

1. E
2. A
3. B
4. C
5. D

Short Answer

6. The Bantu migrated from Nigeria to the west and south, spreading their farming and ironworking skills.

7. Trade made these kingdoms wealthy.

8. The slave trade increased in the 1500s because Europeans started to ship Africans to the Americas to grow sugarcane and other cash crops.

Answer Key

Millions of Africans were torn from their homes and families. Entire villages disappeared, local economies collapsed, and kingdoms weakened.

9. Under colonial rule, Africans had fewer rights and economic opportunities than the Europeans who lived there. European colonists also forced Africans to work in harsh conditions in mines and on large farms called plantations.

10. When forming their colonies, European countries often threw together ethnic groups that did not get along. After these colonies became independent, conflict sometimes erupted between the ethnic groups, resulting in civil wars.

Section Quiz 20-2
CULTURES AND LIFESTYLES

Matching

1. C
2. B
3. E
4. D
5. A

Short Answer

6. AIDS is lowering the life expectancy in some southern African countries.

7. Many Africans south of the Sahara are malnourished because farmers cannot grow enough food. Farmland has been ruined by overuse and soil erosion. Frequent droughts also have damaged crops. In addition, in the past, governments exported most goods to boost their national economies and left little food for the people.

8. As many rural Africans move to cities, families are changing from extended families, with several generations living together, to nuclear families, with a husband and a wife and their children.

9. Arabs introduced the Arabic language and the religion of Islam. Europeans introduced languages like English and French and the Christian religion.

10. The griots of West Africa are storytellers who pass their stories from generation to generation.

Chapter 20 Test, Form A
HISTORY AND CULTURES OF AFRICA SOUTH OF THE SAHARA

Matching

1. F
2. I
3. B
4. H
5. A
6. J
7. D
8. C
9. E
10. G

Multiple Choice

11. D
12. B
13. A
14. B
15. D
16. A
17. C
18. D
19. B
20. C
21. C
22. B
23. B
24. A
25. B
26. B

Essay

27. Between 2,000 and 3,000 different languages are spoken in Africa south of the Sahara. Language is the most important factor in identifying ethnic groups. Rural Africans live in extended families with grandparents, parents, and children living in the same house. Ancestry is important. A clan is a large group of people who are united by a common ancestor in the far past.

Answer Key

Chapter 20 Test, Form B
HISTORY AND CULTURES OF AFRICA SOUTH OF THE SAHARA

Matching

1. G
2. D
3. I
4. A
5. F
6. H
7. B
8. C
9. E
10. J

Multiple Choice

11. C
12. D
13. C
14. A
15. C
16. B
17. D
18. D
19. B
20. C
21. C
22. A
23. C
24. C
25. D
26. A

Essay

27. Most families live in villages near where they farm. Their houses are made from dried mud with straw or palm leaves for a roof. They raise live-stock and only enough food to feed their families, or perhaps a little extra to sell or trade for other goods.

Section Quiz 21-1
WEST AFRICA

Matching

1. C
2. B
3. A
4. E
5. D

Short Answer

6. Nigeria has to import food because it focuses on cash crops and does not grow enough food crops to feed its people.

7. Chad is landlocked and lacks a good transportation system to develop its oil resources. Nigeria is one of the world's major producers of oil, and nearly all of the country's income is based on oil exports.

8. Large herds overgraze and damage the land. The soil blows away from the land, which is stripped bare. Over-grazing and extreme dryness have led to desertification

9. Mauritania, Mali, Burkina Faso, Niger, and Chad make up the Sahel.

10. The region receives plentiful rainfall that supports rain forests.

Section Quiz 21-2
CENTRAL AND EAST AFRICA

Matching

1. C
2. B
3. D
4. A
5. E

Short Answer

6. Djibouti has an excellent harbor at its capital, Djibouti. Somalia has few natural harbors.

7. Uganda, Rwanda, and Burundi are landlocked.

8. Ecotourists visit other countries to view the country's natural wonders.

9. The Congo River is the country's main transportation route. It also provides hydroelectric power to the country.

10. More than a million people died in Sudan in the last century due to a civil

war fought between the country's north and south. More than a million people died in Ethiopia in the last century due to a drought that caused a famine.

Section Quiz 21-3
SOUTHERN AFRICA

Matching

1. C
2. B
3. A
4. E
5. D

Short Answer

6. South Africa rewrote its constitution to ensure equality for all of its people and granted the right to vote for all citizens over age 18.

7. South Africa exports minerals such as gold, diamonds, and platinum.

8. Migrant workers from inland southern Africa depend on South Africa for jobs in the country's mines and factories.

9. Their populations are a mix of peoples from Asia and from Africa.

10. Food shortages in Zimbabwe have been caused by disorder and violence resulting from government efforts to turn over land from European control to Africans.

Chapter 21 Test, Form A
AFRICA SOUTH OF THE SAHARA TODAY

Matching

1. G
2. B
3. E
4. I
5. C
6. A
7. J
8. F
9. D
10. H

Multiple Choice

11. A
12. A
13. C
14. D
15. D
16. C
17. D
18. A
19. B
20. A
21. D
22. A
23. C
24. B
25. C
26. A

Essay

27. Governments in this region must deal with strong ethnic and religious differences among the people. These countries also have serious environmental problems, such as overgrazing and deforestation. Finally, they are concerned with developing a better standard of living and more job opportunities for people fleeing to the cities.

Chapter 21 Test, Form B
AFRICA SOUTH OF THE SAHARA TODAY

Matching

1. G
2. H
3. F
4. J
5. I
6. B
7. A
8. C
9. D
10. E

Multiple Choice

11. B
12. A
13. D
14. A
15. B
16. C
17. B
18. D
19. A
20. B
21. A
22. C
23. A
24. D
25. C
26. A

Answer Key

Essay

27. The countries of Rwanda and Burundi have ethnic conflicts that they have not resolved. Kenya and Tanzania have few ethnic problems. In addition, the economies of Tanzania and Kenya are able to provide a better living for their people.

Unit 7 Posttest
AFRICA SOUTH OF THE SAHARA

Matching

1.	B	**6.**	H
2.	F	**7.**	C
3.	E	**8.**	J
4.	D	**9.**	G
5.	A	**10.**	I

Multiple Choice

11.	D	**15.**	C
12.	B	**16.**	A
13.	A	**17.**	A
14.	C	**18.**	D

Essay

19. People in Africa south of the Sahara suffer from malnutrition. They also lack clean water to drink as well as adequate sanitation facilities. Terrible famines have killed many people, and diseases such as malaria are widespread.

Unit 8 Pretest
SOUTH ASIA

Matching

1.	E	**6.**	F
2.	D	**7.**	G
3.	I	**8.**	C
4.	J	**9.**	H
5.	B	**10.**	A

Multiple Choice

11.	B	**15.**	A
12.	C	**16.**	D
13.	D	**17.**	C
14.	D	**18.**	A

Quiz 22-1
PHYSICAL FEATURES

Matching

1. D

2. A

3. C

4. E

5. B

Short Answer

6. The Hindu Kush, the Himalaya, and the Karakoram were formed by tectonic plate movements that resulted in the South Asian subcontinent separating from Africa and colliding with Asia.

7. The people of South Asia depended upon the Ganges, the Indus, and the Brahmaputra for farming, transportation, and trade.

8. The Western Ghats block seasonal rains from reaching the Deccan Plateau, giving it a dry climate. The rains fall on the Karnataka Plateau instead, giving it a wet climate with dense rain forests.

9. Most countries of South Asia rely on imported oil to meet their energy needs.

10. The people of Nepal rely on wood for heating and cooking. The clearing of trees causes erosion and flooding, and the burning of the wood contributes to air pollution.

Quiz 22-2
CLIMATE REGIONS

Matching

1. E
2. D
3. B
4. A
5. C

Short Answer

6. The Himalaya block winds and rain from going north. Instead the rains move west to the Ganges Plain, bringing water needed for farming.

7. Bangladesh has a wet climate and receives heavy rainfall. These rains help crops grow, but they also can cause flooding and destroy crops.

8. South central India has a tropical dry climate. Because of this, the area's deciduous trees are green during the wet season but turn brown during the long dry season. Southern Sri Lanka has a tropical wet climate. The area receives regular rainfall and is always green with lush rain forests.

9. The Thar Desert in eastern Pakistan receives little or no rain, while Bangladesh receives abundant rainfall.

10. Above 16,000 feet, temperatures are always below freezing, snow never disappears, and little vegetation survives.

Chapter 22 Test, Form A
PHYSICAL GEOGRAPHY OF SOUTH ASIA

Matching

1. B
2. A
3. G
4. D
5. H
6. C
7. J
8. F
9. I
10. E

Multiple Choice

11. C
12. D
13. B
14. A
15. C
16. C
17. C
18. A
19. A
20. C
21. D
22. D
23. A
24. D
25. A
26. D

Essay

27. The heavy rains of the monsoons are good for growing crops, but too much rain may cause floods that kill people and animals, ruin crops, destroy homes, and wipe out roads.

Chapter 22 Test, Form B
PHYSICAL GEOGRAPHY OF SOUTH ASIA

Matching

1. E
2. H
3. I
4. F
5. G
6. B
7. J
8. A
9. C
10. D

Multiple Choice

11. D
12. A
13. C
14. B
15. A
16. B
17. B
18. C
19. B
20. B
21. D
22. A
23. C
24. A
25. B
26. D

Essay

27. The number of cars in the region's cities has risen rapidly in recent decades, which means more exhaust fumes make the air in urban areas dangerous to breathe. In rural areas,

many villagers cook and heat their homes by burning wood, kerosene, charcoal, or animal dung. These substances release smoke and chemicals.

Quiz 23-1
HISTORY AND GOVERNMENTS

Matching

1. D
2. C
3. A
4. E
5. B

Short Answer

6. The Buddha taught that people suffer because they are too attached to material things, which are not lasting. He believed people can be released from attachments by following the Eightfold Path.

7. Mohandas Gandhi and his followers boycotted, or refused to buy, British goods, which helped gain independence for the region.

8. Nepal has always been free of European rule, but Sri Lanka was ruled by the British until 1948.

9. Priests had the highest status. Warriors came next, followed by farmers. At the bottom were unskilled laborers and servants.

10. The people had cities with carefully laid-out streets, ceremonial gateways, and buildings to store grain. The cities also had plumbing, sewers, and other technology. The people made copper and bronze tools, clay pottery, and cotton cloth, and they had a writing system.

Quiz 23-2
CULTURES AND LIFESTYLES

Matching

1. D
2. A
3. E
4. C
5. B

Short Answer

6. Pakistan has developed an expanded irrigation system, boosting farm incomes. India's government is working to provide electricity, drinking water, better schools, and paved roads to rural areas.

7. In India and Pakistan, several generations of a family often live together in the same house.

8. Hindus avoid beef because they view the cow as sacred. Muslims avoid pork because they consider pigs unclean. Jains avoid all meat because they reject violence of any kind and aim to protect every living creature.

9. Mumbai is sometimes called Bollywood because it is the center of the Indian film industry.

10. In South Asia, upper- and middle-class people live in comfortable homes or high-rise apartments. Poor people crowd into cheap apartments or flimsy shacks, or even sleep on the streets.

Answer Key

Chapter 23 Test, Form A
HISTORY AND CULTURES OF SOUTH ASIA

Matching

1. E
2. H
3. G
4. F
5. I
6. A
7. D
8. B
9. C
10. J

Multiple Choice

11. B
12. B
13. D
14. A
15. A
16. A
17. B
18. D
19. A
20. B
21. A
22. B
23. D
24. A
25. B
26. D

Essay

27. In 1947 India was divided into mostly Hindu India and mostly Muslim East and West Pakistan. In 1971 East Pakistan declared its independence. After a brief civil war, it became the new country of Bangladesh.

Chapter 23 Test, Form B
HISTORY AND CULTURES OF SOUTH ASIA

Matching

1. H
2. G
3. B
4. J
5. C
6. F
7. A
8. E
9. I
10. D

Multiple Choice

11. A
12. D
13. C
14. C
15. D
16. A
17. C
18. B
19. C
20. A
21. A
22. C
23. A
24. C
25. A
26. A

Essay

27. Many people who live in urban areas of South Asia face widespread poverty. Large numbers of people have inadequate housing or are homeless. Children often beg in the streets for food or money to buy food. Unemployment, pollution, disease, crime, and lack of clean water are common problems in urban areas.

Quiz 24-1
INDIA

Matching

1. E
2. D
3. B
4. A
5. C

Short Answer

6. In India, wages are low, and the country has large numbers of workers who are educated, skilled, and fluent in English.

7. India's government is divided into three branches—the executive, the legislative, and the judicial. Each branch has specific rights and responsibilities that the other branches cannot interfere with.

8. In the 1970s, India's economy slowed. To boost growth, the government reduced its controls and moved

Answer Key

toward a free market economy. In addition, business shifted to private ownership, and foreign investment was encouraged to create jobs. Today India has one of the world's most rapidly growing economies.

9. India developed new strains of rice, wheat, and corn that produce more grains. It also built dams to store water for irrigation during the dry season.

10. India has rich deposits of coal and also mines iron ore, manganese, diamonds, and bauxite. Deep-sea fishing is another important contributor to India's economy.

Quiz 24-2
MUSLIM NATIONS

Matching

1. C
2. E
3. A
4. B
5. D

Short Answer

6. Bangladesh disputes use of the Ganges River with India, and Pakistan disputes control of Kashmir with India.

7. It is difficult for Bangladesh to build a successful nation because it is densely populated and has few resources.

8. Bangladesh is unable to feed its growing population because farmers there have few modern tools, and they use outdated farming methods. In addition, floods often drown crops and cause food shortages.

9. They become temporary workers in other countries to escape poverty.

10. Pakistan's military has often forced elected leaders out of office and seized power.

Quiz 24-3
MOUNTAIN KINGDOMS, ISLAND REPUBLICS

Matching

1. C
2. D
3. A
4. E
5. B

Short Answer

6. In Bhutan, the government limits the number of tourists to protect the country's cultural traditions.

7. The Nepali are mostly Hindu. They accuse the Bhutia, who are mostly Buddhist, of discrimination during years of rule by powerful Buddhist kings.

8. The major religion of the Maldives is Islam, and the religions of Nepal, Bhutan, and Sri Lanka are primarily Hindu and Buddhist.

9. None of the Maldives Islands are more than 6 feet above sea level. Some scientists believe that global warming will cause ocean levels to rise and completely cover the islands.

10. The Tamils and the Sinhalese have fought a civil war since 1983. The minority Tamils claim they have not been treated justly by the majority Sinhalese. They want to set up a separate Tamil nation in northern Sri Lanka.

Answer Key

Chapter 24 Test, Form A
SOUTH ASIA TODAY

Matching

1.	F	6.	E
2.	A	7.	H
3.	I	8.	B
4.	C	9.	D
5.	J	10.	G

Multiple Choice

11.	D	19.	C
12.	D	20.	D
13.	D	21.	C
14.	C	22.	A
15.	A	23.	B
16.	B	24.	A
17.	B	25.	D
18.	C	26.	A

Essay

27. Many American businesses hire workers in India to do certain jobs because India has a large number of skilled, educated, English-speaking workers whose wages are low. Many of India's software developers and tech support people work for American companies. India also has a large number of doctors, scientists, and engineers who perform research, writing, and other tasks for American companies.

Chapter 24 Test, Form B
SOUTH ASIA TODAY

Matching

1.	B	6.	I
2.	H	7.	A
3.	G	8.	F
4.	J	9.	D
5.	E	10.	C

Multiple Choice

11.	C	19.	A
12.	A	20.	A
13.	A	21.	D
14.	C	22.	B
15.	B	23.	C
16.	D	24.	D
17.	B	25.	B
18.	D	26.	C

Essay

27. Most of the people in Bangladesh are Muslim and very poor. In both urban and rural areas, people face serious threats from natural disasters. Heavy monsoons cause riverbanks to overflow almost yearly, and cyclones also cause flooding. Floods drown crops and cause food shortages.

Unit 8 Posttest
SOUTH ASIA

Matching

1.	D	6.	C
2.	F	7.	E
3.	G	8.	H
4.	I	9.	J
5.	A	10.	B

Multiple Choice

11.	C	15.	B
12.	C	16.	B
13.	A	17.	C
14.	D	18.	D

Essay

19. Under the Gupta Empire's Hindu rulers, trade increased and ideas were exchanged with other parts of the world. As a result, science, mathematics, medicine, and the arts thrived.

South Asian mathematicians developed the numerals 1 to 9, which we still use today.

Unit 9 Pretest
EAST ASIA AND SOUTHEAST ASIA

Matching

1. I
2. B
3. F
4. C
5. A
6. H
7. D
8. E
9. J
10. G

Multiple Choice

11. D
12. A
13. B
14. B
15. C
16. C
17. A
18. D

Quiz 25-1
PHYSICAL FEATURES

Matching

1. D
2. E
3. A
4. B
5. C

Short Answer

6. Japan is an archipelago, or a chain of islands. This isolated Japan from the Asian mainland and allowed it to develop a unique culture.

7. The Mekong region provides a good place to grow rice because of its warm temperatures and heavy rains.

8. Brunei is rich in petroleum, whereas the Korean Peninsula is a major coal producer.

9. The region extends from the mountains of inland China to the Pacific shores of Japan, and from the highlands of northeastern China to the tropical islands of Indonesia.

10. Teak is used to make buildings and ships. Mahogany is used to make wall paneling and high-quality furniture.

Quiz 25-2
CLIMATE REGIONS

Matching

1. E
2. D
3. A
4. B
5. C

Short Answer

6. Cold Arctic winds bring harsh winters to Ulaanbaatar, Mongolia. Winter monsoons and a cold ocean current flowing southwest along Japan's Pacific coast bring harsh winters to Hokkaido.

7. Sea breezes keep temperatures low in Singapore, whereas high altitudes keep parts of New Guinea cool.

8. The Taklimakan is a desert in western China that receives less than 0.5 inches of rain per year. Little vegetation and few people live there. The rain forests of Indonesia are home to a tremendous variety of plants and animals.

9. Mongolia has a dry steppe climate that receives only enough rain to support grasslands for cattle and sheep. Vietnam has a humid subtropical climate with moderate summer and winter temperatures that are good for growing rice.

10. China has the greatest variety of climates in East Asia and Southeast Asia. It is the largest country in the region and also has the greatest range of latitudes and landforms.

Answer Key

Chapter 25 Test, Form A

PHYSICAL GEOGRAPHY OF EAST ASIA AND SOUTHEAST ASIA

Matching

1.	C	6.	D
2.	I	7.	H
3.	E	8.	G
4.	F	9.	J
5.	A	10.	B

Multiple Choice

11.	D	19.	A
12.	C	20.	B
13.	A	21.	D
14.	A	22.	B
15.	B	23.	B
16.	D	24.	B
17.	A	25.	C
18.	C	26.	B

Essay

27. Few people live in the mountainous regions of East Asia. Most of East Asia's population lives on fertile low-land areas such as the North China Plain and the Manchurian Plain. In Southeast Asia, river valleys are densely populated. Southeast Asia's major rivers include the Irrawaddy, the Salween, the Chao Phraya, and the Mekong. More people live along the coasts, where the climate is mild. Fewer people live inland where temperatures are not moderate.

Chapter 25 Test, Form B

PHYSICAL GEOGRAPHY OF EAST ASIA AND SOUTHEAST ASIA

Matching

1.	H	6.	E
2.	J	7.	I
3.	D	8.	A
4.	C	9.	F
5.	G	10.	B

Multiple Choice

11.	C	19.	A
12.	C	20.	C
13.	D	21.	A
14.	A	22.	C
15.	B	23.	B
16.	A	24.	B
17.	C	25.	A
18.	B	26.	D

Essay

27. The climate zones of the region include dry continental, wet continental, tropical, and highland. The dry continental climate is very cold in winter and ranges from desert to grasslands. The wet continental climate zone, such as Northern China, has warm summers and cold, snowy winters. Southeast Asia's tropical climate is warm all year. Heavy rains fall for many months. The highland climate zones are cool and somewhat dry.

Quiz 26-1

HISTORY AND GOVERNMENTS

Matching

1. C
2. D
3. B
4. E
5. A

Short Answer

6. Traders from India spread Hinduism, traders from the Arab Empire spread Islam, and traders from Europe spread Christianity.

7. The Chinese and Japanese isolated themselves to keep out European influences. In the late 1800s, Europeans used powerful warships to pressure the Chinese to open their ports. U.S. naval officer Matthew C. Perry pressured the Japanese to end their isolation and open their country to foreign trade.

8. The Korean War helped boost Japan's economy because the United States poured $3.5 billion into Japan's factories to provide supplies for U.S. troops.

9. Following Japan's example, these four countries have built strong, modern economies.

10. Relaxed government control has allowed factory managers to decide what goods to produce and what prices to charge, and farmers are allowed to sell their crops for a profit.

Quiz 26-2
CULTURES AND LIFESTYLES

Matching

1. B
2. C
3. D
4. E
5. A

Short Answer

6. Mandarin is found in the north and is China's official language. Another major dialect, Cantonese, is spoken in southeastern China.

7. Japan has little ethnic diversity. About 99 percent of the population is ethnic Japanese. Indonesia, however, has great ethnic diversity. More than 300 ethnic groups live throughout Indonesia's islands.

8. Both Daoism and Shinto show a strong reverence for nature. Shinto stresses that all parts of nature—humans, animals, plants, rocks, and rivers—have their own spirits.

9. Mongolian yurts are large circular structures made of animal skins that can be packed up and moved from place to place.

10. Pagodas have several stories with tiled roofs that curve up at the edges. In East Asia, these buildings serve as temples.

Chapter 26 Test, Form A
HISTORY AND CULTURES OF EAST ASIA AND SOUTHEAST ASIA

Matching

1. I	6. E
2. B	7. H
3. D	8. C
4. A	9. J
5. F	10. G

Multiple Choice

11. C	19. B
12. B	20. B
13. A	21. D
14. A	22. B
15. B	23. A
16. C	24. D
17. B	25. D
18. D	26. B

Essay

27. In 1979 the government enacted a policy that encouraged families to have only one child. Population growth has slowed, but it continues to grow by millions of people per year.

Chapter 26 Test, Form B
HISTORY AND CULTURES OF EAST ASIA AND SOUTHEAST ASIA

Matching

1. G
2. C
3. H
4. E
5. A
6. J
7. F
8. I
9. D
10. B

Multiple Choice

11. B
12. D
13. C
14. A
15. C
16. B
17. C
18. A
19. B
20. C
21. C
22. A
23. D
24. C
25. D
26. D

Essay

27. The artists often paint rugged landscapes of their countries. Their works reflect the strong reverence for nature that is part of both Daoism and Shinto.

Quiz 27-1
CHINA

Matching

1. B
2. D
3. A
4. C
5. E

Short Answer

6. China's economy has changed to allow greater economic freedom. For example, people can choose their jobs. However, the Chinese government still keeps tight control over all political activities. It denies individual freedoms and acts harshly against Chinese citizens who criticize it.

7. Chinese leaders believe that Hong Kong and Macao will help boost economic growth because both have successful businesses in manufacturing, trade, and finance.

8. In general, people in China's cities have a higher standard of living than do people in rural areas.

9. The rapid growth of industrial and farm output has caused pollution. Burning coal causes polluted air. Factory wastes, sewage, fertilizers, and pesticides also have poisoned water.

10. The governments of Taiwan and China both claim the right to rule all of China. Despite this political difference, Taiwanese businesses are investing in mainland China, helping fuel its economic growth.

Quiz 27-2
JAPAN

Matching

1. C
2. D
3. E
4. A
5. B

Short Answer

6. Japan's long life expectancy and low birthrate are a challenge for its economy because they create a large, aging population and a shortage of young workers. These workers will have to pay more taxes to support health care benefits for the elderly.

7. Japan lacks military might, but it is a strong world economic power.

8. Japan has been able to grow its economy by importing raw materials

Answer Key

and producing goods to sell to other countries. Japan's modern factories use new technologies to make their products quickly and carefully.

9. Bunraku is a kind of theater that uses puppets to tell stories. No is a traditional form of theater in which actors tell stories through precise movements.

10. The Japanese have adapted to the crowded conditions of Tokyo by building smaller homes and living in apartments. Rooms often have little furniture because they are used as a living space during the day and as a sleeping area at night.

Quiz 27-3
THE KOREAS

Matching

1. E
2. A
3. D
4. B
5. C

Short Answer

6. The Korean Peninsula juts out from China between the Sea of Japan (East Sea) and the Yellow Sea.

7. South Korea used trade to build its economy by exporting many of the goods made in the country. In comparison, North Korea's foreign trade has declined since the fall of communism in Eastern Europe and the Soviet Union.

8. South Korea's farms are organized into many family farms, whereas North Korea's farms are organized into large, government-owned, collective farms. South Korea's family farms are more productive.

9. After World War II, Korea became a divided country. Troops from the Communist Soviet Union took over northern Korea, and American troops occupied the southern half of the country. In 1950 North Korea attacked South Korea in an effort to unite all of Korea under Communist rule. This began the Korean War.

10. South Korea has gained influence in world affairs by becoming an economic leader.

Quiz 27-4
SOUTHEAST ASIA

Matching

1. D
2. A
3. C
4. E
5. B

Short Answer

6. Indonesia's government has difficulty uniting the country because its people belong to many different ethnic groups and live on many different islands.

7. The standard of living in Singapore is high because of its productive economy and because its free port makes it an important center of trade. Laos is economically poor. Most people in Laos are farmers, and industry is largely undeveloped because of isolation and years of civil war.

8. Myanmar's military government runs its economy. Vietnam's Communist government runs its economy.

9. Foreign rule has had no influence on the culture of Thailand. It is the only Southeast Asian country that was never a European colony.

Copyright © by The McGraw-Hill Companies, Inc.

407

10. The major islands of Indonesia are Sumatra, Java, and Celebes.

Chapter 27 Test, Form A
EAST ASIA AND SOUTHEAST ASIA TODAY

Matching

1. C	**6.** A
2. F	**7.** I
3. H	**8.** B
4. D	**9.** G
5. J	**10.** E

Multiple Choice

11. C	**19.** A
12. D	**20.** B
13. C	**21.** B
14. D	**22.** C
15. B	**23.** A
16. A	**24.** C
17. A	**25.** B
18. C	**26.** A

Essay

27. China has permitted some free market reforms. Today people can choose the jobs they want and where to start their own businesses. Workers can keep the profits they make, and farmers have some control over the crops they grow and sell. As a result, China has one of the world's fastest-growing economies. Farm output has risen rapidly, and industry also has boomed. Many companies in China are jointly owned by Chinese and foreign businesspeople. A large middle class has emerged.

Chapter 27 Test, Form B
EAST ASIA AND SOUTHEAST ASIA TODAY

Matching

1. H	**6.** F
2. D	**7.** A
3. J	**8.** G
4. B	**9.** E
5. I	**10.** C

Multiple Choice

11. C	**19.** D
12. A	**20.** B
13. B	**21.** D
14. D	**22.** B
15. C	**23.** D
16. D	**24.** A
17. B	**25.** B
18. A	**26.** D

Essay

27. In world trade, Japan faces competition from South Korea, Taiwan, and China. Life expectancy is high, and the birthrate is low. The aging population may soon result in a shortage of workers, causing the need for increased taxes to support the elderly. Pollution, particularly acid rain, is a problem. Because of Japan's location on the Pacific Rim's "Ring of Fire," destructive earthquakes are a constant threat.

Unit 9 Posttest
EAST ASIA AND SOUTHEAST ASIA

Matching

1. B	**6.** C
2. G	**7.** I
3. H	**8.** A
4. E	**9.** D
5. J	**10.** F

Answer Key

Multiple Choice

11. C	15. B
12. B	16. B
13. C	17. D
14. C	18. D

Essay

19. Western China has a steppe climate with dry continental air blowing across from the west. In winter, arctic air makes the temperatures very low. Grasses grow well in this region. The Gobi is a large desert in Northern China. It is too dry for farming, and few people live there. China's east coast has a humid subtropical climate. Summers are very warm and winters are mild. Pacific winds bring much rain.

Unit 10 Pretest
AUSTRALIA, OCEANIA, AND ANTARCTICA

Matching

1. H	6. A
2. F	7. E
3. C	8. B
4. D	9. I
5. J	10. G

Multiple Choice

11. C	15. D
12. B	16. C
13. A	17. D
14. B	18. C

Quiz 28-1
PHYSICAL FEATURES

Matching

1. A
2. D
3. E
4. C
5. B

Short Answer

6. The Canterbury Plains are New Zealand's largest area of nearly flat land. They are the country's best farming area.

7. The North Island of New Zealand has many hot springs because it lies along a fault line where two tectonic plates meet. These hot springs provide geothermal energy.

8. Tahiti was formed by volcanic activity. Coral, or skeletons of millions of tiny sea animals, formed the Marshall Islands. New Guinea was formed centuries ago by the rising and folding of rock from the ocean floor.

9. The continent's rugged and frozen landscape and an agreement among many nations prevent the tapping of Antarctica's minerals.

10. The koala is a marsupial, or a mammal that carries its young in a pouch. The kiwi is a flightless bird. The koala is found in Australia, and the kiwi is found in New Zealand.

Quiz 28-2
CLIMATE REGIONS

Matching

1. C
2. B
3. A
4. D
5. E

Short Answer

6. Islands with higher elevations tend to have more rain and cooler temperatures, whereas islands with lower elevations tend to be drier and warmer.

7. Many New Zealanders make a living by raising livestock.

8. Far northern Australia is affected by the rising of the dry, hot air of interior Australia, which pulls in the moist warm air of the ocean to the north. The result is monsoon rains.

9. Antarctica is so cold because it does not receive the direct rays of the sun. Because it is so cold, the air can hold little moisture, and little precipitation falls. This makes the continent a desert.

10. The northern third of Australia is located in the Tropics. As a result, it is warm or hot year-round. The rest of the country lies south of the Tropics and has warm summers and cool winters.

Chapter 28 Test, Form A
PHYSICAL GEOGRAPHY OF AUSTRALIA, OCEANIA, AND ANTARCTICA

Matching

1. G   6. J
2. C   7. B
3. E   8. F
4. I   9. H
5. A   10. D

Multiple Choice

11. C   19. C
12. A   20. A
13. B   21. D
14. D   22. B
15. A   23. B
16. D   24. B
17. C   25. A
18. D   26. C

Essay

27. The northern, eastern, and southwestern coasts of Australia have mild climates and enough rainfall to support the population. Most of the interior of Australia is too dry to farm, and the climate is too extreme.

Chapter 28 Test, Form B
PHYSICAL GEOGRAPHY OF AUSTRALIA, OCEANIA, AND ANTARCTICA

Matching

1. G   6. E
2. J   7. B
3. A   8. D
4. C   9. F
5. I   10. H

Multiple Choice

11. C   19. C
12. D   20. A
13. D   21. C
14. A   22. B
15. B   23. C
16. C   24. B
17. B   25. C
18. A   26. A

Answer Key

Essay

27. High islands were formed by volcanoes that erupted under water. Low islands were formed by coral, or skeletons of millions of tiny sea animals. Continental islands developed from the movement of Earth's tectonic plates.

Quiz 29-1
HISTORY AND GOVERNMENTS

Matching

1. E
2. D
3. B
4. A
5. C

Short Answer

6. Early Aborigines had no large settlements. They traveled in small family groups, gathering plants, hunting, and looking for water. Early Maori set up villages and farmed the land. They also hunted and fished.

7. Captain James Cook claimed Australia for Britain. He also visited several Pacific islands, circled Antarctica, and produced accurate records and maps of the area.

8. The Antarctic Treaty was signed by many countries in 1959. In it, they agreed to share Antarctica for peaceful scientific research.

9. The first settlers of New Guinea were from Southeast Asia. They spread throughout Oceania by using large double canoes they had developed for traveling long distances and by reading the stars for location.

10. Australia has a federal government, with power divided between the national government and the states and territories. In New Zealand, the central government holds all major powers.

Quiz 29-2
CULTURES AND LIFESTYLES

Matching

1. D
2. B
3. E
4. C
5. A

Short Answer

6. People of European descent make up the majority of Australians and New Zealanders. However, increased immigration from Asia and a growing Aboriginal population are changing Australia's diversity, whereas a growing Pacific Islander population is changing the diversity of New Zealand.

7. Pacific Islanders are migrating because of high population density. They have too many people on too little land, resulting in overcrowding.

8. In New Zealand, families of European descent are typically nuclear, whereas the Maori emphasize the extended family, with households having relatives from three or four generations.

9. Maori artisans are skilled in canoe making, weaving, and wood carving.

10. Aborigines believe in Dreamtime, the time long ago when wandering spirits created the world. They believe that all natural things—rocks, trees, plants, animals, and humans—have a spirit and are related to one another.

Answer Key

Chapter 29 Test, Form A
HISTORY AND CULTURES OF AUSTRALIA, OCEANIA, AND ANTARCTICA

Matching

1. D	**6.** C
2. H	**7.** F
3. E	**8.** B
4. J	**9.** I
5. A	**10.** G

Multiple Choice

11. B	**19.** C
12. A	**20.** C
13. D	**21.** C
14. B	**22.** A
15. C	**23.** B
16. C	**24.** A
17. B	**25.** C
18. A	**26.** D

Essay

27. The Aborigines arrived in Australia during the Ice Age about 40,000 years ago. When the Ice Age ended and ocean levels rose, Australia was cut off from the rest of the world. The British began to explore Australia in the late 1700s and sent convicts there in the early 1800s. By the mid-1800s, British farmers and ranchers settled along the coasts and then moved farther inland. The discovery of gold in 1851 added to Australia's population.

Chapter 29 Test, Form B
HISTORY AND CULTURES OF AUSTRALIA, OCEANIA, AND ANTARCTICA

Matching

1. C	**6.** B
2. F	**7.** E
3. I	**8.** J
4. A	**9.** H
5. G	**10.** D

Multiple Choice

11. C	**19.** B
12. A	**20.** B
13. D	**21.** A
14. B	**22.** C
15. C	**23.** D
16. A	**24.** B
17. D	**25.** B
18. B	**26.** C

Essay

27. Australia is a very large country, but much of the interior is sparsely populated because of extremely dry conditions. Most people live along the coasts. There, the population density is high.

Quiz 30-1
AUSTRALIA AND NEW ZEALAND

Matching

1. C
2. E
3. A
4. B
5. D

Short Answer

6. The 1840 Treaty of Waitangi has become the basis for Maori claims to land in New Zealand. A 1992 Australian court ruling has allowed the Aborigines to reclaim land in Australia.

7. Australia's main agricultural activity of raising cattle and sheep makes it a world leader in the export of wool, lamb, beef, and cattle hides.

8. Cutting down trees and overgrazing have led to erosion of the topsoil, and Australian wildlife has been threatened by animals brought in from other areas.

9. New Zealand is producing wood and paper products to help expand its economy.

10. Japan and China purchase large amounts of Australia's mineral and energy resources.

Quiz 30-2
OCEANIA
Matching

1. D

2. B

3. C

4. E

5. A

Short Answer

6. With all of its phosphate deposits gone, Kiribati now relies on foreign aid. Nauru still has some phosphate deposits and is investing abroad and trying to develop service industries.

7. The United States pays to keep military bases on the islands. The bases provide jobs to islanders

8. The Northern Mariana Islands and Guam are territories of the United States.

9. Because of the conflict between Melanesian and South Asian ethnic groups, foreign companies have been afraid to invest money in Fiji. The conflict also has kept tourists away.

10. Samoa and Tonga have developed strong tourism industries, and they earn money from timber exports and cash crops.

Quiz 30-3
ANTARCTICA
Matching

1. E

2. C

3. B

4. A

5. D

Short Answer

6. The countries that signed the Antarctic Treaty have agreed to protect the environment there, which helps preserve Antarctica's wildlife.

7. Global warming could harm whales because the melting ice of Antarctica means the loss of plants that form the diet of krill, which are the main food source of whales.

8. Chemicals from aerosols collect in the atmosphere and, when hit by the sun's rays, change into other chemicals that destroy the ozone.

9. Many countries hoped to find mineral resources by claiming territory in Antarctica. The Antarctic Treaty bans mining on the continent.

10. Geologists believe Antarctica was once connected to Africa and South America.

Answer Key

Chapter 30 Test, Form A
AUSTRALIA, OCEANIA, AND ANTARCTICA TODAY

Matching

1. D		6. B	
2. F		7. C	
3. A		8. I	
4. J		9. E	
5. H		10. G	

Multiple Choice

11. C		19. A	
12. A		20. B	
13. C		21. C	
14. C		22. A	
15. C		23. B	
16. D		24. B	
17. B		25. D	
18. A		26. C	

Essay

27. Some island nations are investing abroad and trying to develop service industries. Others have built strong tourist industries. Samoa has established a program to plant new trees as others are cut down, which helps preserve its timber industry.

Chapter 30 Test, Form B
AUSTRALIA, OCEANIA, AND ANTARCTICA TODAY

Matching

1. G		6. C	
2. A		7. J	
3. B		8. D	
4. H		9. E	
5. I		10. F	

Multiple Choice

11. B		19. C	
12. A		20. D	
13. B		21. A	
14. A		22. D	
15. C		23. C	
16. D		24. B	
17. A		25. B	
18. B		26. D	

Essay

27. Scientists from several countries are cooperating in Antarctica. In 1959 the Antarctic Treaty was signed, which prohibits weapons testing or any other military use. The treaty also forbids mining in Antarctica to protect the environment. Since the 1980s, many countries have banned the use of aerosol cans to help protect the ozone layer, which developed a hole over Antarctica.

Unit 10 Posttest
AUSTRALIA, OCEANIA, AND ANTARCTICA

Matching

1. E		6. D	
2. I		7. A	
3. G		8. J	
4. H		9. F	
5. B		10. C	

Multiple Choice

11. B		15. C	
12. A		16. C	
13. A		17. B	
14. A		18. B	

Essay

19. The Maori and the Aborigines were the first people to live in New Zealand and Australia. Europeans arrived later but soon became the majority ethnic group. For both the Aborigines and the Maori, this meant a loss of land and position. Today these two native groups are trying to regain some of their land and privileges.